THE WORLD OF INSECTS

Fig. 1.—Green Darner Dragon-flies.

(*Frontispiece.*)

THE WORLD OF INSECTS

BY

CARL D. DUNCAN, Ph.D.
Professor of Entomology and Botany
San Jose State College

AND

GAYLE PICKWELL, Ph.D.
Professor of Zoology, San Jose State College

FIRST EDITION
SECOND IMPRESSION

McGRAW-HILL BOOK COMPANY, INC.
NEW YORK AND LONDON
1939

CONTENTS

PAGE

Preface vii

CHAPTER

I. Introduction 3

II. Insect Structures 9

III. How Insects Grow Up 31

IV. The Growing Up of a Swallowtail Butterfly 55

V. Insect Foods and Feeding Habits 66

VI. Some Insect Food-getting Devices 92

VII. How Insects Reproduce Themselves 104

VIII. How Insects Get Air 125

IX. How Insects Move 137

X. How Insects Are Protected 159

XI. Insect Voices 174

XII. Insect Fitness 188

XIII. Insect Orders 205

XIV. Social Life among the Insects 250

XV. The Value of Insects 294

XVI. Injurious Insects and Their Control 301

XVII. Where to Look for Insects 347

XVIII. Rearing Insects 358

XIX. How to Collect and Preserve Insects 377

References 391

Index 395

THE WORLD OF INSECTS

CHAPTER I

INTRODUCTION

NSECTS! One is inclined to speak of them only in superlatives. To treat of them one must use "most," "greatest," "highest," "largest," "widest," "unrivaled" over and over and over.

First of all, they are the most abundant in number of species, or different kinds, of all the animals of the earth. Insects constitute but one of nearly fifty different classes of animals, yet that one class has easily three times as many species as the other forty-nine classes added together. Thus, though there are more than eight hundred thousand named animal species in the world, over six hundred thousand of them are insects. And insects are not yet all named. It is believed, indeed, that before the end is reached as many as ten million insect names will have been catalogued![1]

Not only has the class of insects the most kinds; it also, as one might expect, has the greatest number of individuals. At this minute there may be more insects in your back yard than there are people in your city. One very small portion of your back yard may provide a home for several thousand Argentine Ants. A single hive of Honeybees may be home for fifty thousand individual bees. A single neglected rosebush may have twenty thousand plant-lice on it. And the chances are that Gyp, your dog, will bring a score of insect animals with him when he comes into your home.

Of all classes of animals, insects present the widest distribution. There is almost no niche on the face of the earth, conceivably inhabitable by any animal, that will not have its insects. With the single

[1] All estimates of numbers are taken from C. L. Metcalf and W. P. Flint, *Fundamentals of Insect Life* (McGraw-Hill Book Company, Inc., New York, 1932).

exception of the depths of the sea, they occur wherever plants of any kind can grow.

If success be granted to those animal groups with the widest distribution and the greatest number of species and individuals, then insects have attained unrivaled success. The reason for this success of insects can be traced to several things. Among these are such items as their wonderful adaptive ability, their tremendous and diverse specializations to meet a vast multitude of conditions, their life histories that promote distinct periods of food getting and reproduction, and the possession of wings by many of their orders. Perhaps more important than any of these, though, is the matter of relative size. Insects average smaller than other successful groups, and this has a great significance with respect to available food. As one learned professor put it: "Consider a piece of spoiling meat. Presume it is about the size of your two fists. What are its possibilities as a source of food? You will concede, for instance, that it would not suffice as a meal for one hungry dog; but it could raise a hundred flies!"

Insects seem to have a persistence unequaled by other animals. Perhaps this is because their type of nervous system, marvelous though it is with its fixed or instinctive reactions, seems sluggish in learning. Whatever the cause, recall how that lonely fly came back and back and back, though hands swung and swatters flapped, as if discouragement were no part of the insect's universe. Recall how that one mosquito tortured with its nasty hum through the long hours of night until death or a full meal became its due.

The highest development in social behavior exists among the insects, for in many ways it exceeds that of human society. One cannot but marvel at the caste development in a colony of termites, for instance. And a description of the organization of an ant colony will bring near incredulity that such development can have gone so far in creatures considered so lowly as insects. In this connection the complete domination by a queen-mother in a colony of Honeybees or yellowjackets over a vast brood of sterile daughters, that wear out their lives rearing sisters and brothers, is a matter that the wisest has not, as yet, completely explained.

Insects merit their superlatives, but superlatives alone will not explain the entire interest that insects hold. Though they be, among animals, most abundant and of greatest numbers, with widest distribution, unrivaled success, unequaled persistence, and highest social development, they have yet other characteristics that intrigue. To a boy there is no superlative for the thrill that comes with his first sight of a clear-wing moth as it hums before a thistle blossom; no superlative could express the concentration with which tumble-bugs are watched as they roll a pellet; and there are no superlatives to match the elation that attends the first successful rearing of a brood of *Samia cecropia* moths. Superlatives have not been formulated to express the admiration and wonderment called forth by the beauty in the gold-studded emerald chrysalis of the Monarch Butterfly. There are no superlatives for the sheer pleasure that insects may bring to nature lover, nature student, or nature teacher.

INSECTS DEFINED

Insects are animals, but since every living thing that is not a plant is an animal, it will be seen that this statement does not define an insect. Insects belong to a great division, or phylum, of animals that includes also the crayfishes, crabs, sow-bugs, millipedes, centipedes, spiders, scorpions, mites, ticks, and a few other groups less well known. The phylum that contains this assemblage is called Arthropoda. Arthropod means joint-legged; and that is a characteristic possessed by all these animals. Many vertebrate animals, or those with a backbone, also are joint-legged; so the animals of the phylum Arthropoda must have other distinguishing characteristics. And they have. Examine your fingernail. A layer of material similar to this, consisting chiefly of a substance called chitin, covers the entire body of animals of the phylum Arthropoda and serves as a skeleton. This outer covering is a distinctive thing in itself, but its use as a skeleton is even more distinctive. You have an inner skeleton to which muscles are attached. The Arthropoda do not have an inner skeleton, so the muscles are attached to this outer skeleton. *Insects, then, are members of the Arthropoda because they have jointed legs and an outer skeleton containing chitin.*

Insects may be distinguished from the other members of the Arthropoda by two or three distinctive things. First, insects have three distinct body regions: the head, the thorax, and the abdomen. To the thorax three pairs of legs are attached. Attached to the thorax of most adult insects, also, are wings, one of the most distinctive of all insect structures. No other members of the phylum Arthropoda have just this combination of characteristics. Crayfishes, for instance, have only two body regions and always more than six legs. Spiders are not insects because they have only two body regions and they

Fig. 2.—A Grasshopper Is a Typical Insect.
An insect is an animal with a body covering, or exoskeleton, containing chitin; its body is divided into three regions (head, thorax, and abdomen); it has three pairs of jointed legs and usually two pairs of wings attached to the thorax. These characteristics, taken together, make insects distinct, no other animal group possessing all of them.

have eight legs. Centipedes are not insects because they have only two body regions, yet they have more than twenty legs. And none of these animals has wings! *An insect, therefore, is an animal, a member of the phylum Arthropoda, with three body regions, three pairs of legs, and usually wings in the adult stage.*

The definition of an insect seems clear enough and absolute. For nearly all insects these characteristics are so pronounced that after a little experience one never makes the mistake of calling a sow-bug, a centipede, a spider, or a tick an insect; but eventually one will learn

FIG. 3.—THIS TARANTULA IS A SPIDER, AND SPIDERS ARE NOT INSECTS.
Spiders have a chitinous outer covering, or exoskeleton, and jointed legs, so they are members of the phylum Arthropoda, which also includes the insects. But spiders have only two body regions, whereas insects have three; and spiders have eight walking legs and never have wings.

that in a few cases the definition will not fit. For instance, the young of flies, ants, and many bees have no legs. Some of these, too, show poorly defined body regions. How is one to know they are insects? These cases will have to be learned individually, but that is not hard. (See the chapter on "Insect Orders.") However, since such cases do occur, our definition should be modified to this extent: *An insect is an animal, a member of the phylum Arthropoda, which in the adult stage nearly always has three well-defined body regions and three pairs of legs, and usually has wings.*

POSITION OF INSECTS IN THE ANIMAL KINGDOM

Phylum Vertebrata. Animals with a supporting vertebral column or backbone. Examples: mammals, birds, reptiles, amphibians, and fishes.

Phylum Arthropoda. Segmented animals with jointed legs and an outer skeleton of chitin; breathing variously, by gills or by tracheae.

Class Crustacea. Arthropods with two body regions usually, five pairs of walking legs, and two pairs of antennae or feelers; breathing by means of gills only. Examples: crayfishes, crabs, water-fleas, sow-bugs, and barnacles.

Class Arachnida. Arthropods with two body regions usually, four pairs of walking legs, leg-like feelers, and no true antennae; breathing by means of tracheae or book lungs. Examples: spiders, ticks, scorpions, and daddy-long-legs.

Class Diplopoda. Arthropods with two body regions and two pairs of legs per segment, a total of twelve to one hundred pairs; breathing by means of tracheae. Examples: the millipedes, or thousand-legged worms.

Class Chilopoda. Arthropods nearest the insects in structure but with only two body regions, twenty to more than seventy pairs of legs, one pair per segment, the first pair being modified into fangs; breathing by means of tracheae. Examples: the centipedes, or hundred-legged worms.

Class Insecta. Arthropods with three body regions, three pairs of walking legs all on the thorax, frequently with wings, and with one pair of true antennae, or feelers; breathing by means of tracheae. Examples: all true insects, such as beetles, moths, butterflies, true flies, bees, ants, and grasshoppers.

Other phyla are Mollusca with its clams, mussels, and snails; Echinodermata with its starfishes and sea urchins; Annelida with its earthworms and leeches; Coelenterata with its corals and anemones.

CHAPTER II

INSECT STRUCTURES

THE world of the insect, though it is a part of our world, is very different from our world. To a creature as small as an insect, the world presents problems to be surmounted and opportunities to be made use of which are almost totally different from the problems and opportunities with which we are confronted. A garden pathway on a summer day is a forbidding desert to many a small insect. A dry wind, blowing over a meadow for twenty-four hours, brings a drought too severe to be endured by thousands of tiny leaf-hoppers. To a water-strider (Fig. 181) a pond is a veritable skating rink over which to speed on dexterous feet; but to the flies and other insects which occasionally fall into the water and on which the water-striders feed, the pond is a deadly trap from which, once entangled in its sticky surface film, there is no escape. To one insect the swirling water of a rapid stream is home; to another the damp dark earth; to a third the carcass of some dead vertebrate or the body of a fallen tree. The multitudinous adaptations which enable insects to live successfully in this world of theirs are made possible only by the peculiarities of insect structure.

EXTERNAL STRUCTURES

In comparison with vertebrates, insects are inside-out, upside-down, and decidedly fantastic animals. They are inside-out animals because their skeletons form external shells to the inner surfaces of which the internal organs and tissues are attached (Figs. 10–12, 64, 70, and 72), whereas in a vertebrate the skeleton is an internal framework around which the other organs and tissues are arranged. Insects are upside-down animals because their hearts lie above or behind their alimentary canals (Fig. 10), whereas in a vertebrate the heart lies below or in front of the alimentary canal; and their central nervous systems run along the undersides of their bodies instead of along their backs as in vertebrates. They are fantastic because many of their organs seem to be located with utter disregard for reason. For example, grasshoppers and certain moths have their "ears" on the base of the abdomen just behind the wings (Fig. 4), whereas katydids and crickets, though closely related to grasshoppers, have their "ears" on the front legs just below the knees (Fig. 99). Moreover, a given organ will sometimes undergo radical or abrupt change in function during the lifetime of an individual insect, or the same structure will have markedly different functions in different insects. In the doodle-bug, or ant-lion (Figs. 116 and 117), the Malpighian tubules (Fig. 10)—tubular organs that empty into the intestine—serve as excretory organs when the larva is feeding and growing, but on the completion of the larval stage they abruptly change to silk glands. The silk is spun from the anal opening to make a cocoon (Fig. 116) within which transformation to the adult stage occurs. Following the transformation, the tubules revert to their primary excretory function. Such examples could be multiplied by the score, so strange and various are the insects.

The skeleton. Because the skeleton of insects, like that of crabs, spiders, and other arthropods, is external rather than internal, it is called an *exoskeleton*. It is a layer of tough, often hard, more or less inelastic material which not only covers every part of the body but turns inward at the mouth and anus and lines the front and rear portions of the alimentary canal as well. It turns inward also at the spiracles and lines the breathing tubes or tracheae (Fig. 64).

This exoskeleton, or *cuticle*, as it is also called, is composed of non-living material secreted by the outermost layer of cells of the insect's body. Chemically it is a complex mixture of substances. Its best known constituent, *chitin* is a horn-like substance. The chitin gives the exoskeleton its toughness and whatever elasticity it possesses, but not its hardness, which apparently is due to something else.

The exoskeleton has two principal functions: to protect and support the soft parts of the body and to provide an adequate foundation for the muscles. For the accomplishment of these functions it must be more or less thick and hard, at least in part. If it were hard throughout, however, it would be as much a handicap as an advantage to its possessor, for it would prevent movement and growth.

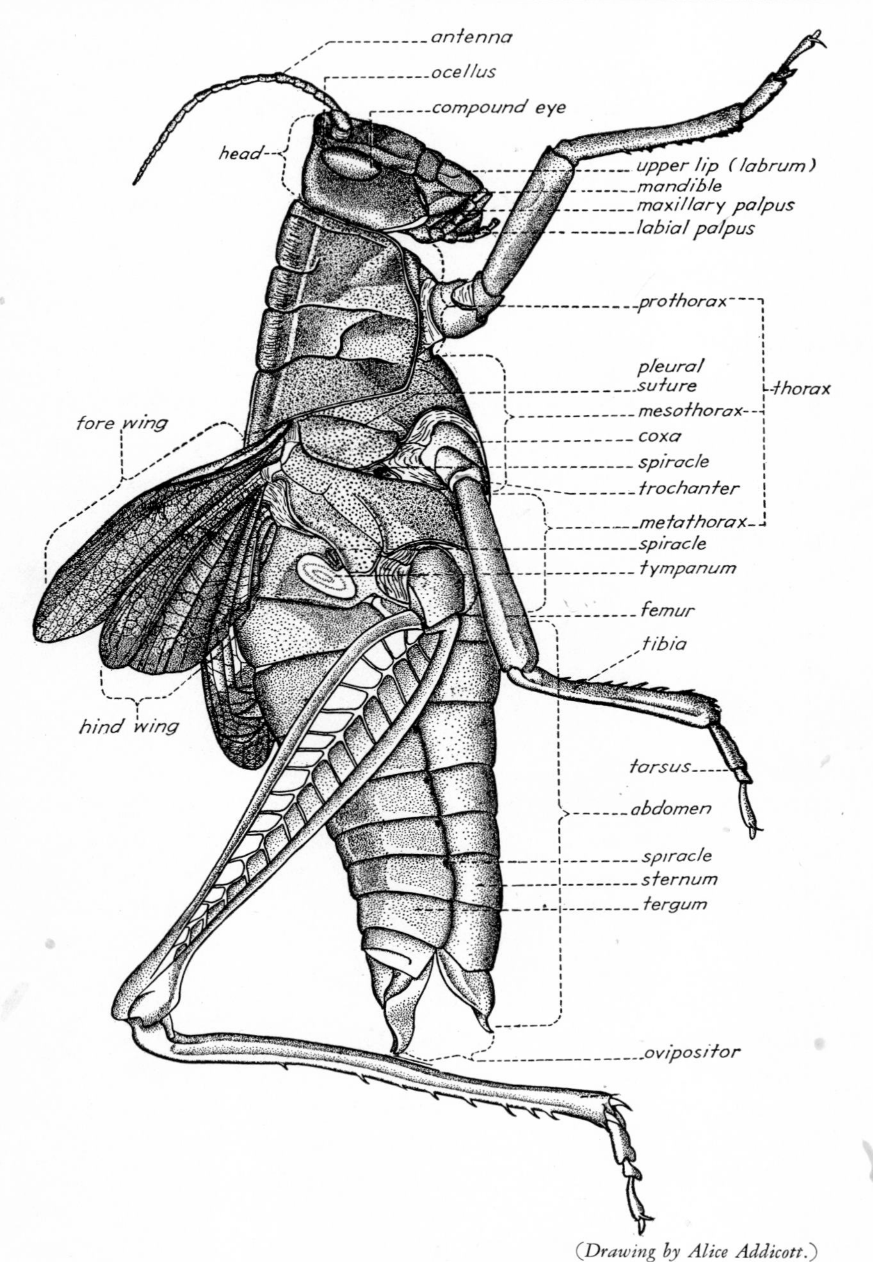

(*Drawing by Alice Addicott.*)

Fig. 4.—The External Structures of a Typical Insect.

This is a side view of a short-winged grasshopper (*Rhomalea microptera*). The grasshopper is relatively unspecialized; therefore an acquaintance with its structures leads to an easier understanding of the structures of the more highly specialized insects.

To make possible the movement necessary in the life of an insect the exoskeleton is thickened and hardened only in part. Many parts are thin and flexible. When these thin parts form broad areas of flexibility they are called *membranes*. Often, however, they are narrow and line-like; then they are called *membranous sutures*. Any groove or impressed line on an insect's body is termed a *suture*. The limited, hardened portions of the exoskeleton are termed *sclerites*. Every sclerite is bounded by sutures—membranous or otherwise, by membranes, or by both sutures and membranes. All these features, as well as several yet to be described, are well illustrated in the body of the grasshopper (Fig. 4).

Many of the sutures and membranes form lines encircling the body and appendages. These mark out or separate the *segments*, or divisions, so characteristic of the bodies and appendages of insects. The segments of an insect's body are not all alike, as are those of an earthworm, nor are they all as distinct and recognizable. Some of the segments are highly specialized; others are not. Some, too, are closely joined together; others are not. As a result of these differences in the development of the segments the body of an insect is partly separated into three main regions: *head*, *thorax*, and *abdomen* (Fig. 4).

The head consists of five or six segments so intimately joined and so highly specialized that their boundaries are in large part no longer discernible. On the head are borne the organs of feeding (Fig. 9) and most of the special sense organs such as the antennae and the eyes (Figs. 7–9). The thorax is specialized for locomotion. It consequently bears the legs, and the wings when these are present, and is filled with powerful muscles to move the wings and legs (Fig. 12). The abdomen is given over chiefly to the functions of digestion, food storage, excretion, and reproduction. It is usually not very muscular, and it usually does not bear any highly specialized sense organs other than some concerned with touch, and possibly in the case of a few insects, with smell.

The support afforded by the hardened sclerites of the exoskeleton, while adequate for all general needs, is insufficient to withstand the strain put upon the skeleton in certain places; so additional strengthening devices are necessary. Several of these are shown diagrammatically in Fig. 5. The more or less vertical line between each wing base and the base of the leg on the same segment is a place that requires extra strength, for it is along this line that the greatest strain occurs when an insect is flying or walking. To provide the needed strength along this line, the exoskeleton is folded inward, much as is shown in

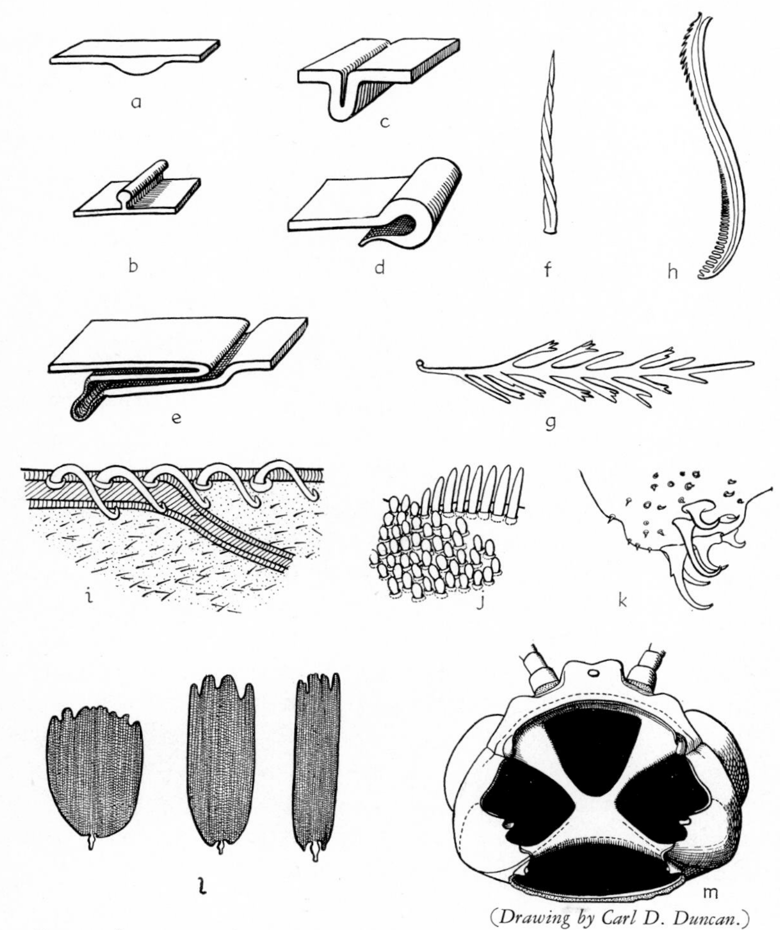

(*Drawing by Carl D. Duncan.*)

FIG. 5.—STRUCTURAL OUTGROWTHS AND MODIFICATIONS OF THE INSECT SKELETON. *a–e* show in diagrammatic form a few of the typical cuticular modifications which strengthen the skeleton in places where it is subject to excessive strain: *a*, simple thickening; *b*, internal bracing ridge; *c*, fold or corrugation; *d*, rolled edge; *e*, reduplication and overlap. *f* to *l* show variously shaped hair-like outgrowths from the cuticle of different insects: *f*, spirally twisted microscopic hair from the wing membrane of a *Polistes* wasp; *g*, pinnate hair from the head of a mosquito larva; *h*, hair from the mouth brush of a mosquito larva, serrate at the base, pectinate at the tip; *i*, hamuli, or curved hook-like hairs, which link the fore and hind wings of a *Polistes* wasp together; *j*, bullet-shaped setae on abdomen of a rove beetle; *k*, locomotor hooks on proleg of an ephydrid fly larva; *l*, three scales from a butterfly's wing; *m*, the tentorium of a grasshopper.

Fig. 5*c*, to form a ridge, the *pleural ridge*, internally, and a strongly marked groove, the *pleural suture* (Fig. 4), externally. This suture looks like a membranous suture, but instead of being more flexible than the rest of the exoskeleton, it is much more rigid. There are many such grooved sutures on the body of a highly specialized insect. They strengthen the exoskeleton in the same way that the grooves in a piece of corrugated iron strengthen the iron.

Another strengthening device found in the insect skeleton is a rolled edge on a sclerite (Fig. 5*d*). If the big sclerite which fits like a bonnet over the top and sides of the prothorax of a grasshopper (Fig. 4) is examined, it may be seen that at the edges of this sclerite the exoskeleton is turned under and rolled back against itself to give the sclerite a rolled edge. This rolled edge is quite similar to the rolled edge on the lid of a pot or kettle, and it strengthens the edge of the sclerite just as the rolled edge of the kettle lid strengthens the lid.

A modification similar to the rolled edge is the so-called *reduplication* (Fig. 5*e*). In a reduplication the edge of a sclerite is simply folded under against itself. This doubles the thickness of the skeleton. Reduplications are to be found on the rear edges of the segments in the abdomens of wasps, bees, and ants, where the edge of each segment overlaps the segment which follows. Two other modifications which increase the strength of the exoskeleton in regions of unusual stress or strain are simple thickening (Fig. 5*a*) and specially developed internal braces (Fig. 5*b*).

The most astonishing, however, of all the strengthening devices in the insect skeleton is the structure known as the *tentorium* (Figs. 5*m* and 9*b*) that is found in the head. The tentorium begins its development as four pockets which form in the head wall, two on the face and two on the back surface. These sink deeper and deeper until they meet inside the head. They then grow fast together, not a trace of their line of meeting remaining, and form a powerful X-shaped brace in the lower part of the skull just above the mouth parts. The tentorium braces the skull against the severest strains that can be put on it during feeding, and these strains, especially in the case of an insect which eats hard wood or dried grains, or even tough weed stems, is considerable!

In addition to the two principal functions discussed in the above paragraphs, the exoskeleton has a variety of less general, or minor, functions. It plays a prominent part in insect locomotion. For example, the wings of an insect (Fig. 4) are essentially flattened pockets of cuticle which grow out from the insect's thorax. The hooks that are called *hamuli* (Fig. 5*i*), which fasten the fore and hind wings of Hymenoptera together and thus ensure their operation as units during flight, are developments of the exoskeleton. So are the locomotor hooks (Fig. 5*k*) which serve the ephydrid fly larva in place of feet as it creeps about over the bottom of the salt-water ponds in which it lives.

Every insect has "hairs" on its body in greater or lesser numbers. The special type of hair-like structure found on insects and related

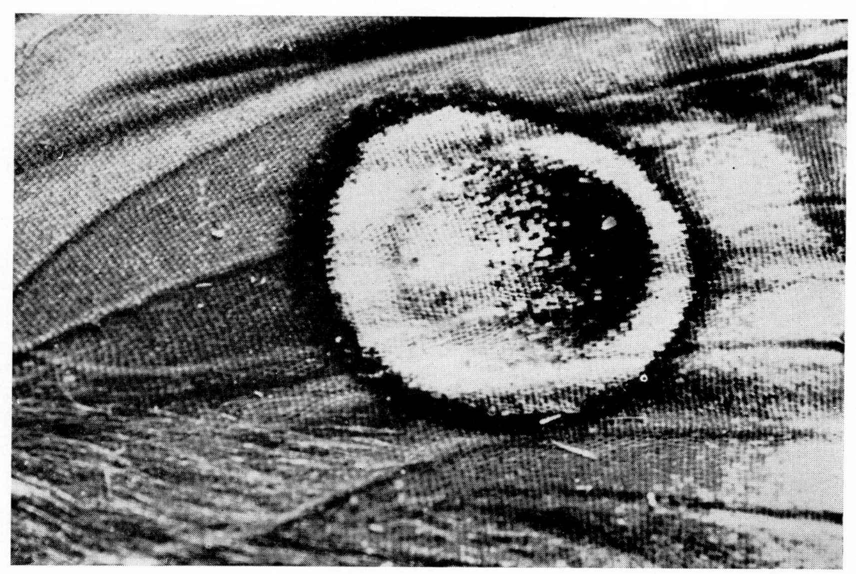

(*Photograph by Lester Brubaker.*)

FIG. 6.—THIS ENLARGED VIEW OF A PORTION OF THE WING OF THE BUCKEYE BUTTERFLY SHOWS THE "EYE," THE VEINS, AND THE SCALES.

The veins form the supporting structure of every membranous insect wing. The scales are flattened and overlapping setae ("hairs") on the wings and are characteristic of all moths and butterflies, and the "eye" is merely an adornment on the wings of certain of them. This "eye" cannot see.

animals is called a *seta* (plural—*setae*). All setae are outgrowths of the exoskeleton, or cuticle, and are variously shaped according to the functions which they perform in the life of the insect. Such setae, when flattened, form the "dust" on a butterfly's wing (Fig. 6). Grouped in elaborate mustaches, they serve as sieves with which the mosquito larva strains microscopic food from the water (Fig. 79).

Most setae, whatever their other functions, serve as organs of touch. Each seta is hollow and up into the hollow runs a tiny nerve. When the seta is bent over by contact with some object a little tug is given to the nerve. Thus the insect is made aware of the nature of its surroundings. Many kinds of specialized setae (Fig. 5) have equally specialized functions, of the nature of which, oftentimes, we are only dimly aware.

The muscles which move an insect's body (Figs. 12, 70, and 72) are attached to the inner surface of the exoskeleton. Many of the muscles are attached to unmodified parts of the skeleton, but others, such as the huge muscles which move the wings, legs, and mouth parts, require a better foundation. To provide this foundation, deep pockets, or *invaginations*, are often formed in the exoskeleton. Each of these pockets projects into the interior of the insect's body as a rod or bar, a rounded process or a broad plate. To each of these processes the muscles concerned are firmly attached (Fig. 12). In some cases the external openings to these invaginations are closed. In other cases they may be clearly seen as pits or depressions in the exoskeleton. The underside of the thorax of the grasshopper shows several of these pits.

Since the exoskeleton of an insect is practically nonelastic, it prevents growth to a large extent. To be sure, an insect may grow a little by "filling out" its skeleton, that is, by stretching out the wrinkles in the membranous parts, but there is an abrupt limit to the amount of such growth. So periodically, as is explained fully in the chapter, "How Insects Grow Up," the skeleton is shed (Figs. 20–23 and 30) and a new one acquired. Between the shedding of the old skeleton and the hardening of the new one the insect expands a great deal.

Thus it may be seen that the exoskeleton is really a marvelous structure. It gives protection by virtue of its position and composition, and support by virtue of its hardness and toughness. Through its various modifications it provides membranes and membranous sutures for movement, grooved sutures and ridges for rigidity where special strength is needed, and special foundations for important muscles. It also aids in locomotion and food getting, and it contributes to the functioning of the nervous system. And lastly, since it may be discarded readily and replaced, it permits growth to occur. Truly an insect without an exoskeleton would be a sorry creature.

Head structures. (Figs. 4, 7–9, and 70). The head of an insect bears the compound eyes, the simple eyes, the antennae, and the mouth parts.

The compound eyes, which are two in number, are large, usually roundish or oval structures on the sides of the head (Figs. 4, 7, and 9). Sometimes, however, they are kidney-shaped, lobed, or even divided. Under a compound microscope the surface of each compound eye appears to be divided into a larger number of hexagonal areas (Figs. 7 and 8). These areas, which are called *facets*, are the outer ends of the units, or ommatidia, of which the compound eyes are composed. The compound eyes of most ground-inhabiting insects, like the ants and many beetles, exhibit only a few facets, and these are compara-

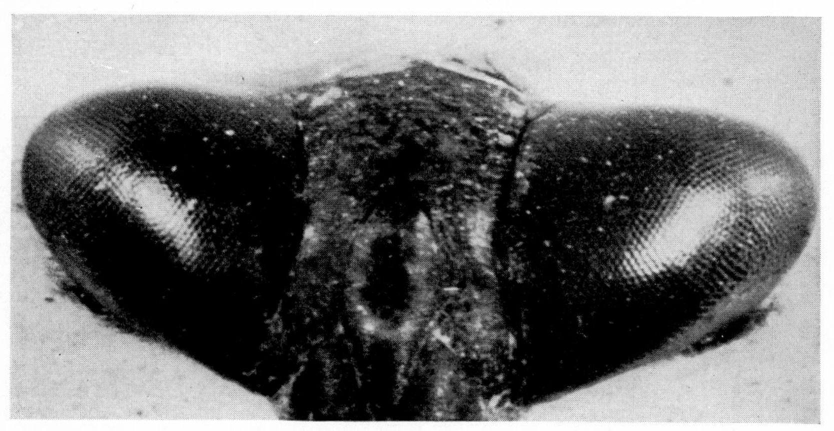

Fig. 7.—Two Enormous Compound Eyes Make up Most of the Head of a Giant Water-bug. Sharp vision is necessary for insects which fly and which hunt food or mates with their eyes, and this vision is provided by remarkable compound eyes that may consist of thousands of units, each one presenting an outer portion, or a facet. The eyes here show many of these facets.

tively large, for the vision of these insects is poor; but the eyes of the dragon-flies and certain wasps, which have very good vision and, in fact, hunt their mates and their prey by sight, have many thousands of facets. Clarity of vision in insects is roughly proportionate to the number of facets in the compound eyes.

The simple eyes, or *ocelli* (Figs. 4 and 9), which are usually three in number, are small bead-like organs set on the top or on the front of the head between the compound eyes. They are ineffective as visual organs and in most cases probably distinguish only between light and darkness, though they may enable the insect to recognize objects at very close range.

The antennae are the familiar "feelers" of the insect. They vary widely in different insects (Figs. 2, 15, 16, 18, 25, 90, 93, 107, 130, and 135). Mostly, however, they are like jointed threads or strings of beads. The "joints" or "beads," as the case may be, are the segments of the antennae. The antennae of nearly all insects are sensitive to touch; hence they are properly to be called *feelers*. They may be more than feelers, however, for the antennae of the males of many moths, and of various ants, wasps, bees, flies, and beetles appear to serve as organs of smell. In male mosquitoes, the antennae appear to function

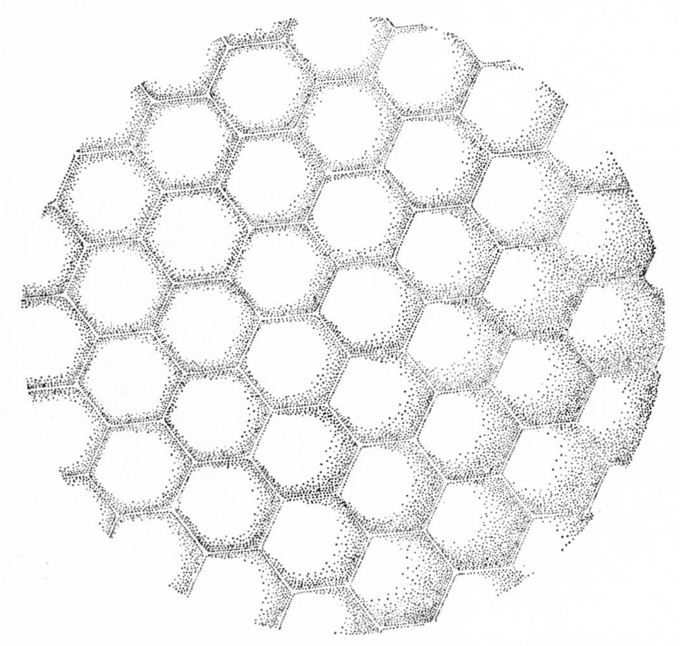

(*Drawing by Tom Rodgers.*)

Fig. 8.—A Portion of the Surface of the Compound Eye of a Dragon-fly, Highly Magnified. A hexagonal facet makes up the cornea of each unit, or *ommatidium*, of the compound eye.

as hearing organs, though other insects, as noted in the beginning of this chapter, have their hearing organs located elsewhere.

The mouth parts, or organs of feeding, are even more varied in form than the antennae, but there are nearly always the same number of mouth parts in all kinds of insects—at least during the embryonic stages. The variations to be observed appear to be merely modifications of one fundamental plan. This plan, and the nature of the mouth parts, may best be understood by studying the mouth parts of some simply constructed insect such as the common Field Cricket (Fig. 9).

In front of the mouth the *labrum*, or upper lip (Fig. 9*a*), hangs as a movable flap from the lower edge of the *clypeus*, which is a part of the skull. Immediately behind the labrum are the *mandibles*, or principal jaws (Fig. 9*c* and *d*). These are large, hard, strong jaws which work from side to side instead of up and down as our jaw does. They are the organs with which the cricket bites and chews its food. Each mandible

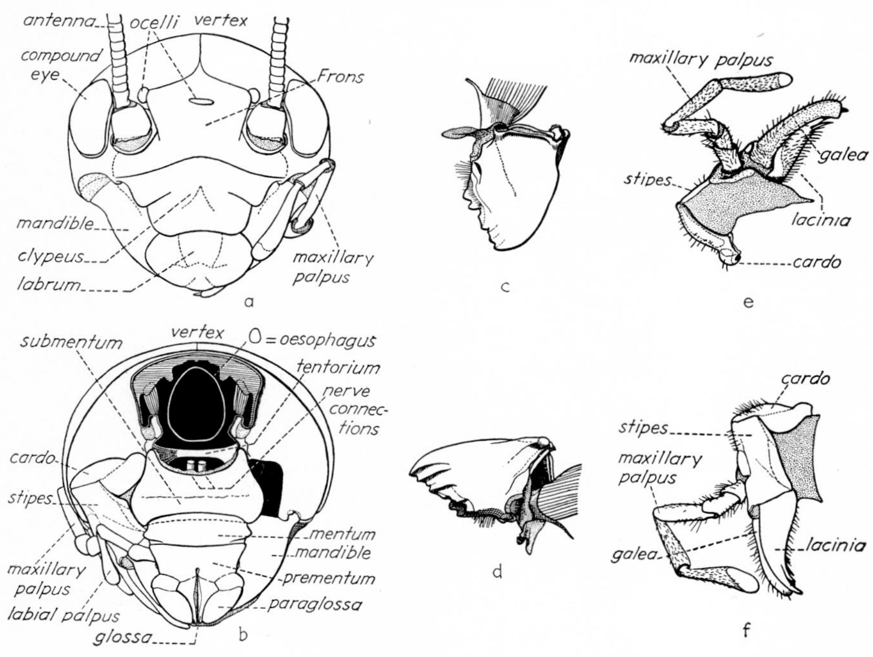

(*Drawing by Carl D. Duncan.*)

FIG. 9.—THE MOUTH PARTS AND OTHER HEAD STRUCTURES OF THE COMMON BLACK, OR FIELD, CRICKET.

Chewing mouth parts represent the primitive type possessed by the ancestors of modern insects. They consist of more numerous parts and are more generalized in character than any others. From chewing mouth parts many specialized types have been developed: *a*, cricket head in face view; *b*, same, in back view; *c*, left mandible, outer (lateral) surface; *d*, same, inner (mesial) surface; *e*, left maxilla from in front; *f*, same, from behind.

bears several strong teeth at the tip and across its inner surface. It is worthy of note that each mandible consists of but a single sclerite.

Behind the mandibles is a second pair of jaws, the *maxillae* (Fig. 9*e* and *f*). These are much more complex than the mandibles. Each maxilla consists of the following parts: a roughly triangular hinge sclerite, or *cardo*, by which the maxilla is hinged to the skull (the triangular shape is best shown in Fig. 9*b*); a rectangular principal sclerite called the *stipes;* and, attached to the stipes, a feeler-like, five-segmented *palpus*, a toothed, jaw-like *lacinia*, and a curved club-like *galea*. In insects such as the grasshopper the galea covers the lacinia like a hood, a fact which explains the name: galea means a hood. In chewing insects, such as crickets, grasshoppers, and beetles, the maxillae act as helpers to the mandibles, manipulating the food, holding it in place, and possibly helping to cut it into bits. In nonchewing insects, the maxillae vary widely. The palpus is a feeler; also, it may be capable of tasting the food.

Lastly, behind the maxillae, is the *labium*, or lower lip (Fig. *9b*). The labium closes the mouth behind, helping to retain the food and to manipulate it as it is being chewed. Like the maxillae, the labium is complex. In fact, the labium represents a second pair of maxillae which have become fused together on their inner margins. When the labium is viewed from the rear, several parts may be recognized. Attaching the labium to the head is a transverse, shield-shaped sclerite, the *submentum*. (In the grasshopper and in some katydids it has the form of a crude crescent.) Next comes a small oblong sclerite placed, like the submentum, crosswise of the head. This is the *mentum*. Following the mentum is a pair of oblong sclerites, joined basally but separate at the tips. Together these constitute the *prementum*. Each half of the prementum bears a three-segmented *labial palpus* on its outer side, a triangular *glossa* on its tip near the midline, and a spoon-shaped *paraglossa* alongside the glossa. The two glossae and the paraglossae are often referred to collectively as the *ligula*. On its inner surface the labium often bears a more or less fleshy structure known as the *hypopharynx*. This serves somewhat as a tongue, aiding in the manipulation of food. Just beneath the tip of the hypopharynx there is a small opening, the outlet of the *salivary glands*.

Thoracic structures (Figs. 4, 107, and 119). The thorax, in all insects except wasps, bees, ants, and other members of the order Hymenoptera, consists of three segments: the *prothorax*, the *mesothorax*, and the *metathorax*. In Hymenoptera, the thorax consists of four segments, for in these insects, what is the first abdominal segment in other insects has been transferred from the abdomen to the thorax. Each of the thoracic segments normally bears a pair of legs, all of which are built on the same plan. Each leg consists of five divisions: the *coxa*, *trochanter*, *femur*, *tibia*, and *tarsus*. With the exception of the tarsus, and occasionally of the trochanter, each leg division consists of but a single segment. The tarsus most commonly consists of five segments, though this number is often reduced by fusion or by loss of segments, to four, three, two, or even one. The trochanter sometimes consists of two segments. In the dragon-flies and in certain families of wasps, the trochanter is in two segments. The coxa and trochanter, as a rule, are short segments by which the leg is hinged to the body. The femur and tibia are long segments containing certain of the leg muscles, but the muscles which move the leg as a whole are found in the thorax (Fig. 12). The femur and tibia are comparable to the thigh and shin joints of a human. The tarsus is plainly a foot.

Not all insects have wings, but when wings are present they are borne by the mesothorax and the metathorax—never by the prothorax. Each wing is a membranous expansion of the body wall, supported and strengthened by thickened line-like parts called *veins* (Figs. 4, 14, 24, 96, 98, and 114). The number and arrangement of the wing veins are important in the classification of insects, for in the wing veins are to be found many of the evidences of relationship on which classification is based. In comparatively primitive winged insects the fore and hind wings were alike in size and structure, but in modern insects generally the wings exhibit considerable differences. In the Coleoptera, or beetles, for example, the fore wings are thick and hard or leathery, and are without obvious veins (Fig. 130). They are called *elytra* (singular: elytron), and they serve only as covers for the hind wings, which are the organs of flight. In grasshoppers and other Orthoptera the fore wings are tough and leathery and are not of much use in flight (Fig. 107), but they are not so highly specialized as the elytra of beetles, for they still exhibit a well-marked venation. Such wings are called *tegmina* (singular: tegmen). The fore wings of true bugs, or Hemiptera, are leathery in the basal portion and membranous in the terminal portion (Fig. 124). They are called *hemelytra* (half elytra) (singular: hemelytron). In the Hymenoptera the hind wings are quite small (Fig. 142) and are fastened to the fore wings by a row of curved hooks that are called *hamuli* (Fig. 5*i*); in the Diptera the hind wings have been so much reduced that they are no longer wings at all, but merely little knobs borne on slender stalks (Fig. 14). Such reduced wings are known as *halteres*.

On the sides of the thorax, in the membranous sutures between the segments or close to these sutures, are two pairs of openings guarded by valves. These are the thoracic *spiracles* (Fig. 4). They are openings into the tracheal tubes (Fig. 64) and are a part of the breathing system of the insect. This is discussed more fully later in the present chapter and also in the chapter on "How Insects Get Air."

Abdominal structures. In comparison with the head and the thorax, the abdomen bears few appendages. In fact, most abdominal segments bear no appendages at all. A typical abdominal segment exhibits only two sclerites, a large *tergum*, or *tergite*, arching over the top and sides of the segment and a smaller *sternum*, or *sternite*, which covers the venter, or underside of the segment (Fig. 4). Pleural sclerites generally are wanting completely, there being only folds of membrane in the pleural (side) regions of the segments.

At the tip of the abdomen is a group of appendages which function in mating and egg laying. Collectively these organs are called the *external genitalia*. In the female the genitalia often consist of four, or of six, prong-like structures, together forming an *ovipositor* (Figs. 4, 93, 110, 111, and 142), a device for placing the eggs when laid. In many Hymenoptera the ovipositor is modified into a sting. The genitalia of insects are discussed more fully in the chapter, "How Insects Reproduce Themselves."

In addition to the genitalia, the abdomen of certain insects bears a pair of anal feelers called *cerci*. In the grasshopper (Fig. 4) the cerci are small and inconspicuous finger-like structures, but in many insects, such as the bristle-tails (Fig. 108) and stone-flies (Fig. 119) they are long and conspicuous. Between the cerci of the bristle-tails there is a third thread-like structure, the *median filament*. The cerci and the median filament are all sensitive to touch stimuli. In an insect like the Jerusalem Cricket (Fig. 107), which lives mostly in burrows underground, the cerci may be important organs, warning the insect of the approach of danger from behind. Many aquatic larvae and nymphs have filamentous or leaf-like outgrowths on the sides of some or all of the abdominal segments. In May-fly naiads (Fig. 68) these serve as gills; their function is doubtful in the dobson-flies (Fig. 78) and alder-flies.

Several of the abdominal segments bear spiracles, one pair to each segment (Fig. 4). These are generally located on the sides of the segments, but usually are not in the membranes as are the spiracles in the thorax. Instead, the abdominal spiracles are located in the sclerites. The number of abdominal spiracles varies in different insect groups, but there are never more than eight pairs. The ninth, tenth, and eleventh segments of the abdomen never have spiracles.

INTERNAL STRUCTURES

In internal construction insects differ as much from vertebrates as they do externally. Their muscles (Figs. 12, 70, and 72), instead of

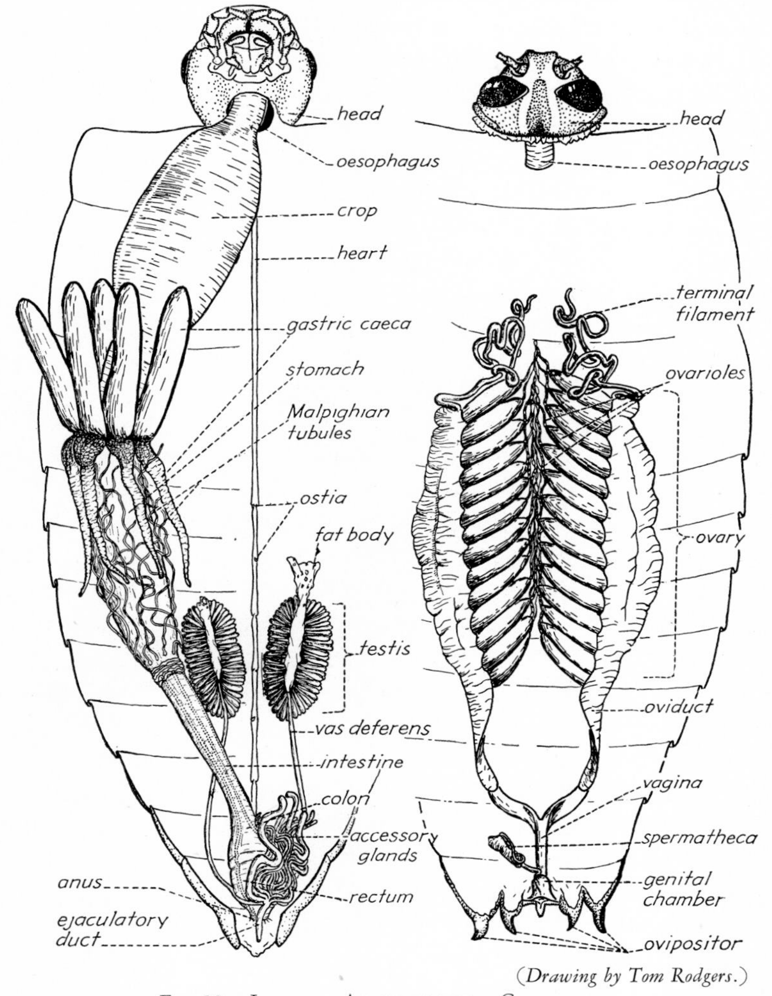

(*Drawing by Tom Rodgers.*)

FIG. 10.—INTERNAL ANATOMY OF THE GRASSHOPPER.
In the left-hand figure the alimentary canal, the heart, and the male reproductive system are shown as they appear in a specimen that has been opened along the under surface. The right-hand figure shows the reproductive system of a female as it appears in a specimen cut along the upper surface.

being tapered at the ends, as is so often true of vertebrate muscles, are usually strap-like and of the same width throughout. Instead of being bound closely to the skeleton with connective tissue, as most vertebrate muscles are, they extend freely across parts of the interior of an insect, much as ropes and belts extend across the interior of a room in a factory. The tubular alimentary canal (Fig. 10), which extends the full length of the body, is suspended in the body cavity by branches of the tracheae, by strands or sheets of connective tissue, and by muscles. Other internal organs are held in place in a similar manner. In most insects the organs are anchored rather firmly so that they will not sag or drift more to one side than to the other, but in insects which move by squirming or wriggling they are only loosely held. In such insects, therefore, the organs surge back and forth with every movement of the body. Around and between the various internal organs of the insect there is a great deal of space, or rather, there are many intercommunicating spaces. These are filled with blood.

The circulatory system. This system is simple. It consists of two parts: the blood-filled spaces referred to above and a single tubular blood vessel called the *dorsal vessel* (Fig. 10). The dorsal vessel lies just beneath the body wall along the back, and extends the full length of the body. Usually it is indistinctly divided into a pulsating part, the *heart*, and a nonpulsating part, the *aorta*. The heart is limited to the abdominal part of the dorsal vessel in most insects, but in some it extends into the thorax. The aorta extends from the heart into the head, where it ends just beneath the brain and above the esophagus. It opens widely into the blood spaces of the head. Along the sides of the heart are pairs of valves, termed *ostia* (singular: ostium), which alternately open and close. The posterior end of the heart is closed, though there may be a pair of ostia very close to this end. Through the ostia blood is taken into the heart. It is then pumped forward through the aorta to the head. There it is poured out onto the brain and other head organs, after which it flows backward through the numerous blood spaces in the body, bathing the various tissues and organs as it goes.

The heart can be seen best, not in a dissected specimen, as might be supposed, for it is delicate and difficult to dissect out, but in living insects, if the right kinds be chosen. Many naked caterpillars have a transparent line down the middle of the back through which the pulsations of the heart may be seen. The best specimens in which to see the heart, however, are certain aquatic insects, because these have transparent body walls. Young damsel-fly naiads, young larvae of midges (flies of the family Chironomidae), young mosquito larvae

(Fig. 65), and newly hatched water-boatmen are excellent for the purpose. In these it is possible not only to see the outlines of the heart, but to see it working! The valves may be seen to open and close, and the white blood corpuscles, the only kind possessed by insects, may be seen to rush into the heart each time the valves open.

The tracheal system (Fig. 64). Typical insects breathe not by means of lungs or gills, but by means of a system of branching air tubes, the *tracheae*, which extend throughout the body and carry air to the very tissues where it is needed. These tracheae open to the outside through the spiracles already discussed. The tracheal system, like the heart, can be seen to best advantage in living aquatic insects—the same kinds in which the heart may be seen. The tracheae are especially clear in the newly hatched water-boatmen. Among nonaquatic insects, newly hatched scale-insects (Fig. 171) make good material for tracheal study. If mounted on a microscope slide, directly in glycerin rather than in water, their tracheae show up quite clearly.

Aside from the heart and the tracheal system, the internal organs of an insect may best be seen by making a dissection. When the body of a suitable specimen—say a grasshopper—is slit open along the back, and the side walls spread apart and pinned down, the internal organs may be readily studied. (In making such dissections a dissecting pan should be used.)

The reproductive organs. Conspicuous among the structures brought to view by making a dissection are the organs of reproduction. Since these are considered fully in the chapter, "How Insects Reproduce Themselves," they will not be described here. A good idea of their form and arrangement in a typical insect may, however, be obtained at this point by referring to Fig. 10, which shows the reproductive organs of the grasshopper.

The alimentary canal. Partially obscured by the reproductive organs and by the fat body is the alimentary canal of an insect. In the grasshopper this consists of a nearly straight tube, as shown in Fig. 10. The tube varies in diameter and in structure in different parts.

Leading inward from the mouth is the *esophagus*. This is often slender and long, but in the grasshopper it is short and thick, and is followed immediately by the large, thin-walled *crop*, or food reservoir. Following the crop in many insects is a thick-walled, strongly muscular part called the *gizzard*, or *proventriculus*. This is lacking in the grasshopper. Behind the crop, or gizzard as the case may be, is the stomach, or *ventriculus*, in which most of the digestion is carried on. On its anterior end the stomach often bears several (usually four) pocket-like outgrowths known as *gastric caeca*. In the grasshopper there are six caeca, and each caecum is divided into two distinct lobes. One lobe of each caecum points forward, the other backward. The gastric caeca are believed by some biologists to be glands which secrete a digestive juice somewhat like the pancreatic juice of vertebrates. Behind the stomach is the intestine. This extends to the anus. The intestine may be divided into a small intestine and a large intestine, as in the grasshopper, or it may lack any visible differentiation.

The labial glands. Associated with the alimentary canal, but not a part of it, there is in most insects a pair of *labial* glands. These generally lie in the thorax beneath or alongside the alimentary canal. They are often called the *salivary glands* because in many insects (cockroaches, butterflies, aphids, and bees) they secrete fluids which moisten and partially digest the food. From the labial gland of each side a tubular *salivary duct* runs forward. These ducts join back of the head to form a *common salivary duct*. This continues forward and discharges the secretion of the glands on the labium just beneath the tip of the hypopharynx (see page 20). In some insects the labial glands are divided into two or more pairs of separate glands, all of which discharge into the common salivary duct.

The labial glands do not always secrete saliva. In fact, they vary greatly in function, in certain insects having no connection with digestion. For example, in caterpillars, in caddis larvae, and in the larvae of cocoon-spinning wasps, the labial glands are silk secreting, at least in part. In some such insects these glands are enormous, extending backward through the thorax into the abdomen. In beetles, on the other hand, labial glands seem to be entirely lacking. In place of saliva, many of these insects regurgitate digestive juices from their stomachs to moisten their food. Incidentally, the brownish liquid which a captured grasshopper, when held in the hand, produces from its mouth in such large quantities, the so-called "tobacco juice" of childhood vocabularies, is not saliva. It is a liquid mixture of partially digested food and digestive juices from the crop, and it is regurgitated as a "protest" against being captured.

The Malpighian tubules. From the anterior end of the intestine, close to its junction with the stomach, some slender tubes arise. These vary from two to many in number (there are many in the grasshopper), but they are always very slender and usually very long. These are the *Malpighian tubules* (Fig. 10). To some extent at least, they take the place of kidneys, removing waste products from the system. The Malpighian tubules usually cling rather closely to the alimentary canal, on the surface of which they wind back and forth, but they may extend freely into the body cavity.

The fat body, or adipose tissue. Whenever we open a grasshopper, a caterpillar, or any other insect to see its alimentary canal, its tracheae, its Malpighian tubules, and other organs described above, we are likely to be impressed with the amount of fatty tissue that is present. In a mature grasshopper or in a crane-fly larva the fat may form only a thin covering over the alimentary canal, a covering that is lace-like and positively beautiful in its construction. In other insects the fat is more abundant, and not only the alimentary canal but other organs are swathed in it. And in some insects, such as the larvae of bees and wasps and most caterpillars, there is so much fat that every nook and cranny of the insect's body seems packed with it. Most of this fat is contained in a single, definite, but elaborately formed organ, the *fat body*. The fat represents surplus food stored against future need. It is more abundant in larvae than in adults, because the larvae must eat and store enough surplus food to nourish the insects throughout the pupal stage and the transformation to the adult stage, for during this period of change no food can be taken. (See also page 52.)

The nervous system. Except for the brain, the central nervous system lies beneath the alimentary canal and the other organs; these must be removed before it can be seen. If the alimentary canal be cut through a short distance behind the mouth and also just in front of the anus, it may be lifted out in its entirety. The tracheae and the remaining fat may then be picked out bit by bit, eventually exposing the nervous system. The removal of internal organs and fat brings to view the muscles of the body wall.

The central nervous system (Fig. 11) consists of two creamy white cords running lengthwise of the body. At intervals these cords are joined, and the junctions are marked by roundish white swellings. The nerve cords are called *connectives;* the swellings are collections of nerve cells and are called *ganglia* (singular: ganglion). In some insects the connectives are joined along their inner sides throughout nearly all their length, so as to look like a single cord instead of two.

Careful examination reveals that generally there is one ganglion for each body segment, except for the hindmost segments, one or more of which lack ganglia. In an adult insect, and in larval insects having thoracic legs, the ganglia of the thoracic segments are larger than those of the abdomen. Tiny, thread-like nerves branch out from the ganglia and extend to the various tissues and organs. The nerves from any one ganglion generally run only to the tissues and organs of the segment containing the ganglion. This fact enables us to understand the greater size of the thoracic ganglia. The thoracic segments are more complex than the abdominal segments; they have legs and wings attached to them, besides having the usual internal tissues and organs

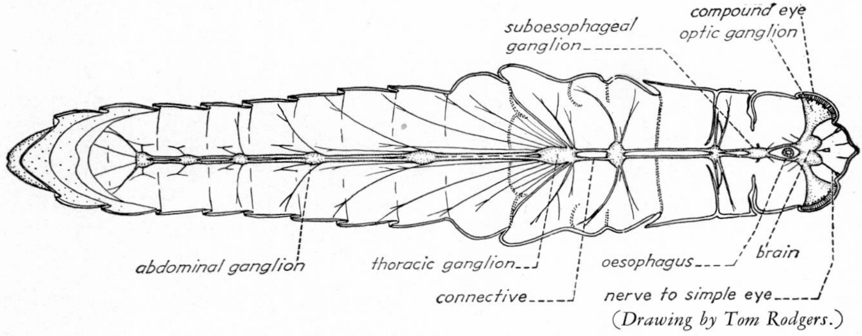

(*Drawing by Tom Rodgers.*)

FIG. 11.—THE CENTRAL NERVOUS SYSTEM OF A GRASSHOPPER.
Note that the nervous system consists of a chain of enlargements, or ganglia, connected by a pair of longitudinal nerve cords.

Therefore more nerves are needed in these segments and more nerve cells are required to govern the activity of the more numerous nerves; hence the ganglia are larger.

In the head will be found two ganglionic masses, so called because they are more complex than ordinary ganglia. One of these lies beneath the front end of the esophagus. It is called the *subesophageal ganglion*. It sends nerves to the mouth parts. Really, it is a fusion of the three ganglia of the three head segments to which the mouth parts belong. Immediately above, or on top of the esophagus, is the *supra-esophageal ganglion*, the *brain* (Figs. 11 and 70). The brain, like the subesophageal ganglion, is compound. It, too, is the product of the fusion of primitively distinct ganglia. The number of these is somewhat in doubt. From the sides of the upper part of the brain two large processes extend to the compound eyes. These processes are the so-called *optic lobes*. The pair of connectives which connect the brain with the subesophageal ganglion pass downward, one on each side of the esophagus, so as to form a sort of ring or collar around the esophagus. These connectives are called, therefore, the *circumesophageal connectives*, and the ring which they form around the esophagus is called the *nerve ring* or *nerve collar*.

The muscles. The muscles of insects are discussed at some length in the chapter entitled "How Insects Move," and will be but briefly treated here. As has already been pointed out, most insect muscles are in the form of straps or ribbons which are of the same width throughout (Figs. 12, 70, and 72). They are not spindle-shaped with pointed ends, as is true of so many muscles in vertebrates. Whether this fact

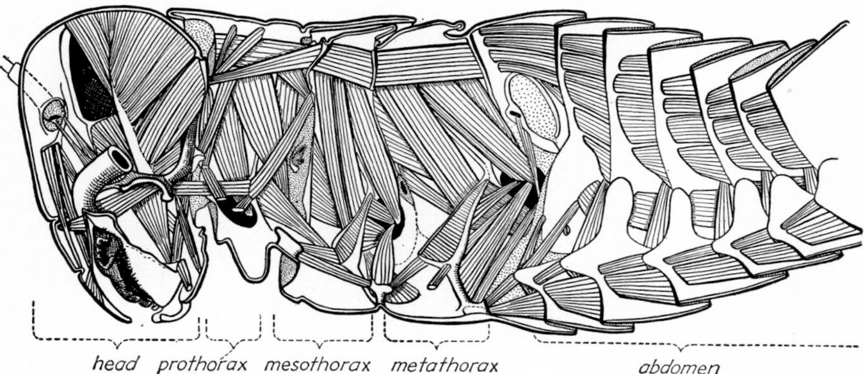

(*Drawing by Carl D. Duncan.*)

FIG. 12.—INSECT MUSCLES ARE FASTENED TO THE INNER SURFACE OF THE SKELETON. Insect bodies are moved by sheets and bands of muscle tissue attached to the inner surface of the cuticle, or exoskeleton. To ensure greater effectiveness the skeleton in many places bears internal ridges and rod-like processes to which the muscles are attached. This figure shows most of the muscles in the right half of a grasshopper, viewed from the inside.

has any special significance is not clear. It seems probable that it is due merely to the fact that insect muscles are attached to a continuous shell-like exoskeleton, whereas most of the muscles of vertebrates are attached to slender bones where the space for attachment is restricted. Not all insect muscles are strap-like, however. Some of those which work the jaws and the legs are slender at the end that is attached to jaw or leg, but broad at the opposite end. They are thus conical or fan-shaped. A few are spindle-shaped.

Many insect muscles lie so close to the exoskeleton that they appear to be part of the body wall. They are so numerous and their arrangement so complex that a complete and satisfactory classification has not yet been devised for them. For our purposes, however, little classification is necessary. We merely need to recognize that most of the muscles of the body wall are longitudinal, transverse, or oblique. The longitudinal muscles serve to bend the body in various directions; the transverse muscles are involved in the movements by which breathing is accomplished and, in certain larvae, in the movements of locomotion. In larvae, the transverse muscles often are numerous and short, and they encircle the body, hence are called *circular* muscles. The oblique muscles are used whenever twisting movements of the body or of the organs are required.

CHAPTER III

HOW INSECTS GROW UP

In the world of the larger and more familiar animals development is apparently simple and the most reasonable of happenings. What is more logical than that colts should grow up gradually to be horses, calves to be cows, kittens to be cats, and puppies to be dogs? In fact, all this seems so natural and proper that were anything else to occur we should be amazed. True, many newly hatched birds are not so suggestive of their parents as colts and kittens are of theirs, but they are obviously birds. It is chiefly the lack of feathers that makes them appear strange for a while. But suppose things were different!

Suppose rabbits were hatched as tiny creatures from eggs no larger than beans. Suppose that, instead of being helpless for several days and requiring the care of their mother, they were immediately strong and independent, voracious creatures which devoured enormous quantities of food, and often doubled in size in a few hours. Suppose, furthermore, that every few days each rabbit would discard a layer of skin and all the fur from its entire body, together with the linings from its mouth, esophagus, lungs, and intestines, only to emerge from the castoff coverings and linings with new and better ones. Suppose that eventually the rabbits changed into objects, apparently inanimate and resembling nothing so much as a lot of smoked hams hung up in a meatshop, or a lot of hibernating turtles with legs folded tight and motionless against their sides and with heads drawn into their shells. And then, as a climax, suppose that the rabbits suddenly burst forth from their smoked-ham or hibernating-turtle forms to appear as full-fledged eagles with powerful wings capable of carrying them over mountain crests and up and down the intervening valleys. If rabbits were to present to us such a kaleidoscopic drama of development, we should consider them most extraordinary creatures. And they would be most extraordinary! Yet such transformations occur daily in the world of insects.

INSECT METAMORPHOSIS

Butterflies. Nearly everyone is familiar with the life of a butterfly. From the inconspicuous eggs laid by the butterfly there emerge *caterpillars* (Figs. 26, 29–34, 38, and 58), smooth or hairy, green, brown, gray, streaked, or spotted according to kind; yet none of them bears the least obvious resemblance to its parents. After a period of feeding and growth, during which the "skin" is cast several times (usually four or five) and the caterpillar grows enormously, each one transforms into a *pupa* (Figs. 35 and 137), or *chrysalis* as it is sometimes

FIG. 13.—TO EMERGE FROM ITS HARD BARREL-LIKE PUPARIUM, THIS FLY "BLOWS UP AND SUCKS IN ITS FACE" IN THE ACTION OF ITS PTILINUM.

The ptilinum is a reservoir that fills and empties with blood as the fly expands and compresses its abdomen in breaking the walls of its puparium. The picture shows the ptilinum fully expanded.

called, a totally different-looking creature, yet hardly more like the butterfly than the caterpillar was. Not until the pupa has lain or hung immobile for several days or weeks, outwardly quiescent but inwardly undergoing a complete remaking, does the winged, highly colored, erratic *adult* butterfly (Figs. 36, 37, and 135) appear.

True flies. The transformations of common flies are even more profound (Figs. 13, 14, and 177). The fly adult lays tiny cigar-shaped white or cream-colored eggs, which hatch into headless, legless, worm-like young, termed *maggots*. These can move about only by squirming, and are dominated, like the caterpillars, by an overpowering desire to eat and grow. On the completion of their larval stage (young insects of worm-like form are called *larvae*), the fly maggots change into brown barrel-like, creatures quite incapable of movement. These are called *puparia* (Fig. 177). A *puparium* is simply the last larval "skin." Instead of being cast off, as with most insects, this last skin is merely loosened from the insect's body, shortened a little, and thickened. Inside the puparium the maggot changes to a typical pupa, the form of which foreshadows that of the full-grown fly. The puparium thus constitutes a sort of cocoon (see pages 39 and 41). Such is the course of development in the case of the House-fly, the Stable-fly, blow-flies, and others of the same and related families. Less specialized flies, on the other hand, do not form puparia. They

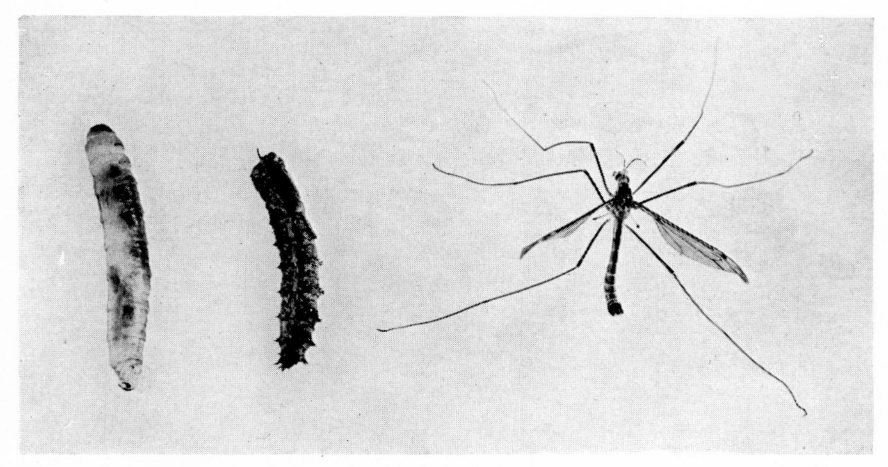

FIG. 14.—BEFORE THERE CAN BE A LONG-LEGGED ADULT CRANE-FLY THERE MUST BE A PALE, SQUIRMING MAGGOT AND A BROWN OR GRAY PUPA.

The crane-fly larvae or maggots are often common in damp leaf mold or beneath loose bark on dead trees in the spring; there they feed on decaying vegetable matter. There, too, the larvae transform into stiff, brownish pupae, which give rise later to long-legged winged adults.

cast the larval skin and become naked pupae (Fig. 14). But whether naked pupae or pupae enclosed in puparia are formed, the end result is the same. There emerge flies, many of which, as a result of recent enlightenment, we have come to regard as enemies, but which are nevertheless amazing beings and, except in the case of a few kinds specifically concerned in the transmission of human diseases, not dangerous at all! Flies are among the world's most highly perfected mechanisms, and are capable of feats of flying beside which the loops, tail spins, and power dives of the finest airplanes are but tame performances.

In emerging from their puparia, the more specialized flies present an astonishing spectacle. The end of the puparium is broken open by main strength, exerted from inside by the fly; but not until the puparium opens at the end do we see how this is done. Then we observe an almost unbelievable sight. A sort of trapdoor, bearing the fly's antennae and bending downward on a hinge line just above the proboscis, opens up in the fly's face and from behind it (between it and the eyes) there swells out a relatively enormous balloon-like sack of membrane. Out it swells; then is withdrawn into the head. This performance may be repeated several times, the trapdoor on the fly's face turning down and up each time. This strange sack is the *ptilinum* and is used on but one occasion, on the emergence of the fly from the puparium. At this time the fly squeezes its abdomen, syringe-like, with its body muscles, forcing blood up through the thorax into the head. The blood surges forward, filling and distending the ptilinum, creating an enormous pressure against the resisting puparium. Finally the puparium can withstand the strain no longer; it cracks open across the end and for a short distance down the sides. The side pieces bend backward and the fly struggles out, an odd-looking creature, deficient in coloring and with small crumpled-looking wings. Shortly, however, its color deepens, it grows strong, its wings expand, straighten, flatten, and acquire the glossy iridescence so characteristic of them, the trapdoor on the fly's face folds back into place and the strange ptilinum shrinks like a deflating balloon and is withdrawn into the fly's head completely out of sight, never to be used again.

Metamorphosis. Changes such as those undergone by the flies and butterflies during their development are known as *metamorphoses*. In fact, any change in form and structure is a metamorphosis, but not all insects exhibit so profound a metamorphosis as do flies and butterflies. Many change much less, and some change hardly at all, except in size. Nor is the change always of the same character or accomplished in the same manner. According to the amount and kind of metamorphosis, therefore, insects may be segregated into four main groups.

TYPES OF METAMORPHOSIS

Direct development. Such primitively wingless insects as the so-called Silverfish, or Fish-moth (Figs. 108 and 170), and its relatives, belonging to the order Thysanura (see Chapter XIII for an explanation of the term *order*), and the spring-tails, belonging to the order Collembola, undergo no obvious transformations. The young resemble the adults closely except in size. They are said to exhibit *direct development*, or to undergo no metamorphosis. All other groups of insects exhibit *indirect development*.

Gradual metamorphosis. The members of certain other orders, such as the grasshoppers, crickets, katydids, and cockroaches, of

Fig. 15.—The Chief Change in the Gradual Metamorphosis of Milkweed Bugs Is the Addition of Wings.

Always the young have the appearance of true bugs, but in the beginning there is no evidence of wings. Wing pads then appear and in the last molt of the nymph the wings assume full and functional size. All these stages are present here.

the order Orthoptera (Figs. 2, 20, 62, 88, 90, 93, 95, 97, and 110); the earwigs, of the order Dermaptera (Fig. 128); the termites, of the order Isoptera (Figs. 159 and 160); the true bugs, comprising the order Hemiptera (Figs. 15, 21, 43, 61, 75, 105, and 181); and their relatives, the plant-lice, leaf-hoppers, spittle-bugs, and cicadas, making up the order Homoptera (Figs. 19, 39, 49, 63, 84, 98, 172, and 173), undergo a limited amount of metamorphosis. In these groups the newly hatched young resemble the adults more or less, though they lack wings, differ in bodily proportions, and often (Fig. 126) have their legs and mouth parts adapted for functions somewhat different from those of the adults. Young insects of this character are called *nymphs* instead of larvae.

As the nymphs grow and molt their "skins," they gradually acquire wings and other features, making them more and more like the adults. For this reason their metamorphosis is termed *gradual metamorphosis*. The wings appear as little flattened pads, attached to the hind margins of the thoracic segments and held closely against the

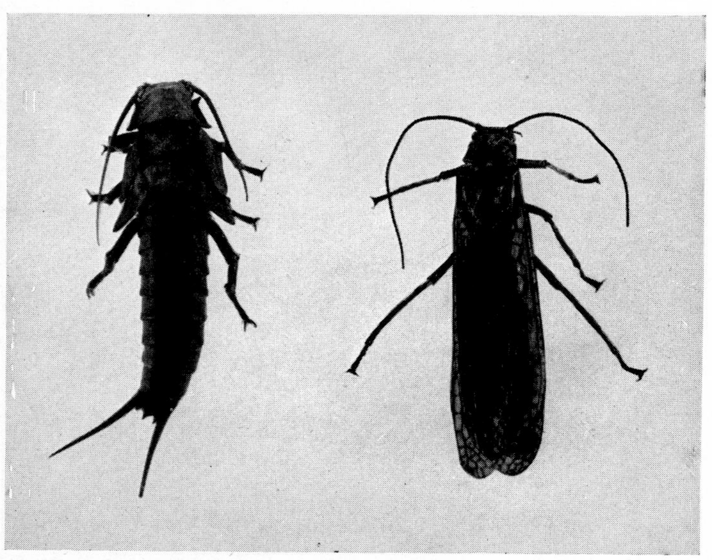

FIG. 16.—AS THEY GROW UP THEIR ONLY CONSPICUOUS CHANGE IS THE ADDITION OF WINGS, SO STONE-FLIES ARE SAID TO HAVE INCOMPLETE METAMORPHOSIS.

The young of insects with gradual metamorphosis are called *nymphs*, but the young of stone-flies, like the young of dragon-flies and May-flies, possess gills and other special features adapting them to live in water, so they are called *naiads* instead of nymphs. Like nymphs, however, they show the promise of wings, as they grow, in the triangular wing pads on the thorax (see the insect on the left). At the last molt these pads produce the long wings of the adult (the insect on the right).

body of the nymph (Figs. 15 and 124). At each molt these *wing pads* increase in size and finally, at the last molt, they are replaced by the large, functional wings of the adult. The amount of change which occurs at this last molt varies greatly among the different kinds of insects exhibiting gradual metamorphosis. In the grasshoppers, crickets, and cockroaches, and also in most of the true bugs, the change is only a little greater than it is at any one of the preceding molts. In certain others, however, such as the cicadas, whose young exhibit peculiar structural specializations that are lost in the transformation, the change at the last molt is much greater (Figs. 19 and 126).

Incomplete metamorphosis. The members of three orders of insects—the dragon-flies and damsel-flies, of the order Odonata (Figs. 1, 22, 53, 69, and 81); the May-flies, of the order Ephemerida (Fig. 68); and the stone-flies, of the order Plecoptera (Figs. 16, 119, 120, and 121)—undergo a somewhat more complex metamorphosis. As in the case of insects which undergo gradual metamorphosis, the young of the members of these three orders acquire wings gradually. They also are sufficiently like the adults in most structural features that a careful examination would enable us to recognize them.

All of them are aquatic, however, and all possess a number of peculiar features, such as gills (Fig. 68) and special locomotor mechanisms, which obscure their identity more or less. Hence they appear superficially to differ markedly from the adult forms which they eventually assume. The final transformation, therefore, seems considerable. The aquatic young of these insects are called *naiads* to distinguish them from nymphs; and the developmental changes which the insects undergo in growing up are referred to as *incomplete metamorphosis*.

Complete metamorphosis. The transformations of butterflies and true flies have already been discussed, so they need not be considered again, except to say that they exhibit the most indirect development of all insects and, therefore, *complete metamorphosis*. Illustrations of the stages in the life cycle of additional members of the orders Lepidoptera, to which the butterflies belong, and of Diptera, to which the flies belong, are to be found in Chapter XIII (see Figs. 138 and 139, also 177). Other insects which undergo complete metamorphosis are: the beetles, making up the order Coleoptera (see Figs. 25, 129, and 178); bees, wasps, ants, ichneumon wasps, and their relatives, making up the order Hymenoptera (see Figs. 141, 142, 144, and 154); dobsons, ant-lions, and lacewings, comprising the order Neuroptera (see Figs. 17, 78, 115–117, and 180); fleas, of the order Siphonaptera (Figs. 140 and 169); caddis-flies, of the order Trichoptera (Figs. 132–134); and scorpion-flies and hanging-flies, of the order Mecoptera (Fig. 131). In all these there are four well-marked stages in the life history: egg, larva, pupa, and adult.

It is commonly supposed that these four stages are as sharply differentiated in all insects which undergo complete metamorphosis as they are in butterflies and typical flies; but this is an erroneous supposition. Only certain orders of insects produce larvae that are as worm-like as caterpillars or fly maggots, and an even smaller number produce pupae that are as immobile as those of butterflies. In most insects with complete metamorphosis, the pupae resemble the adults rather closely, so closely in fact that they are little more than quiescent nymphs with legs and antennae folded against their bodies (Figs. 17 and 25). On the other hand, some pupae are capable of

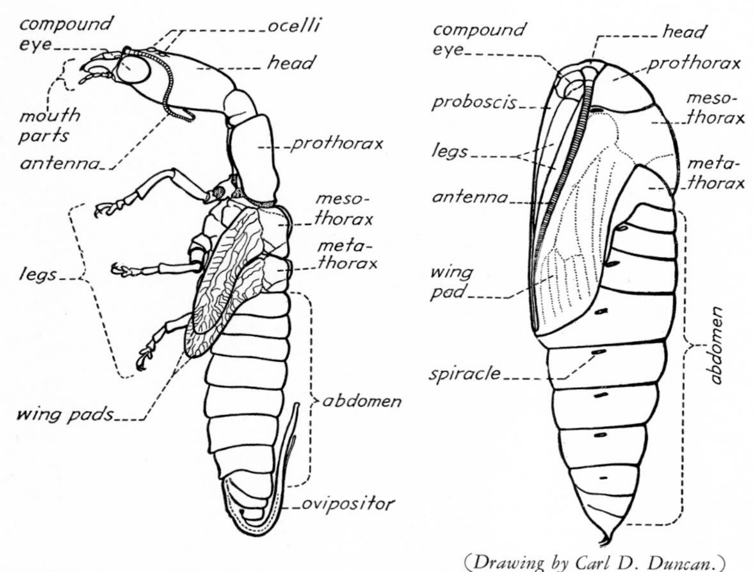

(*Drawing by Carl D. Duncan.*)

FIG. 17.—SIMILARITY TO A NYMPH IS OBVIOUS IN THE ACTIVE PUPA OF A RUBBER-NECK BUG; SUCH A NYMPH-LIKE CONDITION IS CONCEALED IN THE QUIESCENT PUPA OF A MOTH.

The pupae of insects which undergo complete metamorphosis are like modified nymphs of insects which undergo gradual metamorphosis. Compare the nymph-like pupa of the rubber-neck bug, with its free legs, antennae, and wing pads, with the nymphs of grasshoppers and true bugs. Then note that the smooth moth pupa has the same leg, antenna, and wing parts, only they are folded tightly against the body and "pressed" into its surface. In live moth pupae these parts appear as if covered by a glaze which all but obscures them.

considerable activity. Mosquito pupae (Fig. 65) and caddis-fly pupae (Fig. 132) are able to swim vigorously. The pupae of rubber-neck bugs (Fig. 17) are able not only to creep about, an ability which increases as the adult stage approaches, but even to snap their jaws at enemies. And there are some insects, such as certain carrion beetles of the family Silphidae, in which both larvae and pupae resemble the adults almost as much as stone-fly naiads resemble stone-fly adults. Yet we say the metamorphosis of the stone-fly is incomplete whereas that of the beetles and the other insects in question is complete. The distinction is based on two facts. The stone-fly obviously acquires its wing pads gradually and, except for the actual time spent in molting, feeds throughout its entire period of immaturity. Beetles and other insects which exhibit complete metamorphosis spend most of their immature existence without wing pads, acquiring them only at the next to the last molt. Upon the acquisition of wing pads, these insects cease to feed, become quiescent and, unless disturbed, remain quiescent throughout the pupal stage. From these facts, then, it may readily be seen that, although complete metamorphosis and incomplete metamorphosis are really distinct, there are several degrees of complete metamorphosis, some of which are but little removed from incomplete metamorphosis.

The cocoon. Many insects which undergo complete metamorphosis form a cocoon at the close of the last larval stage, to cover and protect them during the pupal stage. This cocoon (Figs. 18, 116, 174–176, and 179) is confused in the minds of many persons with the pupa, though in reality it is an entirely different object. The pupa is the living insect, the cocoon is a nonliving envelope fashioned by the insect while it is still in the larval stage. Within the cocoon the larva transforms into the pupa.

Cocoons often are composed entirely of silk, spun from the modified salivary glands of the larva, but various other materials may be combined with the silk. Hairy caterpillars, such as those of the tussock-moth (Fig. 179), shed their hairs at spinning time and weave these in with the silk of their cocoons. The caterpillars of many moths, on the contrary, make no cocoons at all. Some, like the caterpillars of the sphinx moths, burrow into the ground as the time for pupation approaches, and make oval chambers in the earth which serve as cocoons and inside of which the transformation to pupae takes place (Fig. 27). Butterfly caterpillars appear never to make cocoons. The larvae of crabronid wasps, which often nest in rotten logs, combine tiny bits of rotten wood with the silk of their cocoons. Other insects, such as the ant-lion (Figs. 115–117 and 180), use sand grains as accessory material. When silk is used, it does not always come from the salivary glands. In the case of many Neuroptera, the doodle-bug, for example, certain of the excretory organs are modified into silk glands and the silk produced by them is spun from the anus!

The puparia of flies (Fig. 177) as mentioned on page 33, may be thought of as one kind of cocoon. Though formed of the last

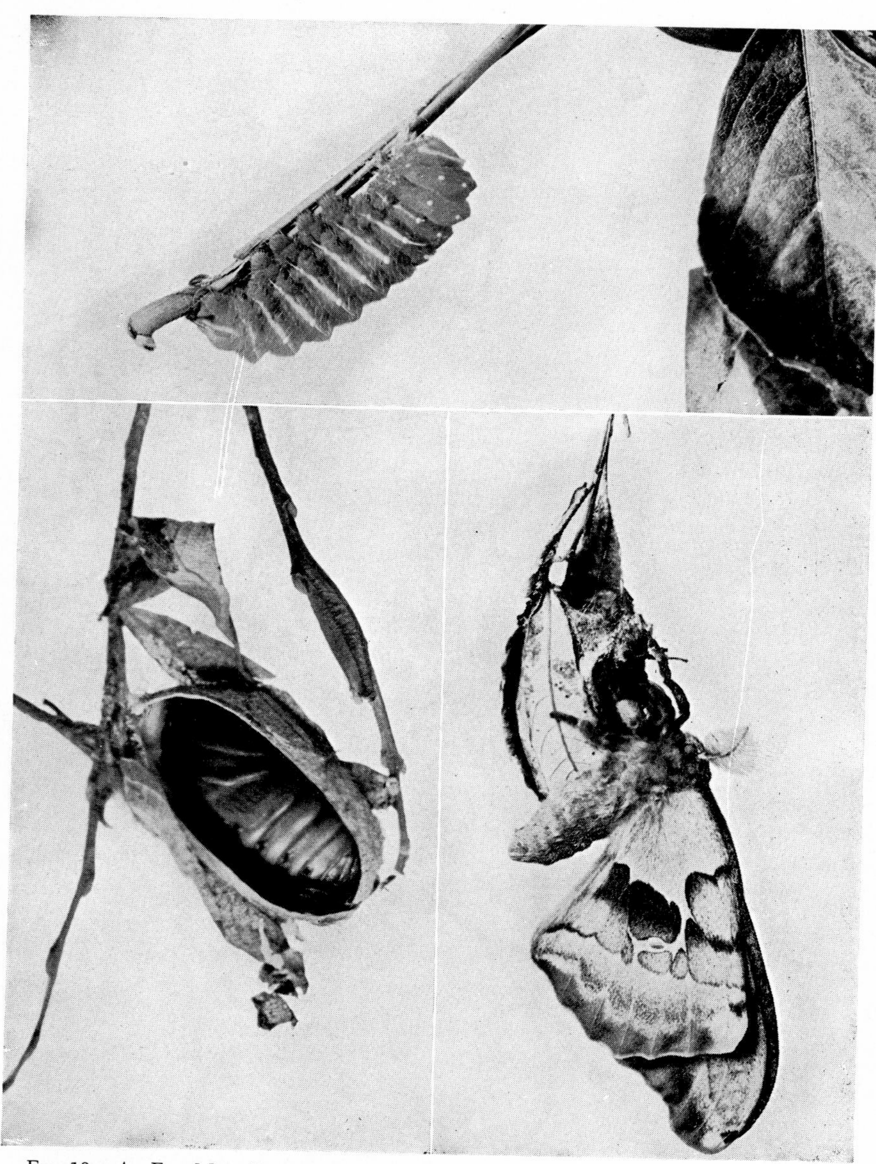

FIG. 18.—AN EGG MUST PRODUCE A CATERPILLAR, THE CATERPILLAR MUST CHANGE TO A PUPA, AND THE PUPA MUST CHANGE TO THE ADULT, IN THE COMPLETE METAMORPHOSIS OF THE POLYPHEMUS MOTH.

Above is the caterpillar at rest just prior to spinning its cocoon; below at the left is the cocoon cut open to show the pupa; at the right is the glorious creature (*Telea polyphemus*) that culminates this growing-up process of complete metamorphosis.

larval skin instead of being secreted, puparia surround and protect the pupae of flies as effectively as any typical cocoon would do.

GROWTH PROCESSES IN INSECTS

The insect skeleton. As has been explained in Chapter II, the outer layer of an insect's body, its so-called "skin," is not a layer of living cells, as is the skin of most animals, but is the insect's skeleton. The secretion that becomes the skeleton is liquid at first but shortly congeals and hardens. During the congealing process it is soft and flexible and is capable of considerable enlargement, but once thoroughly hardened no further enlargement is possible except a slight stretching, and this only in the thinner and more membranous portions. During most of an insect's life the cuticle adheres firmly to the underlying cells of the body wall. Only at the time of molting does it become loosened.

When an insect larva or nymph emerges from the egg, and again immediately after each molt, its skeleton is much too large for it. The skeleton at this time is wrinkled and there are extensive infolded membranous portions between segments and between the hardened subdivisions of segments. As the larva or nymph feeds, it "grows into" its skeleton, just as a boy "grows into" a suit of clothes, filling the latter and taking up the slack.

The molting process. When all the wrinkles have been smoothed out and the skeleton fits tightly, the young insect prepares to molt, or shed its cuticle. It ceases feeding, empties its intestine, usually crawls to some shelter, and becomes quiescent. Then the cells of the epidermis, which have been relatively inactive during the preceding feeding period, secrete a new exoskeleton beneath the old one, and loosen the old one. The new exoskeleton congeals but does not harden until after the old exoskeleton is cast off. The loosening of the old skeleton is brought about by a *molting fluid* (also a secretion of the epidermis) which dissolves the inner layer of the old skeleton.

At the approach of the moment for casting, the insect swallows a large quantity of air, or of water if it be an aquatic insect, or it employs some other as yet unknown mechanism, and in consequence swells considerably. The swelling generates a pressure too great for the old skeleton to withstand. The latter, therefore, suddenly splits down the back and the insect with its new soft skeleton begins to emerge through the break. The place at which the splitting

FIG. 19.—A BURLY CICADA NYMPH CRAWLS OUT OF THE GROUND AND BECOMES AN ADULT CICADA WITH THE MAGIC OF METAMORPHOSIS.

The last nymphal skeleton splits down the back (upper left) and the adult partly emerges; it swings then to grasp the old skeleton (upper right) and pulls out the remainder of the body. Wings, that were but stubs as it came forth, lengthen visibly as blood is pumped into their veins (lower left); and before twenty minutes have elapsed, full form is complete (lower right) and hardening begins. No Prince Charming ever put aside the clothing of a chimney sweep for the glittering attire of royalty with a magic more marvelous than this.

occurs is always the same for each species and is determined ahead of time by lines of weakness in the skeleton. Gradually the insect works its way out of the old skeleton, which is then abandoned (Figs. 19, 20–22, and 30).

Enlargement immediately after the molt. The newly emerged and somewhat enlarged insect is soft, weak, and pale in coloring, but it has more left to do than merely to harden, strengthen, and color up. It must enlarge still more. For a few seconds or several minutes, depending on its kind, while its new skeleton is still soft, the insect continues to swallow air or water and to stretch.

FIG. 20.—A MATURING MALE FIELD CRICKET ENLARGES AND HARDENS HIS LAST SKELETON ALONGSIDE THE USELESS NYMPHAL EXUVIA FROM WHICH HE HAS JUST EMERGED.
With rapidly swelling body, the form of an adult, and pale wings that will quickly harden into resonant musical instruments, this male cricket enacts the miracle of molting and transformation which takes place in the life of every insect, a miracle which would be unbelievable if it did not transpire before our very eyes.

Many insects, especially while undergoing the final molt to the winged state, employ another mechanism also. In stretching the body appendages, they contract their powerful abdominal muscles and force blood from the tissue spaces of the abdomen through the thorax and out into wings, legs, and antennae, thus expanding the latter to their full size. In all probability, however, the insects would not be able to generate the necessary blood pressure by muscular contraction were it not for the fact that their stomachs are distended with air or water. The abdomens of the insects which exhibit this last behavior shrink visibly as the blood is forced out of them into the appendages (Figs. 36 and 37), but the shrinkage is much less than the expansion which occurred during the molting. The end result of the remarkable procedure of molting is that, without feeding, the insect enlarges to such an extent that it would be quite impossible for it to be put back inside the discarded skeleton (Figs. 19–21, 36, and 37). Moreover, it is in possession once more of an ample, much wrinkled skeleton which through active feeding it must "grow into" and fill out. Such is the nature of the molting

Fig. 21.—The Giant Water-bug on the Right Came out of the Old Skin on the Left Just a Few Minutes before This Picture Was Taken.

The bug is still a nymph, not more than two-thirds grown, and it must molt at least once more before becoming mature, but note how rapidly it expands to larger dimensions. In a few minutes it has swelled to more than twice its former size and could not possibly be put back into its former "clothing." By this process of shedding hardened "garments" that are no longer adequate, and then swelling before the new ones harden, insects make room for growth. In the cast-off skeleton, note the white threads in the tear along the back. These are the linings of tracheal tubes which were peeled out, too, when the bug came forth.

process, a process which occurs from two to twenty times, depending on the kind of insect.

It is worth noting that the rapid, or in some cases sudden, enlargement of an insect at molting is not the same sort of thing as the gradual and much slower growth between molts. Enlargement at molting is merely an expansion, not an increase in body substance. In fact, there is an actual decrease in body substance at molting; and in spite of their larger size newly molted insects, making due allowance for swallowed air or water, weigh less than they did before the molt. The loss in weight is partly accounted for by the weight of the discarded skeleton. It is partly due, also, to the fact that food is consumed in the tissues of the insect in releasing the energy needed to accomplish the stretching. The growth of body substance, for which the enlargement at molting is a preparation, comes after the molt is completed when feeding is resumed once more.

Skeletal linings. At this point two other facts command our attention. One is that at every molt the insect sheds not only the

FIG. 22.—A DRAGON-FLY EMERGED FROM THE RENT IN THE BACK OF THIS OLD NAIAD COVERING AND THEN FLEW AWAY FROM THESE CAST-OFF CHILDHOOD CLOTHES.

From the hind margin of the thorax the cases of wing pads show. From these the dragon-fly pulled out the wings that expanded and carried it away. White lines show at the base of the rent. These are linings of tracheal, or breathing, tubes that were shed, too, as the old skeleton was cast off.

skeletal covering of its body but also the linings of its mouth, esophagus, and gizzard, the lining of its intestine, and the lining of its large *tracheae*, or breathing tubes. Since all these parts are lined with cuticle which is continuous at the mouth and anus with the skeletal covering of the body, they, too, must cast off their cuticle periodically to provide for the enlargement necessitated by growth (Figs. 21–22). A little reflection as to what all these changes entail will make clear what an extraordinary process molting is and what a remarkable experience it must be for an insect.

Every winged insect an adult insect. The second of the two facts referred to in the preceding paragraph is that, once having attained functional wings, no insect, excepting only the May-flies, ever molts again; and few insects, except the queens of termites and certain species of ants, ever increase materially in size. A winged insect

FIG. 23.—THE NEVADA BUCK MOTH CATERPILLARS LEAVE THEIR DISCARDED EXOSKELETONS AT THE TIPS OF STEMS.

In the business of growing up, insects leave behind many discarded suits of "childhood clothing." In some cases these suits are eaten by the former wearer, but not the spiny coats of the Nevada Buck Moth.

is a full-grown insect, and the old belief, still rather widespread, that little flies grow up to be big flies, and the belief that big flies lay the eggs for all other kinds, are pure myths. May-flies alone, out of all the myriad kinds of winged insects, molt after their wings become functional, and they molt but once more. The fertile females of termites and the queens or workers of certain ants are exceptions to the general rule that insects do not materially increase in size after attaining wings. The abdomens of these insects, owing to the development of great numbers of eggs in their ovaries or, in the case of worker honey ants, to the swallowing of enormous amounts of food, may enlarge through the stretching of the membranes between the segments until a proportionately tremendous size is attained and the insects are quite incapable of locomotion.

THE RELATION OF MOLTING TO METAMORPHOSIS

Molting is a necessity, because of the external nature of an insect's skeleton. It is also an opportunity, for during each molt, while the newly forming skeleton is soft and plastic, there is a chance for the insect to accomplish some of the changes which constitute metamorphosis.

FIG. 24.—IN ITS COMPLETE METAMORPHOSIS THE NEVADA BUCK MOTH WAS FIRST AN EGG, THEN A SPINY CATERPILLAR, AND AFTERWARD A PUPA BEFORE IT BECAME A MOTH.

Eggs of this moth are clustered like corn grains on a cob around the stem on the right. In the upper left are the exoskeletons, or exuviae, that the caterpillars cast to uncover the pupae of the lower left. On the right is a moth so recently emerged from the pupa that its wings are not yet expanded, and another with wings fully expanded.

Gradual metamorphosis and incomplete metamorphosis. In the case of insects having gradual metamorphosis or incomplete metamorphosis, the wing pads of the nymph or naiad, respectively, increase a little at each molt to provide room for the development of wing tissues within, and body proportions change so as to approximate more and more closely those of the adult (Figs. 15, 16, 19, 21, 109, and 124). By the time the last molt is reached, most of the work of transformation has been done and completion of the metamorphosis is easily accomplished.

Complete metamorphosis. In the case of insects having complete metamorphosis, the matter is not so simple. An insect larva molts time after time and no wing pads appear. Nor does the larva seem to change otherwise, except that it increases in size and its abdomen becomes proportionately larger. Then suddenly, all at one molt, it seems to change utterly and become, within the space of minutes, a pupa. Now, as has been pointed out already, a pupa looks something like a nymph if it be the pupa of a bee, a wasp, a beetle, or some neuropteran; less like a nymph if it be the pupa of a moth or a butterfly—except that, typically, it is quiescent (Figs. 17 and 27). It usually is not active and it does not feed as nymphs do. Its legs, antennae, and wing pads are folded against its sides and, in the case of butterflies and some moths, so closely cemented to the body wall and so smoothed over that only the outlines of the parts show. The quiescent character of insects at this time is the fact that suggested the name *pupa*, which is the Latin name for doll.

Internal development of wing pads in larvae. The suddenness of the transformation from larva to nymph-like pupa is more apparent than real, for the wing pads and, in the case of legless larvae such as fly maggots and the grubs of wasps and bees, the leg pads develop gradually, just as truly as wing pads develop gradually on nymphs, but they develop internally. Some time during the larval stage, tiny pockets form in the epidermis underneath the cuticle. In the bottom of each pocket a tiny wing bud or leg bud appears. (The term *bud* is used here to supplant the term *pad*.) The mouths of the pockets close so there is no external indication of their presence. In these pockets the wing and leg buds increase in size, molt by molt, much as the wing pads of nymphs do. There is this difference. The internal wing and leg buds of larvae do not appear quite so early as the external wing pads of nymphs, and they do not enlarge so rapidly until near the end of the larval stage.

The prepupa. At the close of the larval period the last larval cuticle is loosened from the body but is not cast off immediately. It is retained long enough to protect the insect during its transformation to the pupal form. First, the wing buds and leg buds move out of their pockets and come to lie alongside the body just beneath the loosened larval cuticle. Then the body segments change in shape until they resemble more or less closely the segments of the adult, and the thorax becomes differentiated from the abdomen. Eventually the larval cuticle is cast and the pupa is disclosed. During the transformation from larva to pupa beneath the loosened larval cuticle, the insect is known as a *prepupa*.

From the foregoing discussion it will be seen that the larval stages of an insect with complete metamorphosis correspond in a general way to all but the last, or the last two, nymphal stages of an insect with gradual metamorphosis, and that the pupa corresponds to the last nymphal stage. Larvae, however, differ from nymphs not only in the manner of development of wing pads and legs, but also in the fact that their heads are usually more simplified and their abdomens tremendously enlarged proportionately, chiefly through elongation. A partial explanation of this fact is that larvae seem to hatch from the eggs at an earlier stage of development, embryologically speaking, than do nymphs. Larvae also exhibit many structural specializations which are peculiar to them and are not possessed by nymphs. Nevertheless, it is clear that, in certain respects, larvae may be thought of as highly modified nymphs.

SIGNIFICANCE OF METAMORPHOSIS

An explanation of gradual or of incomplete metamorphosis appears simple enough. It is merely a process of development under the restrictions imposed by an external skeleton. An explanation of complete metamorphosis is not so easy, though the account given in the following paragraphs doubtless comes fairly near to the truth.

Complete metamorphosis and specialized environments. Insects with complete metamorphosis, as a rule, during some part or all of the life cycle inhabit more specialized environments or have relatively more specialized feeding habits than insects with gradual or incomplete metamorphosis. Moreover, the respects in which complete metamorphosis differs from these other types of metamorphosis represent adaptations to ensure successful living in these more specialized environments and with these more specialized feeding habits. Witness the larvae of beetles which burrow in soil or in the wood of trees (Figs. 25, 73, and 106); the larvae of ant-lions covered by dust and lying in wait for their prey (Fig. 180); the larvae of flies submerged in the flesh of a decaying animal; or the larvae of bees and wasps packed in waxen or paper cubbyholes (Figs. 154 and 155) and waiting to be fed by their nurses, the worker adults. Contrast the lives of such larvae with the lives of the free-ranging nymphs of grasshoppers, katydids, and true bugs (Figs. 15, 109, and 110), which feed more or less promiscuously on the soft tissues and juices of green plants.

Such insects as the termites, which have special modes of living and specialized food habits and yet exhibit gradual metamorphosis, appear on first thought to cast doubt on the statements just made. The doubt quickly disappears, however, when it is noted that the worker and toiler termites, which rarely leave their specialized environments, have become somewhat larviform (Figs. 112 and 160). Typical worker termites no longer develop even vestiges of wing pads but remain soft-bodied and big-abdomened all their lives. And note what has happened to those relatives of the grasshopper, the Jerusalem Cricket (Fig. 107) and the camel crickets (Fig. 110), which have forsaken the free-roving life of their ancestors and have taken up their abode in the soil and in the burrows of rodents. Never a trace of wing pads appears on them, and their abdomens, like those of the termites, remain permanently soft.

Differences in habits and habitats of larvae and adults. Another point of great significance is that the young of insects with complete metamorphosis generally inhabit environments differing from those of the adults or have different food habits, or both. It is the young which, through evolutionary changes in past ages, have made most of the adaptations to new foods and habitats. This is what has made them larvae. Adult insects have in most cases retained the free-roving habits, though they have not necessarily remained general feeders. Specialized habitats for young insects often are localized and widely separated. Specialized food supplies are restricted in quantity and temporary in character. It is generally necessary, therefore, that the adult insects possess functional wings and efficient legs to enable them more readily to find mates and to seek out the favorable larval environment or food supply in which to lay their eggs. In accordance, then, with these needs, the thorax of the adult is relatively large, strongly braced, and heavily muscled, to make it an efficient machine for carrying the insect about, and the abdomen is largely given over to the development of the reproductive organs.

To the larva, on the other hand, has been given the business of preparing for the momentous transition from a grub-like or worm-like creature, restricted in its activities and in the range of its wanderings, to the comparatively versatile, free-living, far-ranging adult. How, during the ages of insect evolution, has the larva acquired the ability to prepare for this transition?

Larval specializations. First, as already noted, it has eliminated, to the extent required by its particular environment, the encumbering legs and wing pads. To the beetle larva, gnawing its way through solid wood, wing pads would be a liability, a danger; they have been withdrawn into the body. To wood-boring larvae, to larvae that burrow in soil, and to fly larvae squirming through the flesh of a dead animal or a pile of decaying vegetable matter, speed in running can have little if any importance. In such insects we find that legs have often been reduced to mere stubs, or even done away with entirely and fleshy tubercles substituted for them (Fig. 73).

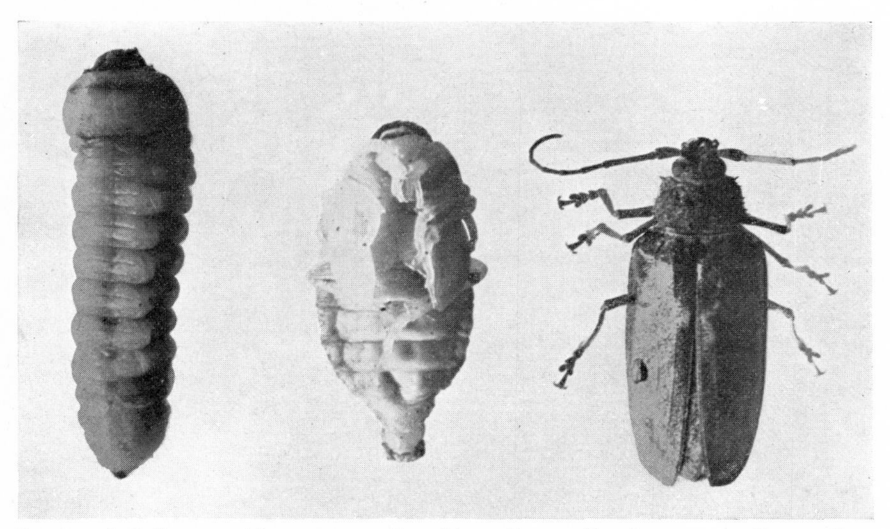

FIG. 25.—IT IS COMPLETE METAMORPHOSIS THAT MAKES POSSIBLE THE CHANGE FROM LEGLESS GRUB TO NYMPH-LIKE PUPA TO WINGED ADULT IN THE LIFE OF THE PINE SAWYER.

Complete metamorphosis has made possible great specializations in the life of an insect—specializations in eating and reproduction. Because of this type of metamorphosis the legless grub on the left can spend its time cutting tunnels, with chisel-like mandibles, through dead pine trees. Eventually this grub transforms into the pupa in the center, that resembles a nymph because of its free legs and wing cases. Finally, as the pupa sheds its covering, the winged adult Pine Sawyer (*Ergates spiculatus*) appears.

Larvae living in concealment not only do not need legs and wings, but they hardly need heads. The need for heads, with their specialized sense organs, is associated with speed in locomotion and the consequent necessity of avoiding obstacles; with exposure to enemies and the necessity for recognizing them in time to flee or prepare for combat; with a free-ranging life and the necessity of finding food, mates, and shelter from a distance. The most specialized types of larvae, living surrounded by mountains of food, protected from most enemies, and unable to range far and wide, have no need for specialized heads, and have dispensed with them (Figs. 46 and 177).

The larva spends its time eating. It does little else. It eats enormous quantities of food, not only to provide for its own growth but to accumulate a sufficient surplus to meet all the requirements of the pupal stage when feeding will be impossible. Some larvae eat still more, storing a surplus even for the adult stage. The adults which develop from such larvae have dwarfed mouth parts and partake of no food (Figs. 18 and 179). It is this business of feeding that provides

Fig. 26.—Less Than Three Weeks Will Pass before the Monarch Caterpillar on the Lower Side of the Stem Will Become as Large as the One on the Upper.

The caterpillar on the lower side of the milkweed stem is about two days old and has molted once. In three weeks it will molt several more times (and eat its cast skin each time) and will multiply its size by several hundred-fold to become as large as the fully-grown Monarch caterpillar on the upper side of the stem.

an explanation of the apparently disproportionately large abdomen of the larva. A large abdomen is needed to contain the extensive digestive apparatus employed in feeding. Abundant storage space is needed to hold the accumulated surplus of food. If the abdomen of a highly specialized insect larva be opened, the space between the internal organs and the body wall will be seen to be almost completely filled with surplus food in the form of fat.

The significance of the pupal stage. The answer to the question as to why there should be a quiescent, nonfeeding pupal stage seems to be that the transition from the immature feeding machine to the free-ranging adult reproductive machine is too great to be accomplished at a single molt. The changes are too profound. During the course of evolution, then, the rest periods associated with the last and next to the last molts were gradually lengthened to encroach on the intervening feeding period. More and more time was needed for the

(Photograph by Lester Brubaker)

FIG. 27.—AN OVAL CHAMBER IN THE EARTH SERVES AS A COCOON FOR THIS PUPA OF A TOBACCO HORNWORM.

Unlike the caterpillars which spin cocoons, the Tobacco Hornworm and many other moth caterpillars burrow into the soil and there, by pressing the earth outward in all directions, construct oval pupation chambers which protect them as completely as any cocoon ever made. Butterfly caterpillars, with few exceptions, neither spin cocoons nor burrow, but form naked, exposed pupae. To transform to a moth the Hornworm pupa covering must split open and the proboscis be pulled forth from the "pitcher handle," the wings from the pads above the "handle," and the big pursy abdomen from the segments with their spiracles for breathing which show above and behind the wing pads.

adaptive changes preparatory to the attaining of adulthood. Finally, feeding in the last immature stage was eliminated entirely. The feeding needs, ordinarily met during this last stage of immaturity, were transferred to the stages preceding, and the pupa as a distinct stage in the development of insects came into being.

In the discussion as presented here the impression may have been given that the larval stage became definitely established before the pupal stage. This may have been true in certain insect groups, but it was not true in others. In many cases the evolution of the larva and the quiescent pupa probably occurred simultaneously. In other insects, such as certain species of thrips and of termites, a quiescent pupa was developed long ago, but there is as yet no specialized larval stage. At least the young of these thrips and termites are no more worm-like than are the young of other species. Moreover, although a definite pupal stage exists, it is customary to refer to these insects as undergoing gradual metamorphosis.

Physiological specialization in the pupal stage. The evolution of complete metamorphosis did not stop with the differentiation of larval and pupal stages. The pupa, as well as the larva, has become still more specialized. In the highest insect types, such as the true flies and the higher Lepidoptera and Hymenoptera, much of this additional specialization is physiological. Behind the immobile skeletal exterior there is amazing internal activity, the entire insect being remade. The changes involved in this remaking are poorly understood as yet, but we do know that, not infrequently, nearly the whole of the internal organs of the pupa disintegrate into a nutrient-charged liquid. Only here and there little islands of functional cells remain, and around these as centers the insect is rebuilt.

When the regeneration is complete, the new insect lies packed in the pupal cuticle awaiting the stimuli which will awaken it to renewed activity and cause it to burst forth a fully developed, scintillating adult. Truly, insects are extraordinary creatures!

CHAPTER IV

THE GROWING UP OF A SWALLOWTAIL BUTTERFLY

DETAILED photographic studies have been made of a swallowtail, the Western Parsley Butterfly (*Papilio zelicaon* Lucas). Because these studies cover all phases of larval life, pupation, and emergence of the adult from the pupa, a separate chapter is presented on this example of complete metamorphosis. It will serve as a guide to present the general picture of the amazing changes that occur in this type of growing up.

The Western Parsley Butterfly occurs commonly in the lowlands of the Far West, and is the most conspicuous swallowtail of this region. The beautiful adult is a prize for the net of every butterfly collector and can frequently be seen throughout the spring, summer, and fall months. Though the larvae feed on several species of the Parsley family, they are found most abundantly on Sweet Fennel or Sweet Anise (*Foeniculum vulgare* (L.) Gaerth). This introduced weed is common along the roadsides, and clumps of it can hardly be examined carefully without disclosing eggs or larvae of this butterfly. The material was brought to the laboratory and the full life history observed and recorded in pictures (Fig. 28).

Eggs and larvae. The eggs are spherical, creamy-white structures and are attached separately to the food plants. The larva at hatching is spiny, essentially black, with a white saddle over one and a portion of a second of the central abdominal segments. In addition to this saddle, tiny white spots make a tessellated pattern over the remainder of the body (Fig. 30). This condition is in surprising contrast to the smooth, black, orange, and green creature of the later larval life.

Fig. 28.—These Are Materials of a Laboratory Butterfly Farm.
On this cluster of Sweet Fennel may be seen larvae, a pupa, and an adult of the Swallowtail Butterfly.

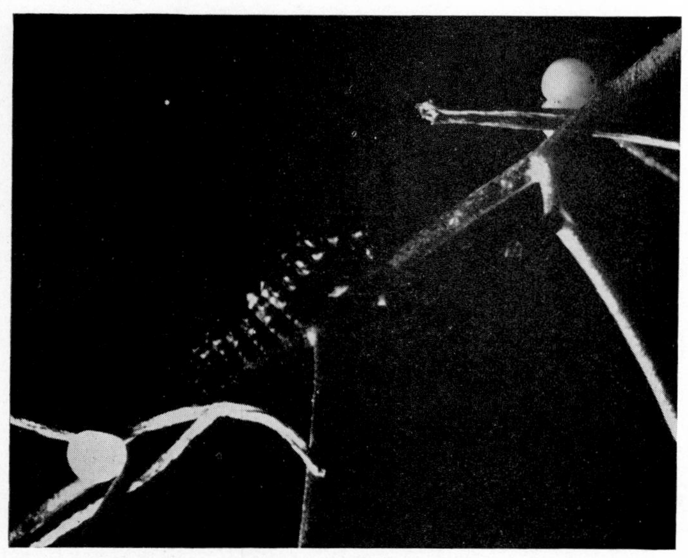

Fig. 29.—Here Are Eggs of the Swallowtail Butterfly and a Recently Hatched Larva.
The eggs are attached singly to the food plant, and the larva in the beginning is spiny and black with white spots.

The larva, as is characteristic of the larvae of most insects with complete metamorphosis, feeds voraciously and constantly upon its

FIG. 30.—THIS SWALLOWTAIL LARVA IS CRAWLING AWAY FROM ITS EXOSKELETON WHICH IT HAS JUST MOLTED.

FIG. 31.—THESE THREE STAGES IN THE LIFE OF SWALLOWTAIL LARVAE SHOW STRIKING CHANGES. A newly hatched larva is "peering" from behind the central twig. The larva at the right has molted two or three times and is about one-fourth grown, and the larva at the left is nearly full grown but is still eating.

food material, except at the period of molt. At this time also, as is characteristic, the larva is quiet for a period, then molts its exoskeleton, leaving the latter in the manner shown in Fig. 30. This is what one would expect. Our observations did not show that the exoskeleton is ever eaten as is the case with certain lepidopterous insects such as the Monarch Butterfly.

Molting by the young larva of the swallowtail, while it has its spiny exoskeleton, is repeated three or four times. In a later molt, usually the next to the last, it loses its spiny covering with the black-and-white saddle and presents the last larval form, which is smooth and strikingly green and black, with occasional orange spots within the black blotchings (Fig. 31).

FIG. 32.—SCENT SACS, OR *Osmeteria*, ARE POPPED FORTH FROM THE FIRST THORACIC SEGMENT TO DRIVE SWALLOWTAIL ENEMIES AWAY.

These sacs, as the name indicates, throw into the air a pungent odor, which may be a satisfactory defense against birds.

Like all lepidopterous larvae, the growth of the swallowtail is prodigious during warm weather. In one definite record the growth was completed in seventeen days. In that length of time the larva multiplied its hatching size by several hundred times as is shown by the newly hatched larva of Fig. 31, in comparison with the full-grown larva of the same illustration.

Enemies of the swallowtail. In our experience, the commonest enemy of the swallowtail was a tiny wasp of the family Braconidae (Figs. 174 and 175) that parasitized the newly hatched larvae. The larva of the wasp grew so rapidly within the body of the swallowtail caterpillar that it attained its full growth and emerged while the caterpillar was still only a fourth of an inch in length. While its host still lived and wriggled slightly, the braconid larva spun its cocoon directly beside it. In its spinning the braconid would, from time to time, push up its victim with thrusts of its body as it spun its silk in the cocoon making (Fig. 174).

FIG. 33.—THIS SWALLOWTAIL CATERPILLAR WHEN NEARLY FULL GROWN IS STRIKINGLY GREEN AND BLACK WITH ORANGE SPOTS.

Its simple eyes and minute antennae make it necessary for the larva to search for food by lifting the body and swinging it back and forth. Here it is shown searching and then feeding after the food is found.

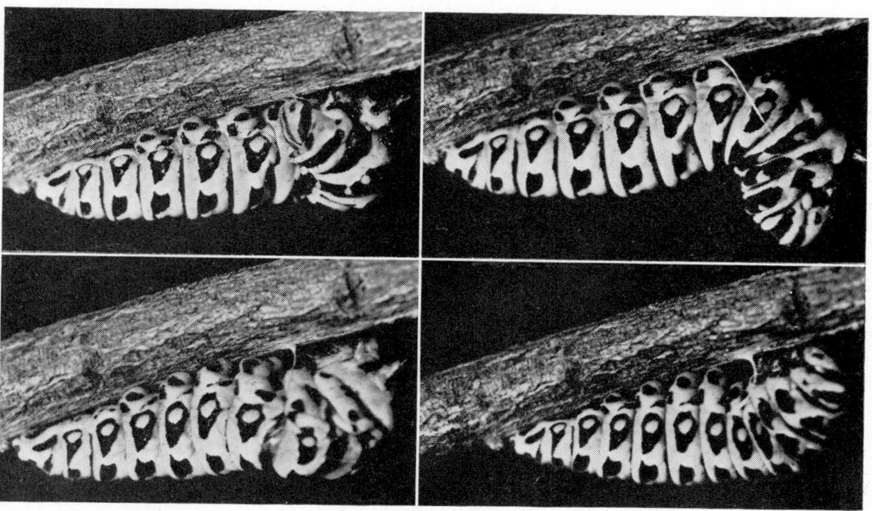

FIG. 34.—THE SWALLOWTAIL LARVA MUST SPIN A GIRDLE TO SUSPEND THE BODY BEFORE IT CAN COMPLETE PUPATION.

Here it is shown with the anal props clasping a pad of silk, and in the various steps that are taken in attaching and spinning the thread that makes the girdle.

Parasitism became more and more pronounced in the swallowtail larvae as the season advanced. There was a characteristic lag in parasitism early in the season, but gradually the parasites built up in number as the season advanced, so that with this swallowtail a large percentage of the larvae collected in August was parasitized.

Defense against enemies. This swallowtail has a striking defensive structure which, though ineffective against braconid wasps, probably is useful against large enemies such as birds. This defensive structure consists of two sacs invaginated in the first segment posterior to the head. These sacs, bright orange in color, are popped forth precipitately (Fig. 32) when the caterpillar is touched or molested. They give off a disagreeable, pungent odor from chemicals which they contain. The sacs, or *osmeteria*, are quickly withdrawn when the enemy removes its molesting presence.

Pupation, the girdle. In its preparation to pupate, the swallowtail larva crawls to the underside of a stem or other support and spins first a pad of silk, then turns and clasps this pad with its anal props. It then builds a slight bed of silk from posterior pad to anterior end. Next it spins the "girdle" which is to suspend the pupa.

In spinning the girdle the larva reaches back to a point just at the side of the first pair of abdominal prolegs for the attachment. With the silk thread apparently held between the first and second pairs of thoracic legs, the larva swings back and away from the stem until the anterior part of the body, including the first pair of abdominal prolegs, is nearly at right angles to the stem. It continues in an arc and swings up to the opposite side of the stem and there makes a second attachment.

To make an attachment the larva works its head back and forth for some seconds as if it were pasting. Then it starts the arc back, out, and to the other side. As it progresses along the thread, it moves the head back and forth through short distances, but farther in one direction than in the other, thus maintaining the general body movement.

Observation shows that the time occupied in working over the entire arc, from one side to the other, is two minutes. Some thirty loops, back and forth, are made. The thread increases visibly in size as the larva works. When the process of girdle making is completed the larva pulls its head back to the thoracic legs and against the stem, and then straightens out. The girdle thus comes to encircle the anterior part of the abdomen of the caterpillar. With one or two stretchings and adjusting movements the process is completed. Almost a full hour was required for the making of the girdle by the specimens observed (Fig. 34).

Pupation, last larval molt. About twenty-four hours elapse from the first evidence of preparation for pupation until the girdle is finished. About thirty-six more hours elapse before the pupation takes place. During this time the insect, now called the *prepupa,* has loosened, one pair at a time, the hold of its abdominal prolegs on the stem. Eventually the entire length of the body, excepting only the anal props, is supported by the silken girdle.

Fig. 35.—The Most Spectacular Molt Performed by the Larva Is That Which Uncovers the Pupa.

Here, from left to right in each row of pictures, are shown the steps by which the last larval cuticle is discarded.

Evidence that the suspended larva is about to molt the larval exoskeleton is shown by its gradual dulling and wrinkling. The larva also throws its head region down and so straightens. Following the straightening of the head, the exoskeleton splits on the dorsal surface near the head; and the larval covering, with a series of telescoping movements, is rapidly worked to the posterior end of the body (Fig. 35).

This simple description gives no hint of the startling things that take place during the brief period while the exoskeleton is being shed. For instance, Fig. 35 shows a striking line along the abdominal wall, which is probably caused by the withdrawal of the linings of the

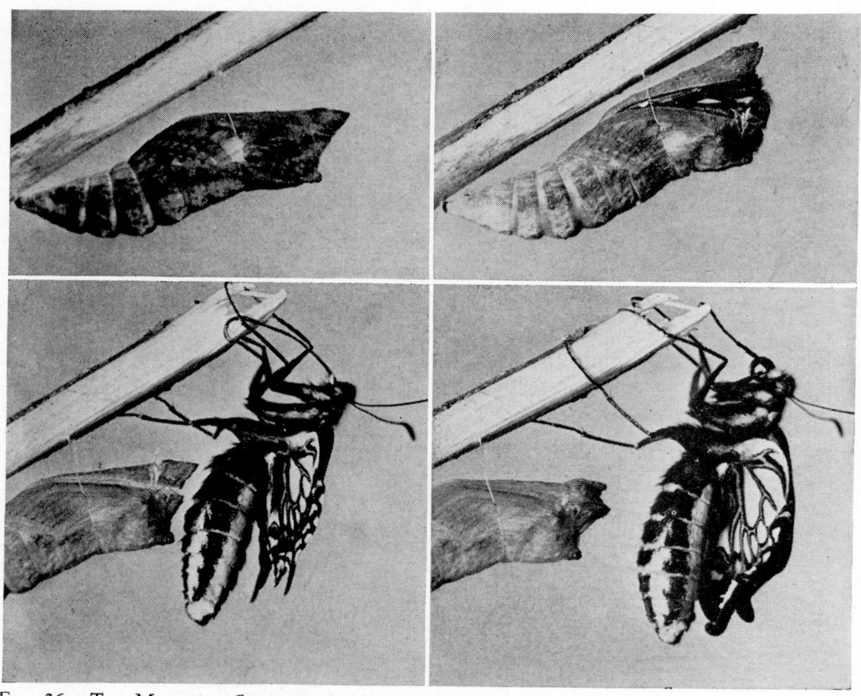

Fig. 36.—The Magic of Complete Metamorphosis Reaches Its Pinnacle in the Emergence of the Adult from the Pupa Case.

Just before emergence, the markings of the wings show through the wing cases and the constrictions of the abdominal segments are pronounced. The pupa case then breaks and the adult crawls forth, with pursy abdomen and tiny wings, to arrange its mouth parts and to fill the veins of the wings with blood that they may expand.

tracheae in the region of the spiracles there. During this process the pupal mouth parts, antennae, and legs, in which the corresponding organs of the adult develop, are pulled forth from the old larval head and thoracic regions, and stretched along the ventral surface of the pupal abdomen.

Lastly, before the larval covering is discarded, a process called a *cremaster* that is covered with tiny hooks and is borne by the tip of the pupal abdomen is withdrawn from the posterior end of the larval skin and seated in the pad of silk that surrounds the abdominal tip. When this has been done, the larval skin is entirely discarded and the pupal form presented.

FIG. 37.—THE SWALLOWTAIL BECOMES A FULLY FORMED ADULT IN A SPACE OF TEN MINUTES AFTER EMERGENCE FROM THE PUPA CASE.

The abdomen becomes smaller by a discharge of material from the anal opening and by the pumping of blood into the wings. The mouth parts are at last fitted together and coiled and the wings are fully formed with the "tails" straight. This gorgeous adult has been an egg, a larva, and a pupa.

The pupa. In twelve cases in which exact records were obtained, the pupa hung in its girdle an average of thirteen and a half days. The shortest period was twelve days; the longest was fifteen. These records were made during the months of July and August, the time becoming increasingly longer as August advanced. During the pupal stage nearly all of the structures that are present in the larva break down and are remade into wings, legs, mouth parts, body wall, and internal organs of the adult.

The adult. When the adult is about to emerge, the black and yellow markings of the wings become visible through the wing pads of the pupa and the creases between the abdominal segments become more pronounced. Within a few hours after these changes first become visible the pupal shell breaks open and the adult emerges.

The line along which the breaking occurs follows the margins of the entire head region and the outer margins of the wing pads. The posterior tip of the lid-like structure remains attached, so the emerging adult lifts it up like a lid and crawls forth. As soon as the adult is free of the pupa covering, the lid drops back to close the abandoned case (Fig. 36).

The adult, with legs and antennae free, climbs to the support from which the pupa case hangs, and the expansion of wings begins immediately. The abdomen is surprisingly pursy in the beginning, and frequently throughout the period of wing expansion quantities of milky fluid are discharged from the anal opening. In addition, the abdomen becomes increasingly smaller because blood is forced from it into the wing veins to cause the expansion of the wings. This change in abdominal size is strikingly illustrated in Figs. 36 and 37.

The wings expand rapidly. In the beginning they show many folds, looking like crumpled paper, but in about ten minutes they acquire their full size and final form. It is truly amazing that such elaborate changes can occur in so short a period. Our proof that the swallowtail was completely formed was indicated by the fact that the "tails" became straight at this point.

In addition to working the abdomen in discharging milky fluid and reducing its size by squeezing liquid into the veins of the wings, the adult butterfly spends considerable time in fitting the maxillae together to make the proboscis. The two maxillae develop separately in the pupa and, in consequence, must be fitted to each other. For some minutes after emergence the adult rolls and unrolls them in the process of seating them firmly together. This activity is well illustrated by Figs. 36 and 37.

Though development of the wings to full size is completed in a period of about ten minutes, the wings are not sufficiently hardened to allow flight until an hour or more has elapsed. Then the now truly magnificent creature, having come through the most remarkable of changes in growing up—having changed from a caterpillar with short legs, chewing mouth parts, simple eyes, and negligible antennae, to a gorgeous adult butterfly with long legs, mouth parts for sucking, compound eyes, long and sensitive antennae, and wings of scintillating beauty—has come to the last stage in that marvelous process of metamorphosis that is complete.

CHAPTER V

INSECT FOODS AND FEEDING HABITS

THE kinds of materials used as food by insects are diverse, though not as much so as the insects which eat them. Many kinds of insects, differing markedly in structure and appearance, may eat the same kind of food. Nevertheless, insect foods embrace an amazing variety of substances.

Variety of insect foods. Insect foods include almost every kind of organic matter which conceivably could furnish nourishment for any living thing. They range from liquids, such as the blood of vertebrates and other animals and the juices of succulent plants, to materials as densely solid as the heartwood of trees; from the tissues of living plants and animals to the dried or decaying remnants of their long-dead bodies. They include the secretions of both plants and animals. They include animal excrement and the microorganisms which share with insects in the decomposition of this same excrement. Even the humus of the soil, which has been derived chiefly from plant remains but has been changed so much that its plant origin is almost unrecognizable, furnishes food for certain insects. In the face of all this diversity an intelligent comprehension of insect foods and of insect adaptations for food getting would be difficult to acquire were it not for a few outstanding facts and relationships.

Classes of feeders. With few if any exceptions, insects may be grouped into four great categories according to the nature of the food they eat. Some species are not particular as to what they eat, consuming indiscriminately both plant and animal matter. They are called *omnivores*, eaters of everything. Many insects restrict their diet to vegetable matter and so are *vegetarians*. Others feed only on the substance of animals. They are *carnivores*. The fourth category is not really distinct, for it is made up of representatives from the other three. It consists of the *scavengers*. Scavengers eat only dead plant or animal material, especially if it be partly decayed. In addition to these fairly well-defined classes there is a small miscellany of insects which are difficult to classify on the basis of foods or feeding habits.

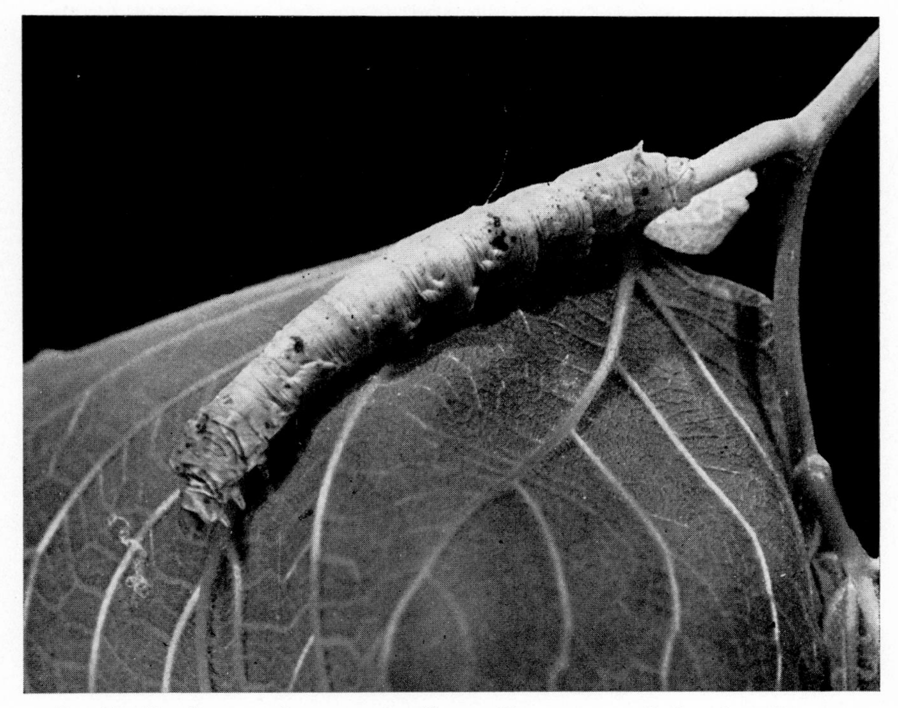

FIG. 38.—THE ORIENTAL SILK-WORM IS A TYPICAL HERBIVORE, FOR IT EATS ONLY LEAVES. This caterpillar of the Oriental Silk Moth (*Bombyx mori*) is a restricted feeder, however, for its diet is limited largely to mulberry leaves.

Whether the primitive ancestors of modern insects belonged to some one or to all of these categories cannot now be determined, but it is interesting to speculate concerning their food habits. There are good reasons for believing that the first insects were vegetarians, though biologists are by no means agreed on this point. For example, it is a well-known fact that the basic food supply of all animals consists of plant life. This is as true for the carnivores as it is for the vegetarians, since the animals which serve as prey to the carnivores are creatures which in turn have eaten plants. Furthermore, carnivores are either fewer in number or smaller in size than the species on which they feed. And the abundance of carnivores is determined more or less directly by the abundance of vegetarians. Hence there must have been vegetarians before there could have been carnivores. It is logical to conclude, therefore, that animals which eat plants are more ancient as a class than those which eat other animals. An obvious corollary to this conclusion is that the meat-eaters have evolved from vegetable-eating ancestors. But what is true for animals as a whole is not necessarily true for any single class of animals, such as the insects. The members of any single class may have displayed uniform feeding habits from their very inception as a class. On the other hand, they may have changed in feeding habits, shifting from one type of food to another or becoming more diversified. It is certain that insects have become more diversified, but their status before diversification began is not certain. If it were, there would be no occasion for our present speculation.

What the first insects on this earth were like we do not know, for the simple reason that no fossil remains of them have yet been found. The best we can do, then, is to study the most ancient types of which we have any knowledge, and formulate our conclusions accordingly. Even then we can reason only indirectly. From a study of the mouth parts of those insect fossils in which the mouth parts have been preserved, we can determine something, for mouth-part structure provides us with the surest clues we have concerning the foods eaten by insects. This fact will be made clear in the next chapter. From the known feeding habits of the nearest living relatives of the earliest fossil insects we can perhaps draw still more valid conclusions, for insects, like men, are judged "by the company they keep."

In the most ancient rocks that are known to contain insect fossils there are remains of a few creatures of doubtful character which appear to have been built on the general plan of the wingless Silver-fish (Figs. 108 and 170), a member of the most primitive order of living insects. If the first insects were of this type, then they were predominantly vegetarians, though they may have had a slight penchant for animal food.

A far more numerous lot in these ancient rocks, however, are the fossils of primitive cockroaches, dragon-flies, and May-flies. There are members, too, of a still more primitive and now long extinct order known as the *Palaeodictyoptera*. Translated, Palaeodictyoptera means "ancient net winged." The nature of the feeding habits of the ancient net-winged insects can only be conjectured, but as to the primitive cockroaches, dragon-flies, and May-flies of long ago, the case is different. They have relatives living today whose behavior illuminates the past of these their ancestors.

All existing May-flies (Fig. 68), so far as is known, are vegetarians. Existing dragon-flies (Fig. 1), without exception, are strictly carnivores. Of modern cockroaches, the more primitive species are vegetarians, the less primitive species often are omnivores. In so far as the habits of these modern May-flies, dragon-flies, and cockroaches throw light on the habits of their ancestors, one may conclude that the ancient May-flies were vegetarians and the dragon-flies were carnivores, whereas the cockroaches may have been either vegetarians or omnivores.

The conclusion just stated does not seem to have got us very far. At the same time, an interesting and valuable by-product of our efforts has come to light. The study of ancient and modern cockroaches, May-flies, dragon-flies, and of the ancient net-winged insects has revealed the fact that none of these insects displays any of the specializations found among modern beetles, bugs, butterflies, flies, bees, and wasps. They may have been omnivores, vegetarians, or carnivores; but no matter what they were, they were general feeders. The specialized orders of insects, and the multitudinous specializations and restrictions in foods and feeding habits that exist among the vegetarians and carnivores of today, have come into existence since the ancient heyday of the insect primitives. Some of the specializations will be considered shortly.

Dependence of insects on plant life. Because all insect food comes originally from green plants, plant abundance determines insect abundance. In any locality or region the abundance of individual insects and the number and variety of insect species are roughly proportionate to the abundance and variety of plant life. For example, insects are more abundant in the wooded strip along a stream or around a lake or pond than they are in the drier fields or prairies away from streams or ponds. They are relatively scarce in desert regions where plant life is scanty, and are extremely abundant in the wet portions of the tropics where vegetation is luxuriant.

This close correlation between plant life and insect abundance is strikingly shown in the spring of the year by the tremendous increase of vegetarian insects. The new growth of succulent green vegetation provides a bounteous food supply for literally millions of caterpillars, beetle larvae, and sucking bugs (Figs. 15, 39, and 124). To these hosts are added millions of bees and other insects which come out from hibernation or emerge as adults from overwintering pupae to feed on the nectar and pollen produced by spring flowers (Fig. 161 and 162). As spring passes into summer and summer into fall there is a slowing down in the rate of plant growth. This is reflected in a corresponding slowing down in the rate of increase of vegetarian insects. In regions of very dry summers, such as the interior valleys of the Pacific Coast states and the deserts of the Southwest, the slowing down of plant growth occurs in early or late spring and is followed in summer by a complete cessation of new growth. In these regions, consequently, there is an early decrease and an ultimate cessation in the multiplication of those insects which feed on new growth.

Not all insects which feed on plants, however, eat the succulent new parts. Many feed on the older, and therefore tougher, parts. Such insects are much less affected by the seasonal changes in plant life and show less variation in seasonal abundance, for the older parts of plants are available more or less continuously throughout most of the year. Such insects as the beetle larvae (Figs. 25, 73 and 106) and termites (Figs. 112 and 160), which feed on dead wood (Figs. 41 and 42), or the scavengers, which subsist on any kind of vegetable debris, exhibit no seasonal fluctuations which can be ascribed to variations in food supply.

OMNIVORES

Typical omnivores are to be found in several orders of insects. The domestic cockroaches, which too often haunt our kitchens and bathrooms, are omnivores. So, also, are the common Black Cricket (Figs. 20 and 93), the House-fly, and various species of yellowjackets (Figs. 147–158). A less widely known but far more interesting omnivore is that big-headed, wise-looking relative of the katydids, the Jerusalem Cricket (Fig. 107), an inhabitant of the semiarid West and Southwest. Jerusalem Crickets in the field and laboratory have been observed to eat potatoes, carrots, and other root vegetables, apples, grasshoppers, earthworms, beetle larvae, and other Jerusalem Crickets. One large captive specimen even killed and partially devoured a baby horned lizard ("horned toad").

VEGETARIANS

Generalized feeders. A number of the better known common insects belong to this group. Several species of destructive grasshoppers and crickets (Fig. 164), the army-worm and other cutworms, the Woolly Bear caterpillars (Figs. 82 and 177), the caterpillar of the White-lined Sphinx Moth (Fig. 162), and the common diabroticas (often incorrectly called *Green Ladybugs*) are vegetarians which consume a miscellany of green vegetable matter. Most vegetarian insects, however, are restricted or specialized feeders; that is, they can eat but few kinds of plants or only special parts of plants.

Restriction to a small number of plants. This is the simplest type of specialization among vegetarian insects. The caterpillar of the Cabbage Butterfly feeds chiefly on cabbage, cauliflower, and Brussels sprouts, but will eat various other closely related members of the mustard family. In addition, it feeds on the quite unrelated garden nasturtium (*Tropaeolum sp.*). The nasturtium seems to be singled out for special favor because of its peppery flavor, which is similar to that of the members of the mustard family. The Oriental Silk-worm (Fig. 38) prefers mulberry leaves but in the absence of these will eat the leaves of Osage Orange.

Some restricted vegetarians feed only on certain of the lower plants. For example, in the water of swift mountain streams there are to be found numerous flattened May-fly naiads, clinging to the stones in the stream bed, getting their food supply by scraping from the slippery rock surfaces the one-celled diatoms and other minute algae to which the slipperiness is due.

Then there are the fungus-eaters, or *fungivores*, as they are called. These fall into two groups: those which feed on the substance of various fungi occurring naturally, and those which cultivate particular species of fungi in gardens of their own making.

The first group includes the well-known "worms" that are found in mushrooms. If any mushroom or "toadstool" more than four or five days old is picked and broken up it will nearly always be found infested with the translucent or whitish larvae of the fungus gnats, or Mycetophilidae. These larvae are so numerous and so active that in a few days they will reduce a large mushroom to a small pile of gray or brown pulp, if they do not consume it entirely. Other species of fungus-gnat larvae may be found beneath loose bark on dead trees and rotting logs, feeding on the molds and other wood-destroying fungi that are present. In company with the latter insects are to be found, occasionally, members of that curious family of Hemiptera, the flat-bugs (Aradidae). With long slender beaks they suck the juices from wood-destroying fungi.

The second group of fungivores includes the fungus-eating ants of our Southwest and of the tropics. It also includes the ambrosia beetles. These small beetles are wood-borers, excavating burrows in the solid wood of recently felled trees. The adult beetles carry about with them, on their heads and mouth parts, the spores of certain fungi. The fungi constitute the *ambrosia* from which the beetles get their name. The spores are "planted" in piles of minute wood chips in the beetle burrows. The spores germinate and produce extensive growths of fungus filaments which derive their sustenance from the chips and from the wood forming the adjacent walls of the burrows. The adult and larval ambrosia beetles then feed on the fungus filaments. Ambrosia beetles are said even to fertilize their "mushroom beds," using their own excrement and that of their larvae. Several species of ambrosia beetles occur in the United States.

Restrictions to certain tissues or parts of plants. Under this heading there are to be noted inmumerable specializations among vegetarian insects. There are *herbivores*, insects which devour only foliage, such as the aforementioned Oriental Silk-worm or the caterpillars of the Gypsy Moth; there are *root-eaters*, such as the white grubs which grow up to be May-beetles and June-bugs; and there are *stem-miners* such as the European Corn Borer and the Asparagus Miner.

Other vegetarians of restricted diet are the *leaf-miners*, insects so small that they are able to live inside a leaf (Fig. 100). They eat the soft green pulp between the upper and lower surfaces of the leaf, making the "mines" from which they get their name. The Chrysanthemum Leaf-miner is a widely distributed species that works in the leaves of chrysanthemums, Shasta Daisies, marguerites, and related plants. All leaf-miners are larval forms. Most of them are the larvae of small moths or flies, but some are beetle larvae and some belong to the order Hymenoptera.

One very large group of restricted plant-feeders, the *juice-suckers*, which includes most of the true bugs, feed only on the juices of plants, sucking these out of the softer tissues with needle-like beaks. Well-known members of this group are the Squash-bug, the Harlequin

Cabbage-bug (Fig. 124) and the Spotted Milkweed-bug (Figs. 15 and 125) of the order Hemiptera. Other forms, belonging to the order Homoptera, are the cicadas (Figs. 19, 98, and 126), leaf-hoppers, tree-hoppers, spittle-bugs (Fig. 84), aphids (Fig. 39), and scale-insects (Figs. 171–173).

Another company of specialized vegetarians, the *anthophilous insects*, includes many adult moths and butterflies, wasps, bees, beetles, and flies, which feed on the nectar produced by flowers

FIG. 39.—APHIDS, OR PLANT-LICE, YOUNG AND OLD, SUCK JUICES FROM PLANTS.
With needle-like piercing beaks, aphids puncture the succulent tissues of green plants and suck out the nutritious contents of living cells. Both the winged aphid, in the middle of the picture, and the wingless one behind it are fully grown.

(Fig. 162) or on pollen, or on both. These eaters of pollen and nectar render an invaluable service to plants and, incidentally, to man in return for the nectar and pollen they take. From flower to flower they carry pollen (Fig. 161), thus ensuring the fertilization of the ovules so necessary for the production of seed. The importance to man of this pollen-carrying service is discussed at some length in Chapter XV.

Seed-eaters. Certain vegetarian insects restrict their diet to seeds. Everyone knows that there are minute weevils which feed on beans, peas, corn, wheat, and other grains. Almost everyone is familiar, too, with the caterpillars of certain small moths, the "worms" which get into flour, corn meal, and various breakfast cereals manufactured from grains. The number of these seed-eaters is legion, for the seeds of practically all plants, except those of extremely small size, are eaten by one or more kinds of insects. Not all seed-eating insects are minute, however. Many of our larger ants are seed-eaters. In the western part of the United States there are several species of harvesting ants which collect and store immense quantities of seeds from weeds and other low-growing vegetation.

Among the most interesting of the specialized vegetarians are the *gall-insects*, makers of some of the peculiar and varied plant growths knows as *galls* (Fig. 40). A gall is an abnormal growth that looks like a wart or a swelling. Many galls are caused by fungi or by mites, and some are caused by worms, but most are due to insects. Most gall-making insects in the United States belong either to the order Diptera or to the order Hymenoptera. Some are members of the order Homoptera and some of the orders Lepidoptera and Coleoptera.

Insect galls are found on many kinds of plants but they are most numerous on oak trees, willows, and wild roses. Two common and widely known galls are the Spiny Rose-gall and the Pine-cone Willow-gall. The former is caused by a gall-wasp (*Rhodites bicolor*). The gall is colored much like a strawberry and often looks as tempting. The Pine-cone Willow-gall consists of a willow bud peculiarly enlarged and modified to resemble a small pine cone. It is caused by a small fly, *Rhabdophaga strobiloides*, the larva of which lives in the center of the gall and feeds on the gall tissues.

The largest of all known insect galls (Fig. 40) is one of the so-called *oak apple* galls and grows on the Garry, Blue, Valley, Scrub, and Leather Oaks of the Pacific Coast. It is caused by the gall-wasp, *Andricus californicus*, and its varieties. In the fall or winter the adult female gall-wasp stings the twigs of the tree and lays her eggs beneath the bark. During the following spring the eggs hatch and the young wasp larvae begin to grow. At the same time, the tissues of the oak surrounding the waspling are stimulated to produce the familiar oak apple. The first indication of the gall is a slight enlargement; then the bark of the twig bursts and the gall shows through, a shiny smooth-surfaced ball which grows rapidly until it attains its maximum size. It is green and succulent to begin with, but ultimately becomes tan-colored, corky, and dry. In the center of the gall are from one to several small oval chambers, each of which contains a wasp larva. The size and shape attained by the gall depend on the number of gall-insects developing within it. If there is but one, the gall may not exceed an inch in diameter and be spherical in shape. If the gall develops as a compound structure around several larvae which hatch from eggs that are laid close together, it may become a huge sausage-shaped growth as much as three inches in diameter and four inches in length. The *Andricus* larva derives its food from the delicate tissue lining the chamber in which it lies. In late summer

Fig. 40.—The Activities of Tiny Gall-wasps Cause Oak Apples to Grow.
The light-colored galls are of the present year; the dark ones are two or more years old and are blackened by sooty fungi.

the larva transforms into a pupa and then into an adult wasp. The wasp cuts its way out of the gall with its mandibles and sometime between October and February, depending on geographic location and environmental influences, emerges to lay the eggs for a new generation.

There are many vegetarian insects which subsist on the wood and bark of trees and shrubs. They are called *lignivores*. Some of these, such as the caterpillars of the Carpenter Moth (*Prionoxystus robiniae*), the larvae of the horn-tail wasps, the beetle larvae known as *round-headed borers* (Figs. 25 and 73) and *flat-headed borers*, eat the solid wood of living or dead trees through which they excavate burrows. In this group, also, are the larvae of the powder-post beetles (Fig. 106), which feed upon dry, thoroughly cured woods. Natives of arid or desert regions where available dead wood is

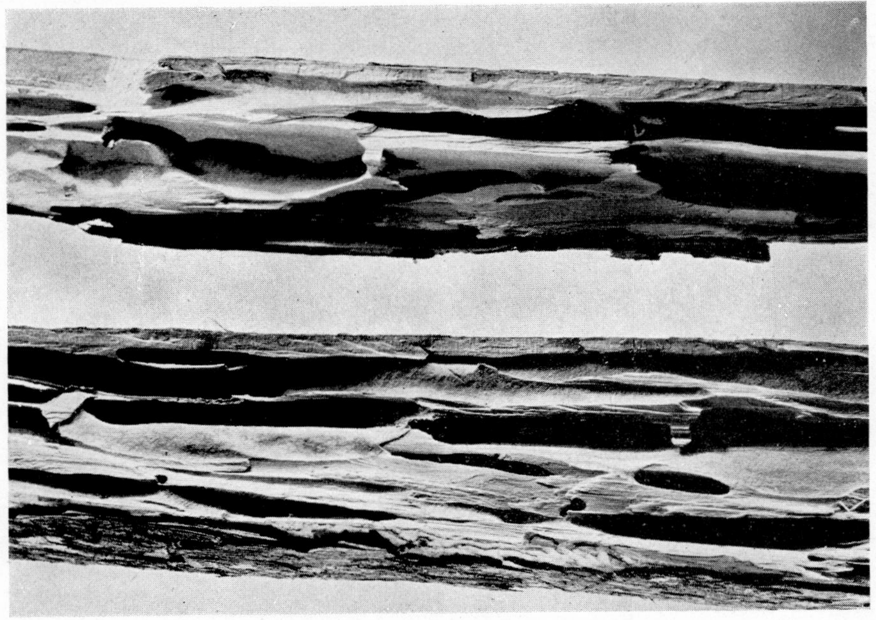

FIG. 41.—THESE GALLERIES, IN DEAD BRANCHES OF MONTEREY CYPRESS, REPRESENT THE WORK OF A DAMP-WOOD TERMITE.

The Common Damp-wood Termite (*Zootermopsis angusticollis*) does not have a true worker caste as do many species of termites, but the work of the colony is done by the immature sexual individuals. These are called *toilers*. Termite activity occurs almost entirely in darkness and obscurity. The galleries do not open to the outside, and often a limb or log may be completely honeycombed without any external evidence of the damage.

likely to be very hard and dry, they have spread to human habitations, to office buildings, stores, and warehouses. They burrow into and destroy pianos, radios, and other furniture, hardwood floors and tool handles (Fig. 42).

Other lignivorous insects prefer wood that is partly decayed though they will eat sound wood that is not living. Of such insects none are more interesting or more important than the termites (Figs. 112, 159, and 160). Dead stumps or fallen tree trunks and limbs are frequently riddled by the burrows of these insects (Fig. 41).

So also are the foundations of wooden buildings, telegraph poles, bridge and mine timbers, stored lumber, and innumerable articles manufactured from wood and stacked on the ground or placed near enough to it to be reached by termites. The activities of termites are treated somewhat at length in Chapter XIV.

A group of insects commonly associated with the lignivores are the *cambium-eaters*. These consist chiefly of the so-called *bark-beetles*. These burrow in and feed upon the delicate cambium layer between the bark and the wood of trees and shrubs, and upon the new layers of living wood and bark immediately adjacent to the cambium

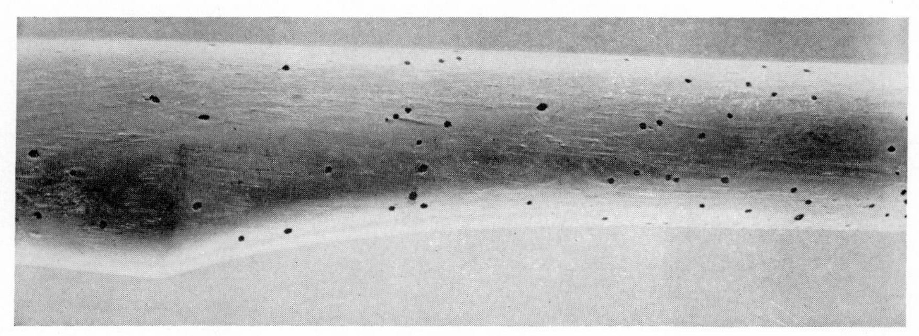

Fig. 42.—Hardwood Tool Handles Are Acceptable Food for Powder-post Beetles.
An unvaried diet of cured hickory wood does not sound appealing, yet powder-post beetles (family Lyctidae) found this ax handle in storage in a hardware store entirely satisfactory. Such beetles get not only food but water from hard woods. The water is liberated as a by-product of the digestion of the wood. The holes were made by the beetles when they emerged as adults.

(Fig. 103). The feeding of cambium insects results in much tree destruction, for the cambium is the tissue that produces all new growth of bark and wood.

CARNIVORES

The term *carnivore* is here employed in a somewhat broader sense than is customary in that it is applied to any creature whose food is of animal origin, whether that food be flesh or some body fluid such as the blood. Strictly speaking, the word *carnivore* means eater of flesh, and so it is not entirely appropriate to the use here made of it; but a term with a meaning of sufficient scope seems not to exist. Moreover, from a nutritional standpoint, a distinction between flesh and body fluids is somewhat arbitrary and of doubtful value.

General carnivores. Like primitive vegetarians, the general carnivores have catholic tastes, for they will eat any insect or other small creature which they find dead, or which they can capture or subdue, so long as it is not distasteful or too hard-shelled. The army ants of the tropics, which fall under this heading, are said to kill even large vertebrates if these are unable to escape by flight. Such large animals are overwhelmed by the sheer force of numbers of attacking ants. As defined above, the group of general carnivores includes predatory species, scavenging species, and species which are indiscriminately predatory or scavenging. All general carnivores, however, have

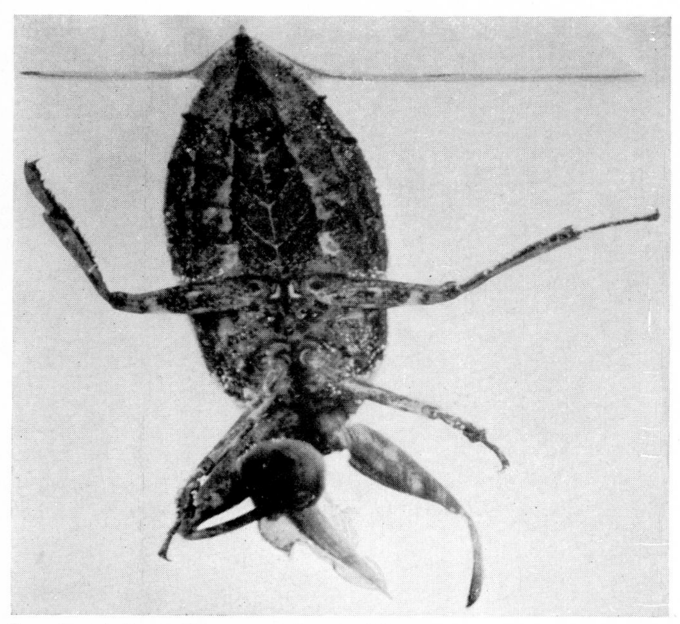

FIG. 43.—A GIANT WATER-BUG SUCKS A MEAL FROM A CAPTURED TADPOLE.
The Giant Water-bugs (this one a *Lethoceros*) are voracious predators which will kill and eat anything from insect larvae and worms to small fishes and newly hatched turtles. This one hangs from the water surface as it consumes the juices of the tadpole it holds with its hooked left foreleg.

one characteristic in common: they are typical flesh-eaters, consuming any or all parts of the creatures which serve as food. The predatory members of the group as a rule devour their prey outright, often while it is still alive.

Dragon-flies (Figs. 1 and 81) are typical general carnivores of the predatory type. The only limitations placed on the animals chosen as food by dragon-flies seem to be limitations of circumstance, not of choice. Being preeminently flying creatures which lack almost wholly the ability to walk or run, their prey also must consist of flying insects. What is true of adult dragon-flies is equally true of their naiad young (Figs. 52, 53, and 80). These consume as prey any aquatic animals available, from one-celled animals (Protozoa), in the case of very young naiads, and smaller crustaceans, worms, and small aquatic insects in the case of partially grown naiads, to large insects or even tadpoles and small fishes in the case of mature large naiads.

The predatory diving-beetles (Fig. 76) of the family Dytiscidae, the tiger-beetles, and the ground-beetles of the extensive family Carabidae, so called because they are common on the ground beneath stones, logs, and miscellaneous debris, are likewise flesh-eating general carnivores. And as with the dragon-flies, the food habits of the larvae of these beetles often are similar to those of the adults. Ground-beetle larvae wander freely in search of food, but tiger-beetle larvae (Fig. 44) live in burrows in the ground and lie in wait at the mouths of their burrows, with jaws agape, ready to seize any wandering insect unlucky enough to stray within reach.

Feeding specializations among the carnivores have occurred in various directions, some having to do with the kinds of food eaten, some with the means of securing it. A classification of carnivores, however, in its main lines at least, usually is based on the manner in which food is secured rather than on the nature of the food or on family relationships. The following classification is a satisfactory one. Those carnivores which capture and kill outright other insects, spiders, mites, worms, snails, and other small animals are called *predators*. On the other hand, those carnivores which live on or within the bodies of other animals, feeding on the tissues and juices of the latter and either not killing them at all or doing so only very slowly, are known as *parasites*.

General predators. These are predatory insects which will feed on any creature which they can capture regardless of the size or the nature of the prey. General predators fall quite naturally into two subgroups. One subgroup consists of the flesh-eating general predators. Many of these, such as dragon-flies, tiger-beetles, and ground-beetles, belong also to the group of general carnivores. They are simply the predatory members of that group. But the group of general predators includes also insects which are not flesh-eaters, and it does not include any scavenging species.

The members of the second subgroup of general predators is made up of sucking types. These cannot devour prey because of the way their mouth parts are made, so they puncture the body of the prey and suck out the liquid portions. Well-known examples of sucking general predators are the Sulcate Rough Shield-bug (*Brochymena sulcata*) of the family Pentatomidae; the assassin bugs (Fig. 125), of the family Reduviidae; the Giant Water-bugs, *Lethocerus* (Figs. 43 and 48) and *Abedus* (Figs. 21 and 61), of the family Belostomatidae; the water-scorpion, *Ranatra* (Fig. 66), of the family Nepidae; and the back-swimmers (Fig. 105) of the family Notonectidae. The so-called Water-tiger, which is simply the larva of a diving-beetle, *Dytiscus*, and the ant-lions, or doodle-bugs (Fig. 117 and 180), which are the larvae of certain Neuroptera (Fig. 115), also belong in this

FIG. 44.—THE PREDATORY LARVA OF A TIGER-BEETLE, REMOVED FROM ITS BURROW. Inside a smooth, vertical or slanting burrow dug in firm soil, its soft abdomen sheltered in the burrow, its stony head at the soil surface with beady eyes alert and with sickle-shaped jaws widely agape, the tiger-beetle larva awaits its prey. The prey: any insect wanderer on the soil surface which ventures within reach of the hungry larva. And lest it be pulled from its burrow by too large and sturdy a victim, or by some enemy, the tiger-beetle larva has forward-curving spines on its back just behind the middle, which it hooks into the wall of its burrow.

category. The ant-lions prey on ants and other small insects which they capture in funnel-shaped traps made in dust or sand. The ant-lions and the several water-bugs just mentioned not only suck the blood from their prey, but also inject into the prey digestive fluids which completely liquefy the tissues so that every bit of nutrient substance may be sucked out.

Restricted predators. Certain flesh-eating predators restrict their diet to one or but a few kinds of prey. Such are the ladybird beetles (Figs. 143 and 178) which feed only on scale-insects and plant-lice, and the lacewing-flies (Fig. 115) of similar habits. The Vedalia Ladybird, which was imported into this country from Australia, eats only the Cottony-cushion Scale and its close relatives.

One very interesting group of restricted predators, made up chiefly if not entirely of various species of wasps, is peculiar in that its members are carnivorous only in the larval stage. The adults of these insects feed chiefly on nectar. Curiously enough, however, it is the adults which capture the prey. The well-known yellowjackets (Fig. 147) and hornets belong to this group. Most of the species in the group, though, are solitary wasps, such as the Thread-waisted Sand Wasp shown in Fig. 142. This particular species, *Sphex nigricans*, is typical of the sand wasps. It is a member of the family Sphecidae.

Fig. 45.—Tree Cricket Wings inside a Pithy Stem Tell a Dramatic Story of Tragedy and of the Growing Up of a Lusty Brood of Hunting Wasps.

Podalonia wasps of the family Sphecidae, meat-eaters in the larval or grub stage, diners on nectar in the days of their winged adulthood, dig out the pith of stems as homes for their young. The burrows are then stuffed with paralyzed tree crickets, crude partitions of pith and vegetable fibers are made to separate brood chambers, an egg is laid among the crickets in each chamber as it is made, and the entrance holes are than loosely plugged with fibers. The fate of the young, thereafter, is left entirely to chance.

Each female *Sphex* digs a burrow in the soil and in the burrow places a caterpillar which it has captured. The wasp then lays an egg on the caterpillar. When the egg hatches, the wasp grub which it produces devours the caterpillar. Thus, though the adult wasp captures the prey, it is the wasp larva of the succeeding generation that devours it. Other species of wasps with similar habits capture grasshoppers, tree crickets (Fig. 45), flies, or even beetles as prey, instead of caterpillars.

Parasites. Parasitic insects are generally believed to have evolved from predatory ancestors. As a general rule, parasites are smaller than the animals on which they feed. The latter are known as *hosts*.

Parasites are classified secondarily in two or more different ways, depending on the point of view. There are, for example, *true parasites*, such as adult fleas (Fig. 169), lice, bedbugs, and mosquitoes (Fig. 65), which merely suck the blood or other tissue fluids and only rarely kill the host. Then there are *parasitoids*, such as the larvae of ichneumon wasps (Fig. 142), braconid wasps (Figs. 174–176), chalcid wasps, and tachina-flies (Fig. 177), which develop usually, though not always, inside the bodies of their hosts. Parasitoids at first feed only on body fluids, but eventually turn internal predators and devour the hosts' tissues, thus killing them.

According to another classification, parasites are segregated into *ectoparasites*, or parasites which live outside the bodies of their hosts, and *endoparasites*, or parasites which live within the bodies of their hosts. Ectoparasites may live permanently on their hosts, as is true, for example, of the head lice and body lice of man. Or they may live intermittently on the host after the manner of fleas and bedbugs. Endoparasites, on the contrary, are obliged to spend their entire existence, at least during their parasitic stages, within the bodies of their hosts.

The two systems of classifying parasites just outlined produce groups which are almost identical, for nearly all true parasites are ectoparasites, and nearly all parasitoids are endoparasites. There are true parasites, however, such as the larvae of bot-flies (Fig. 46), which are endoparasitic, though within the tissues of vertebrates instead of insects; and there are some parasitoids, such as the larvae of certain ichneumon wasps, which are ectoparasitic.

Blood-sucking ectoparasites, such as fleas, bedbugs, mosquitoes, and sucking lice, which have transferred their attention from other insects to vertebrates, are in a sense predators. They are not classed as predators simply because their prey is too large to be killed outright. In feeding habits, such parasites differ in no essential way from assassin-bugs (Fig. 125) and shield-bugs.

Endoparasites. Parasites of this group are in general much more highly advanced than ectoparasites. Many ectoparasites, such as bedbugs and sucking lice, are members of insect orders which undergo gradual metamorphosis. Endoparasites, with few exceptions, belong to orders which undergo complete metamorphosis. Endoparasites, too, are as a rule parasitic only in the larval stage. The adults are free-living though they are not primitive. In fact, the adults are often highly specialized in some connection entirely unrelated to the parasitism of the larvae.

The adult endoparasite lays its eggs either on the surface of the body of its host or just beneath the latter's integument, or skin. When the former is the case, the parasite larvae, on hatching, burrow into the host or are carried in by some special agency. They may, for example, be licked off and swallowed by the host.

The endoparasites are separable into two groups according to the nature of their hosts. If the host is a predator, a scavenger, or a herbivorous animal, the parasite is said to be a *primary endoparasite*. If the host is itself a parasite, then the endoparasite is called a *hyperparasite*.

Primary endoparasites of vertebrates: flesh-flies and bot-flies. Many endoparasites feed on vertebrate animals, especially on mammals. Of these there are two groups. One group, typified by the blow-flies and Screw-worm Fly, are called flesh-flies. Certain of these attack only wounded animals or those suffering from infections of the mouth, nasal passages, ears, or genitals. Such flies lay their eggs or deposit young larvae (which have already hatched within the bodies of their parents) in the wounded or infected parts of their hosts. Many flesh-flies, however, are parasitic only accidentally, being primarily scavengers. They normally lay their eggs in decaying carcasses of dead animals. They are attracted to wounded or diseased animals and parasitize them because the odors emanating from the wounds or infected parts are the same odors which are given off by animal carcasses.

The other group of endoparasites affecting vertebrates may be typified by the bot-flies (Fig. 46). The Horse Bot-fly attaches its eggs to the hairs of the fore parts of horses, especially the forelegs. In a similar manner the Cattle Bot-fly, or Ox Warble, attaches its eggs to the hairs on the hind legs and bellies of cattle. Horses take the eggs of the bot-fly into their mouths when nibbling or biting themselves. While the eggs are still in the mouth the larvae emerge, and in the course of events they are swallowed. In the stomach they complete their development and eventually pass out with the dung to pupate in the soil.

For a long time the life history of the Cattle Bot-fly was believed to be essentially like that of the Horse Bot-fly. Recent investigators say, however, that the Cattle Bot-fly eggs hatch while still on the hairs of the host. The young larvae then crawl down the hairs and burrow through the skin of the cows. For the next few months the larvae wander around through the connective tissues of the host and eventually come to rest beneath the skin of the back. They cut small holes through the skin in order to obtain air while they complete their development. At maturity the larvae squirm out through these "breathing holes," drop to the ground, and pupate.

Primary endoparasites of insects. These are exceedingly numerous in kinds, though most of them belong to but two insect orders, the

Fig. 46.—These Larvae of the Sheep Bot-fly Are Parasites in the Heads of Sheep. The eggs of the Sheep Bot-fly (*Oestrus ovis*) hatch in the body of the female fly, and she deposits the larvae or maggots in the nostrils of sheep and goats. These larvae live in the nostrils or the head sinuses of their hosts and cause them extreme annoyance or even death. After several months the larvae drop from the nostrils, enter the ground, pupate, and then transform to adult flies.

Diptera and the Hymenoptera. The dipterous species belong chiefly to the family Tachinidae (Fig. 177), the hymenopterous species chiefly to the superfamilies Chalcidoidea and Ichneumonoidea (Figs. 142 and 174–176). Nearly every medium-sized or large vegetarian or predatory insect is preyed upon by one or more endoparasites.

Most endoparasites of insects attack only the larval stages of their hosts, though quite a few attack pupae and adults. Even the eggs do not escape parasitism. Imagine a parasite so small that a food supply sufficient for its entire lifetime may be found within a single egg of a moth or butterfly! There are such parasites, tiny wasp-like creatures less than one-fiftieth of an inch in length! One of these egg parasites, which is common on the Pacific Coast, is a parasite on the eggs of the Ten-spotted Psocid, a small gray bark-louse, found on the leaves of trees and shrubs and technically known as *Peripsocus californicus*. The egg parasite is called *Alaptus psocidivorous*.

The feeding of the endoparasites of insects. Endoparasites of insects generally live in the blood-filled spaces making up the body cavities of their hosts. Through these the parasites wander about, avoiding the vital organs and feeding on the blood or on the less vital tissues, such as fat. In some cases, such as that of certain tachina fly larvae, the parasite larvae do not wander about but remain in definite spots attached to the tracheae of the host (Fig. 67). This attachment assures the parasite larvae of an adequate air supply. As a result of the peculiar behavior on the part of endoparasites, the host is not killed outright but continues to feed and to grow, though perhaps more slowly than before. The parasite larvae are thus ensured a food supply throughout their developmental period. On the completion of their growth, and before they transform to pupae, the parasite larvae usually burrow outward through the body walls of the hosts (Figs. 174–176). Certain species of parasites are exceptions to this rule, pupating within the hosts. The unfortunate host is killed, though not always immediately, by the emergence or maturing of the parasites.

Anyone who so desires may rear many of these parasites for himself. It is necessary only to collect a number of caterpillars and keep them in a cage to secure the parasites. A lamp-chimney cage (Fig. 184) or a cellophane-fronted shoe-box cage (Fig. 183) is satisfactory for this purpose. If Monarch Butterfly caterpillars (Fig. 136), which feed on milkweed, are selected, many of them will fail to transform into pupae, but instead will deliver whitish parasitic fly larvae from their bodies and then die. The fly larvae will transform into elliptical brownish puparia about the size of large wheat grains; and a few days later each of these will give rise to a gray parasitic fly about the size of a House-fly. Woolly Bear caterpillars likewise often yield parasites instead of moths (Fig. 177).

Hyperparasites. According to an old bit of humorous verse by Jonathan Swift:

> So, naturalists observe, a flea
> Has smaller fleas that on him prey;
> And these have smaller still to bite 'em,
> And so proceed ad infinitum.

While not strictly true, for there are limits to all things, these lines pretty well express the facts in regard to the hyperparasites of insects. Not only may the parasites have parasites, but the parasites of parasites may have parasites! As many as five successive stages of parasitism are said to occur! Like the primary parasites, hyperparasites are smaller than their hosts, and when there are several stages of parasitism the last hyperparasites are small indeed!

An example of hyperparasitism may be interesting. The Green Peach Aphis, *Myzus persicae*, which feeds also on numerous other plants including cherry, plum, potato, tomato, lettuce, eggplant, carnation, and rose, supports both primary parasites and hyperparasites. It is affected by no less than four species of primary parasites, all of which are minute wasp-like insects smaller than the aphis itself. Of these four primary parasites, only one (*Praon simulans*) is not known to possess hyperparasites. Another primary parasite (*Aphelinus semiflavus*) has only a single species of hyperparasite. Of the remaining two species of primary parasites, one (*Aphidius phorodontis*) is afflicted with three species of hyperparasites and the other (*Diaeretus rapae*) with four!

Indirect parasites. There is one group of insects, the members of which are chiefly Diptera and Hymenoptera, which are parasitic only in an indirect way. These usually do not feed directly on the bodies of their hosts, but appropriate the stores of food which the latter have accumulated for their own young.

Among the indirect parasites which are common are several species of medium-sized gray flies. One of these parasitizes a black and yellow crabronid wasp. While the wasp excavates a nest for itself in a rotten log and packs the chambers of this nest with dead bombylid flies, which it has captured and killed, the parasitic fly waits near by. In each chamber the wasp lays an egg, the bombylid flies in the chamber being intended as food for the wasp grub which is to hatch from the egg. But the parasitic fly does more than wait while the wasp is excavating and provisioning its nest. In the intervals during which the crabronid is away capturing bombylids, the parasite sneaks into the nest and lays its eggs. Since the eggs of the parasite hatch quickly, the result is obvious! The larvae of the parasite consume the bombylids stored by the wasp, and in many cases also the eggs laid by the wasp or even the young wasp larvae which emerge from the eggs.

The Thread-waisted Sand Wasp, *Sphex nigricans* (Fig. 142), which was discussed in the section on predatory insects, is also afflicted by flies which act as indirect parasites, in that they consume the caterpillars collected by the wasps to serve as prey for the wasp larvae.

SCAVENGERS

The scavenging insects, as was pointed out earlier in this chapter, owe their distinction as a class to the fact that they feed on dead organic matter, especially that which is in process of decay. It is frequently impossible, however, to distinguish clearly between matter which has begun to decay and that which has not. In view of this fact, it is likewise impossible to limit sharply the class of scavenging insects. We know that the processes of decay begin almost immediately after a plant or animal dies. For the purposes of this chapter, therefore, a scavenging insect will be defined as any insect which feeds on dead plant or animal matter, whether decay is obvious or not. A couple of examples will make the logic of this clear.

A dermestid beetle feeding on the dried skin and wool of a dead sheep in a pasture certainly would be called a scavenger. The same species of beetle may attack a woolen carpet or the woolen upholstery on a piece of overstuffed furniture. Is this beetle any less a scavenger because the wool in the carpet or the upholstery is being used by man? In such a case man does not prevent decay; he simply retards it for a long time. Let us consider another case. The larvae of vinegar-flies (*Drosophila*), which develop in milk that has clabbered and become rancid, are admittedly scavengers, for the milk on which they feed is obviously in a state of decay. What, then, shall we say of the Cheese Skipper, a fly larva which feeds on cheese? We do not commonly regard cheese as spoiled yet, biologically speaking, it is decaying just as truly as is rancid milk. The truth is that, in eating cheese, both man and the Cheese Skipper are acting as scavengers.

A convenient way to classify scavengers is to divide them into scavenging omnivores, vegetarians, and carnivores. Scavenging omnivores are relatively few in number and are unimportant as a group. Scavenging vegetarians and carnivores are numerous.

Scavenging vegetarians. This group includes a diverse lot of insects ranging from the larvae of boring beetles and termites, which will eat essentially sound wood as readily as they will obviously decaying wood, to species which feed upon the humus of the soil. Every pile of rotting weeds is inhabited by many scavenging vegetarians. The layer of fallen leaves and twigs which accumulates beneath trees and shrubs, though partially consumed by bacteria, fungi, worms, sow-bugs, and millipedes, is fed on also by numerous scavenging insects. The larvae of March-flies and of several of our common crane-flies (Figs. 14 and 71) feed on such vegetable debris and on humus. In feeding on humus, the insects, after the manner of earthworms, usually swallow soil and digest the humus out of it.

With the scavenging vegetarians also are to be included the insects which feed on the dung of herbivorous vertebrates. Since the dung consists chiefly of undigested portions of the vegetable foods eaten by the vertebrates, it is not very different in character from other decaying vegetable debris. Many of the scarab beetles, both as larvae and as adults, and the larvae of many flies, feed on dung. The common House-fly is a dung-feeder in its larval stage. The Stable-fly, which resembles the House-fly but which, unlike the latter, is a blood-sucker in the adult stage, feeds in its larval stage on a mixture of dung and straw.

Scavenging carnivores. The best known of the scavenging carnivores are the larvae of blow-flies, those brilliant, iridescent, blue-green or bronze-green relatives of the House-fly that are known to every one, and the larvae of flesh-flies. The latter are almost always a neutral gray but varying in the intensity of the gray, so that a pattern of conspicuous longitudinal stripes is produced on the thorax and a less striking, checkered pattern on the abdomen. The carcass of every dead vertebrate provides sustenance for hundreds or thousands of blow-fly larvae. Hardly does the body of a dead animal become cold before blow-flies and flesh-flies appear as if by magic, though actually attracted by the odors given off by the carcass. Eggs are laid or squirming, already hatched young are deposited, and the consumption of the carcass begins. A few days later only the skeleton, together with portions of the skin, the tougher tendons and ligaments, and the hair remain.

Other insects always to be found about carrion are beetles of several families. These are the carrion beetles (family Silphidae), the hister-beetles (family Histeridae), the rove-beetles (family Staphylinidae), and the dermestid beetles (family Dermestidae). A few of the carrion beetles and perhaps all of the dermestids (all those that visit vertebrate carcasses) are actually scavenging carnivores but the others are predatory, feeding chiefly on the larvae of blow-flies and flesh-flies.

The dermestids, both as adults and as larvae, feed principally on the drier parts of a carcass left after it has been deserted by the flesh-flies. In fact, the dermestids keep working on animal remains until the bones have been cleaned of every vestige of consumable material. For this reason they are sometimes made use of by zoologists in the preparation of vertebrate skulls or skeletons for exhibition purposes. After the preparator has removed most of the flesh from the skeleton of an animal the skeleton is put into a box or jar with a few dermestid beetles to complete the cleaning of the bones.

Dermestids also consume innumerable dead insects, as every insect collector learns sooner or later to his sorrow. Specimens must be kept in tight boxes and fumigated periodically if they are to escape the ravages of these little scavengers. Dermestids are very common out-of-doors in old moth cocoons, where they consume both the silk of the cocoons and the dried exuviae and secretions contained in them. They are similarly to be found in abandoned wasp nests and beehives.

The fondness of dermestids for hair, feathers, and silk has led to their becoming household pests, as has already been noted. Furs, woolens, and silks of every sort, feather goods, and toys in which these materials are used, unless given adequate protection are commonly damaged by dermestids.

Allied in feeding habits to the hair-eating dermestids are the clothes-moths, the depredations of which are too well known to need discussion. It should be stated, however, that only the larvae of clothes-moths are destructive.

In the same general category with the dermestids are to be placed the larvae of fleas and the peculiar insects making up the order Mallophaga. Flea larvae (Fig. 140) eat the loose hairs and skin scales which fall from dogs, cats, and human beings and accumulate in cracks and the corners of rooms and kennels. The Mallophaga are known as biting bird-lice (Fig. 122). The latter name is not a good one, for though there is scarcely a bird without them, many Mallophaga live on mammals. Without exception, however, they feed on feathers, hair, and the dead surface scales of the skin of their hosts. The only significant difference in habits between the

Mallophaga, on the one hand, and the flea larvae and dermestids, on the other, is that the Mallophaga secure their food material while it is yet attached to the bodies of their hosts, whereas flea larvae and dermestids do not eat it until it has fallen or until the animal from which it is derived is dead.

MISCELLANEOUS

There remains for final consideration a motley assemblage of diverse insects whose feeding habits do not fit into any of the categories already discussed. All of them in one way or another feed upon secretions of either plants or animals.

Myrmecophiles. Within the colonies of nearly all species of ants there may be found at times beetles, flies, and other insects, often of grotesque form, which are not killed and devoured by the ants, as might be expected, but are tolerated or even cared for by the ants just as pets or domestic animals are cared for by men. Such foreign residents within the ant colonies are termed *myrmecophiles*, which means "lovers of ants." The "love," however, is mutual, for at the bottom of this strange association between ants and myrmecophiles there is often a feeding relation by which the ants benefit. Many myrmecophiles, in return for the food or care received from the ants, produce secretions of which the ants are very fond. In fact, it is to secure these secretions as food that the ants care for the myrmecophiles. Among the common myrmecophiles of this class occurring in the United States are certain large black Scarabaeid Beetles.

Other myrmecophiles do not produce secretions, and are more tolerated than cared for by the ants. One of these, a small member of the cricket family belonging to the genus *Myrmecophila*, is common in ant nests throughout the United States. It is about one-eighth of an inch in body length, oval in shape, flattened like a cockroach, and tan colored. *Myrmecophila* licks the surface of the ants' bodies to secure the dried saliva left by the ants during their cleaning operations. Whether it eats any other food material is not known to the authors.

Feeders on honeydew. As a final group there are many ants, bees, wasps, and flies which feed on the sweetish material known as *honeydew*, which is produced by aphids (Fig. 145), scale-insects (Figs. 127 and 171–173), leaf-hoppers, tree-hoppers, and fulgorids. Honeydew was originally thought to be a true secretion produced by the insects in question. We know now that it is really a somewhat concentrated and slightly altered extract of the juices of the plants on which aphids and their kind feed. These bugs suck the food-laden cell sap from the tissues of plants. Only a small part of the food material and some of the water in the sucked-out cell sap is used by the bugs. The remainder is passed through the alimentary canal undigested and is deposited on leaves and twigs or is dropped to the ground beneath as honeydew. Since honeydew is highly nutritious and is produced in tremendous quantities, it constitutes a food supply of considerable importance for ants, bees, wasps, and flies.

CONCLUSION

From the foregoing discussion we see that insects have become as diversified in feeding habits as they have in body form and structure. From a presumably homogeneous group of ancestors they have evolved into a heterogeneous class with a diversity of feeding habits unparalleled in the animal kingdom. We see, furthermore, that this diversification has proceeded along certain definite lines. The generalized herbivores gave rise to specialized herbivores and perhaps to omnivores and predators. The predators subsequently produced the parasites and these in turn produced the hyperparasites. From all groups, except the parasitic ones, there have developed, as offshoots, groups of scavengers. With such infinite possibilities as the insects have manifested in adapting themselves to so many kinds of food, is it any wonder that they have become the dominant animal life of the earth?

CHAPTER VI

SOME INSECT FOOD-GETTING DEVICES

In the chapter, "Insect Foods and Feeding Habits," a discussion was given of the manifold types of foods that insects eat, and also something in general concerning the many modifications of insects adapting them to these types of foods. To supplement this material, more detailed information of a small series of insects will be given here, together with descriptions of some of the devices developed by insects for their diverse food habits.

The insect mouth. Modifications for different types of food should be presented most impressively by the mouth. One need think only of the mouth of a dog or cat, both typically adapted to eat flesh, and compare it with the mouth of the plant-grazing horse or cow, for this to be granted. Comparable variations in mouth structure, to correspond to variations in food habits, are found among insects, as among other animals, except that among insects the variations are more numerous and more diverse, because the food habits are more diverse, than in any other animal group. To a somewhat less extent other parts of the insect's anatomy also are modified to assist the mouth parts in their particular method of food getting.

In general the mouth of an insect can be likened to a human mouth in that it has an upper lip, jaws, and a lower lip. Of course, such a comparison is merely superficial, for no insect mouth has the appearance of a human mouth—quite the contrary; however, the parts can be kept in mind easily by such an analogy. In the case of an insect, as was brought out in Chapter II, the upper lip is called the *labrum*. The jaws are of two types: upper jaws called *mandibles*, and lower jaws that are called *maxillae*. The lower lip is called the *labium* (Fig. 9). These four kinds of mouth parts serve as the basic structures which have undergone almost an infinity of modifications for different types of food getting; and though insect mouths have come to be as diverse as those of a grasshopper and a House-fly, still some or all of the basic parts can be recognized in spite of their enormous changes.

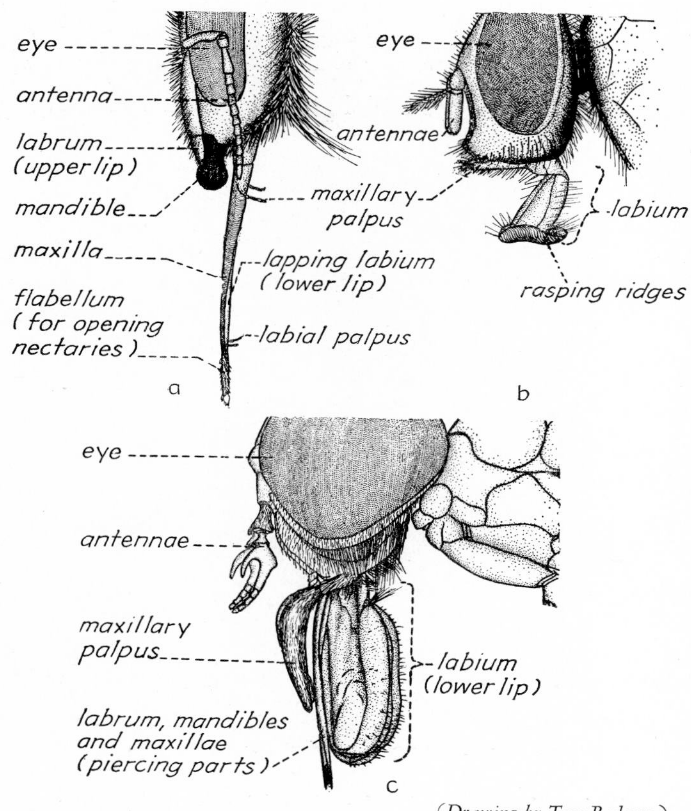

(*Drawing by Tom Rodgers.*)

FIG. 47.—INSECT MOUTH PARTS AS FOOD-GETTING DEVICES.

Variations in feeding habits of insects are followed by striking modifications of the mouth parts. (*a*) The chewing and lapping mouth parts of the bumblebee in which the mandibles remain as big chewing teeth, but the maxillae and labium have been elongated to form a lapping tongue for gathering nectar and other fluids. (*b*) The head and mouth parts of the House-fly in which nearly all of the mouth parts have disappeared except the labium or lower lip, which, with its rasping ridges and capillary grooves, breaks down solid foods as they dissolve in liquids regurgitated from the stomach, and then sponges them up. (*c*) The head and mouth parts of a horse-fly, which has its labrum, mandibles, and maxillae developed into piercing stylets for sucking blood.

For instance, the generalized plant-chewing insect, such as a grasshopper, has all the mouth parts present and but little modified; the bees possess mandibles for chewing, but their maxillae and lower lip have become elongated and specialized for lapping. The true bugs no longer have any chewing mouth parts, for both mandibles and maxillae have been elongated into sharp stylets, all four of which are enclosed in the grooved lower lip, the whole assemblage being adapted for piercing and sucking (Fig. 48). Most butterflies and moths have lost the labrum and mandibles altogether, but the maxillae, with grooves on their inner surfaces, have been prolonged and fitted together to form a long sucking tube, or siphon, that is coiled up and tucked in between the labial palps when not in use (Fig. 50).

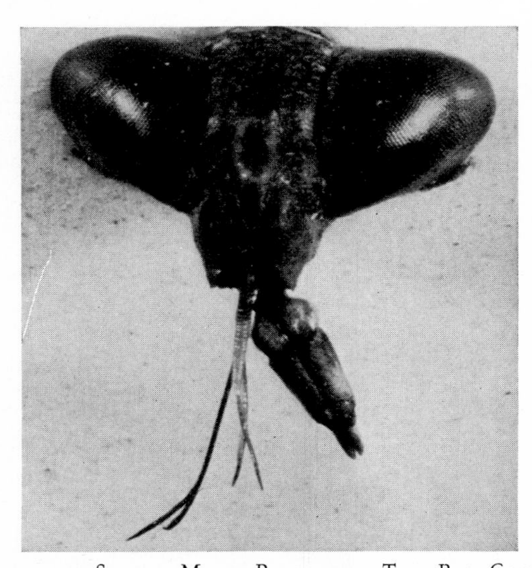

Fig. 48.—The Piercing and Sucking Mouth Parts of the True Bugs Consist of Four Stylets Encased in the Lower Lip.

Here the slender stylets, two of which are mandibles and the other two maxillae. are shown removed from the labium (lower lip) of a Giant Water-bug.

The House-fly has lost practically all of its mouth parts except the labium, which has become a tube that can be folded and is supplied with a curious series of ridges at the tip so that it can be used for rasping or sponging and for sucking.

For good reasons the mouth parts of the chewing insect are believed to be the most generalized and the most primitive. They include all the parts, and these parts are less modified than in any other type of mouth. In fact, they have served as the basic type from which many different lines of mouth parts have diverged in the course of an evolution that has adapted insects to their multitudinous types of food. One line of evolution has led off to culminate in piercing and sucking mouth parts; another has led to chewing and lapping mouth parts; in another direction a line has led to types that merely suck or siphon; still another direction has at last provided mouth parts that rasp, or sponge, and suck. In these various modifications some parts of the original type have been altered to take on new functions and other parts have remained as in the original and primitive form, or have been lost altogether. These insect mouth part modifications, then, become one of the most interesting things in insect structure, for they present a most amazing evolution. A few of these will be discussed, and since they provide the starting point, the chewing mouth parts will be considered first.

Chewing mouth parts. These primitive mouth parts are possessed by the insects of the order Orthoptera—the grasshoppers and their relatives; by the Coleoptera—the beetles; by the larvae of the Lepidoptera—the moths and butterflies; by many larvae and some adults of the Hymenoptera—the bees, wasps, ants, etc; and by the insects of a few orders of less importance. In these the mouth parts are used to chew plant stuff, or they are used to catch and to chew other animals.

Chewing mouth parts (Fig. 9) consist of the four principal kinds of organs already listed, and none of them greatly specialized. The labrum is simple and serves the ordinary function of an upper lip, that is, to assist in holding food that is being chewed. The mandibles are heavy and tooth-like, with blunt projections on their inner margins. They serve as the grinding organs, and for fighting, for tearing, or for holding. The maxillae are more complicated because each has several parts: an outer antenna-like sense organ used for smell or taste, called the *maxillary palp* (or palpus); next a slender, smooth, spoon-like lobe; then an inner blade with teeth. The maxilla serves to draw food inward and assists also in chewing. Both mandibles and maxillae work from side to side and so against each other, not up and down as do the jaws of higher animals. The labium has also a pair of palps, the *labial palps* (or palpi), which probably are sensory organs, but otherwise it serves merely as a lower lip and closes the mouth on the lower side. Lastly, there is a tongue-like structure, the hypopharynx.

Chewing and lapping mouth parts. Specializations have developed in all directions from the primitive chewing mouth parts. These specializations have seized upon some one or more of the mouth parts and have exaggerated such parts for functions that chewing mouth parts could not accomplish. Let us consider, first, a line of specialization that has led to modified maxillae and to a greatly modified labium, or lower lip, a labium that has become much more than a mere device to close the lower side of the mouth. In the insects exhibiting this specialization the mandibles have retained their chewing function, but the maxillae and labium have become greatly modified for lapping up liquids; and so mouth parts of this type can perform two distinctly different functions.

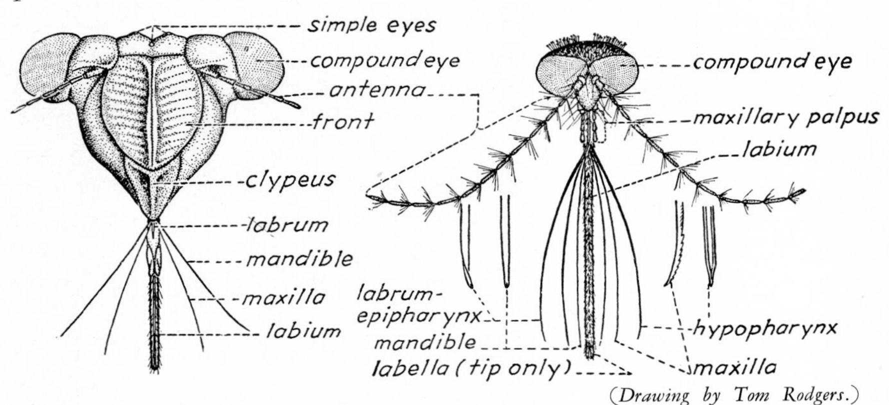

(*Drawing by Tom Rodgers.*)

Fig. 49.—The Piercing and Sucking Mouth Parts of a Cicada and a Mosquito.
The figure on the left shows the head and mouth parts of the cicada, or harvest-fly. Like the mouth parts of all the other members of the order Homoptera and all members of the order, Hemiptera, these mouth parts are adapted for piercing and sucking, and to that end the mandibles and maxillae are developed into piercing stylets. Normally the labium enfolds them all like a sheath. The figure on the right shows the head and mouth parts of the mosquito. These mouth parts consist of six sharp stylets for puncturing your skin, for, in addition to the maxillae and mandibles, there are the labrum-epipharynx and the tongue (or hypopharynx) that are elongated and stiletto-like. All six stylets work together when making a puncture and all are enfolded in the labium when not in use.

Honeybees, bumblebees, yellowjackets, and many other bees and wasps have retained mandibles for making comb, molding wax, chewing wood to make paper, catching living food, and similar functions for which mandibles are especially adapted; but all these insects have the maxillae and labium extended into a long, lapping, tongue-like structure (*a* of Fig. 47). The maxillae and the labial palps fold about the labium to form a tube. The labium is thrust down into a liquid and then withdrawn into this tube where the liquid is brushed off. It is then sucked into the mouth by the action of a powerful sucking pump inside the head. If a bee is watched as it works over flowers, the labium can be seen moving constantly up and down. Many bees have the tip of the labium equipped with a brush-like structure, called the *labellum* or *flabellum*, which is used in opening nectaries as well as in lapping.

Sponging, or rasping, and sucking mouth parts. The extreme in modification of the labium for food getting is shown in the House-fly. In this case not only is the labium highly developed, but the mandibles have disappeared; and of the maxillae only the palps remain. The labium is sufficient. To accomplish its function it is rolled into a tube and on its broad tip curious ridges appear (*b* of Fig. 47). Between these are deep grooves of almost tubular shape. The ridges at the tip are brushed back and forth over the liquid to be taken up, and by capillary attraction the grooves collect the moisture and carry it to a central food channel, from whence it is drawn into the mouth. If the object to be eaten is a solid substance, such as sugar, it is first dissolved by saliva discharged from the mouth, and then the whole is sponged up and drawn back into the mouth. This type of labium is jointed so that it can be folded into a groove on the lower surface of the head when not in use; when in action, it is straightened and thrust downward.

Many near relatives of the House-fly, as well as several other members of the order Diptera, have sponging and sucking mouth parts.

Piercing and sucking mouth parts. For another series of extraordinary insect mouth parts we shall drop back to the chewing type and consider a line of modification in which the mandibles, or maxillae, or both are retained but are highly modified, not for chewing but for piercing. To accomplish this function of piercing, the mandibles and maxillae are drawn out into slender, piercing stylets. In this case neither the labrum nor the labium has any function beyond forming or helping to form a sheath to envelop these stylets (Figs. 48 and 49).

Insects of the order Hemiptera—the true bugs—and those of the order Homoptera—the aphids, scale-insects, cicadas, etc.—have the type of mouth parts in which the mandibles and maxillae form piercing stylets enclosed in a tube formed chiefly by the labium (Fig. 48). With this type of mouth parts, these insects live upon plant juices, puncturing leaves or stems and sucking up the fluids which they find below the surface; or they live upon other animals and suck the blood or juices from their prey. Also because of this type of feeding, these insects cannot be killed by arsenicals or other stomach poisons used against chewing insects, because the piercing and sucking insects extend their stylets through coatings of such poisons into the juices below. They must be controlled by "contact poisons," such as soap, nicotine, or lime-sulphur compound, which kill by touching or suffocating the insect.

In addition to the kind of piercing and sucking mouth parts possessed by true bugs and their relatives, there are several other piercing and sucking types which have been arrived at by other

FIG. 50.—THE FEEDING DEVICE OF A BUTTERFLY CONSISTS OF A LONG SIPHON.
The siphon is composed of two grooved maxillae fitted together to form a tube. It is rolled between the maxillary palps when at rest, but can be stretched into the long "tongue" with which everyone is familiar.

modifications. For instance, mosquitoes have not only the mandibles and maxillae prolonged into piercing stylets, but have the labrum drawn out into a long slender organ, and, from the floor of the mouth, the hypopharynx also, so that six stylets, all told, contribute to the discomfort that a mosquito can cause (Fig. 49). These six stylets are enfolded in the labium. Similar mouth parts are possessed also by such mosquito relatives as the black-flies and horse-flies (Fig. 48). Still other modifications of mouth parts give piercing and sucking types to true lice, to fleas, and to the Stable-fly.

Siphoning mouth parts. When moths and butterflies gather nectar or other liquids, they extend a long tube that everyone has seen

(Figs. 50 and 51). This tube consists of two maxillae, each of which is grooved on its inner surface and so forms half a tube. When the two maxillae are fitted together, a long complete tube is formed. When

Fig. 51.—The Tobacco Sphinx Moth Secures Its Food with a Siphon That Is Longer Than Its Body.

All moths and butterflies with usable mouth parts have siphons formed by the maxillae, fitted together with grooves between. In the sphinx moths this siphon is much longer than that of other moths or butterflies. Everyone has watched sphinx moths hovering like hummingbirds before petunia or nasturtium or other blossoms, while they dipped their siphons into the depths of the flowers. (See also Fig. 162.)

this tube is in action, it is straightened out and liquids are sucked up through it. When it is at rest, it is coiled up between the labial palps (Fig. 50). In this siphoning type, the maxillae and the labial palps are all that remain of the original, primitive, chewing mouth parts.

The grasping labium of dragon-fly naiads. There are many minor modifications in insect mouths; so many, in fact, that a surprise is

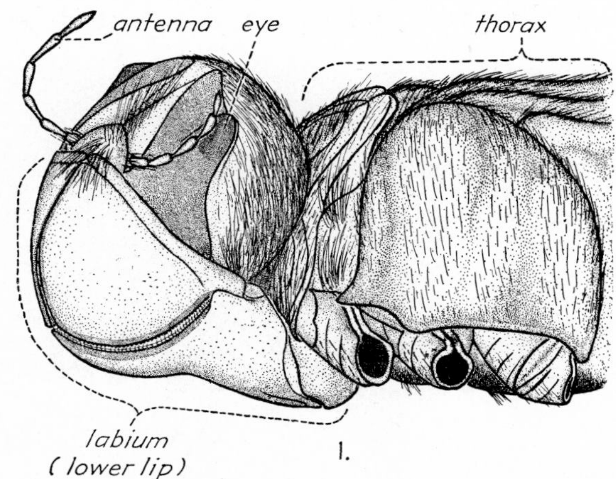

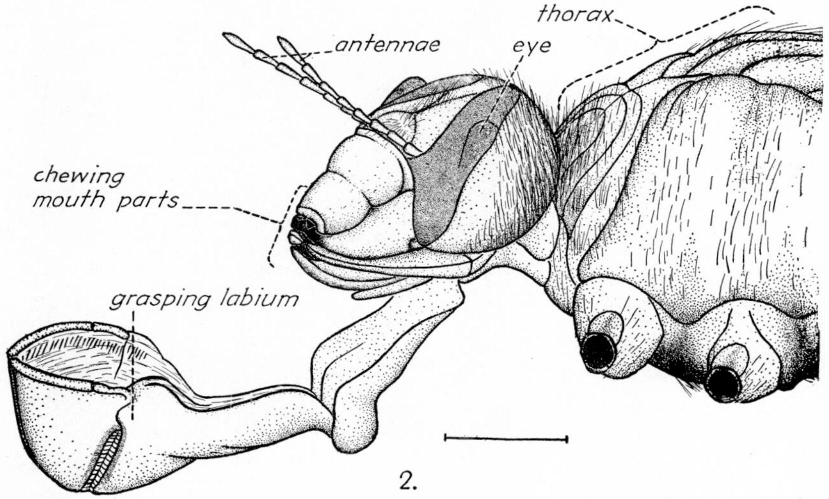

(*Drawing by Tom Rodgers.*)

FIG. 52.—THE MOUTH PARTS OF A DRAGON-FLY NAIAD.

The young dragon-fly, called a *naiad*, lives in the water and there eats mosquito wrigglers and other small aquatic insects, or even tadpoles and small fishes. To get this food, its lower lip, or labium, has been developed into a remarkable scoop or grasping hook. When this scoop is at rest it folds up over the face like a mask (upper figure), but when in action it extends out (lower figure) with lightning rapidity and captures the luckless prey. The other mouth parts are of the typical chewing type. (Hair line indicates actual size.)

in store for anyone who investigates carefully the structures that insects have for their food getting. One of the most unusual of these is the labium of the dragon-fly naiad. Now dragon-flies, both young and old, are carnivores and live chiefly upon other insects. For this purpose their mouth parts, in the main, are of the chewing type. But the naiads, which live in the water, have developed the labium into a remarkable organ by means of which they catch their food. This labium, when at rest, is folded up over the face like a mask

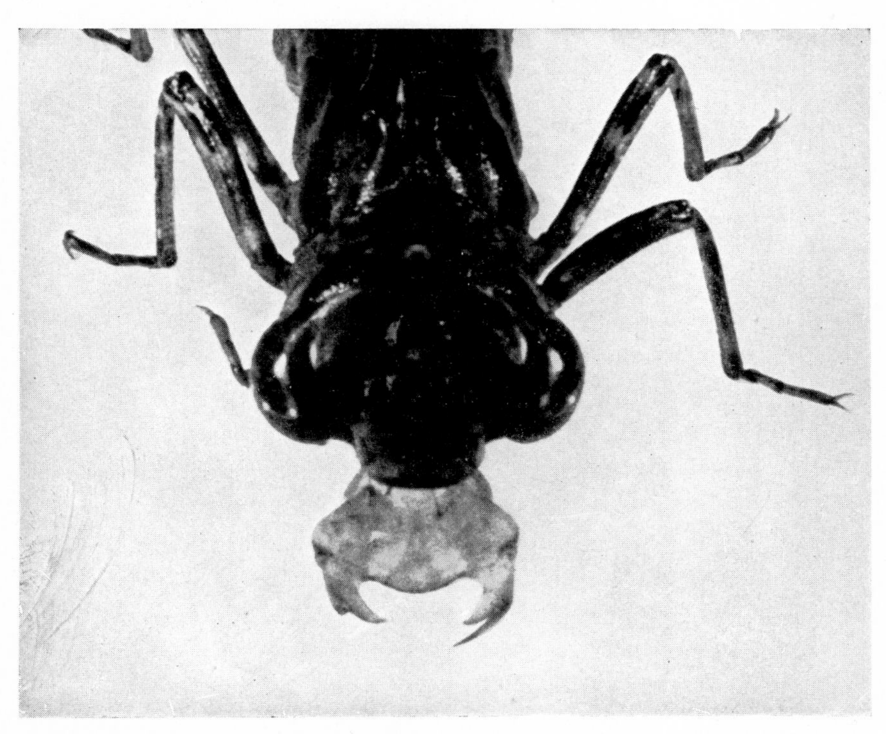

FIG. 53.—THE YOUNG DRAGON-FLY CATCHES ITS FOOD WITH A PREHENSILE LOWER LIP. When not in use, the lower lip folds over the face, but here it is shown extended as it would be in action. In its water home, by its capture of mosquito wrigglers and other aquatic insects, the dragon-fly naiad performs a service in the scheme of nature's balance. When it is grown into adulthood, and speeds on active wings as a mature dragon-fly, it continues this service by capturing grown mosquitoes as it flies.

(Figs. 52 and 53). With the labium in this position, the dragon-fly remains as quiet as a bit of mud or a stick. Should a mosquito wriggler, for instance, flip by, that mask leaves the face, shoots forward on a long elbow that has been folded under the chin, grasps the wriggler in the toothed scoop at the end, and brings it back where the chewing mouth parts soon convert it into dragon-fly naiad. Next time such a naiad comes to your notice, look for this mask over the face; then pull it out to its astonishing length, release it, and watch it fold back into place.

Some other food-getting devices. There are many, many food-getting devices in addition to those that have been listed. Two more of these will be pointed out briefly here. The water-tigers, those bloodthirsty larvae of the Dytiscus diving-beetles, have two long mandibles that

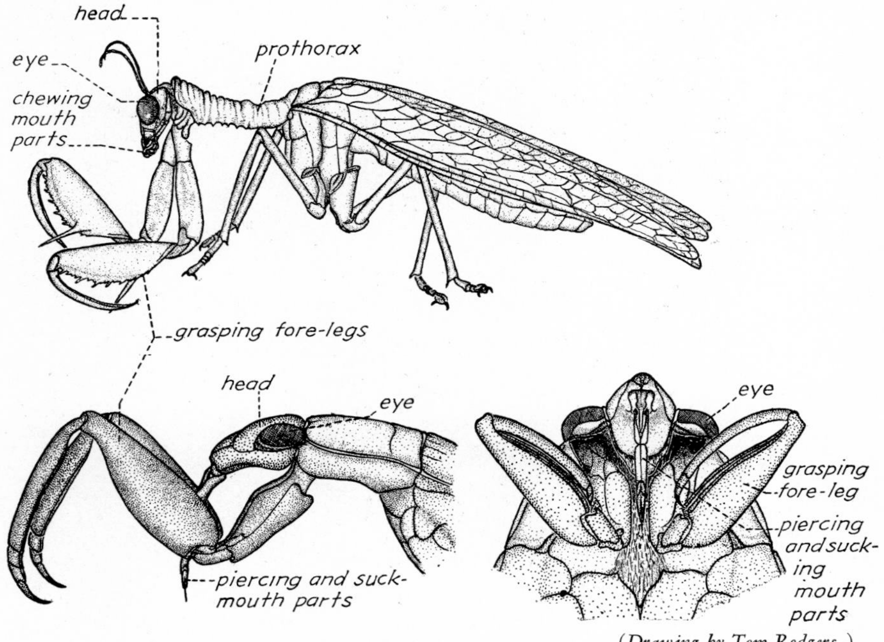

(*Drawing by Tom Rodgers.*)

Fig. 54.—Insect Legs as Food-getting Devices.

In most insects legs merely serve to carry the insect from one place to another. In some, however, the legs may be modified for special methods of food getting. Adult dragon-flies use the legs as baskets to catch insect food on the wing, and the Wingless Hanging-fly (Fig. 131) uses its second and third pairs of legs to catch food as it hangs by the first. The mantispid (upper figure) holds its powerful front legs ready to grasp any luckless insect that wanders near. The forelegs of the Giant Water-bug (lower figures) are also powerful and have sharp hooks at their tips. With these it catches prey as large as tadpoles and small fishes, draws them to its mouth, and sucks their juices with its piercing beak.

are grooved on their inner surfaces (Fig. 76). The water-tiger does not chew its prey, but seizes it with these mandibles, sinks them in, and then sucks out its victim's juices through these grooves. Doodle-bugs (Fig. 117) are similarly equipped for securing the juices of ants and other wandering insects.

Associated with special types of mouth parts there are frequently other modifications of the insect's body that assist. This is especially true of insects that must catch living animal food. For instance, the Giant Water-bug (Fig. 54) has powerful forelegs with hooks at their tips by means of which it seizes its victims and draws them down to its piercing and sucking mouth parts. *Ranatra*, the water-scorpion (Fig. 66), seizes its food in a similar fashion. Mantids and mantispids (Fig. 111) hold their heavy forelegs up in an attitude of prayer, but this is only that they may seize the more readily some hapless insect that wanders near.

When next you come across an insect, remember that among its most interesting features are those having to do with the food it eats and the devices it employs in getting that food.

CHAPTER VII

HOW INSECTS REPRODUCE THEMSELVES

GENERAL FACTS AND PRINCIPLES

All life from life. Reproduction is as universal a characteristic of living things as the fact that they consume food and grow. It is a unique property, for all living things reproduce and no nonliving thing does. Nor does any nonliving thing, or combination of nonliving things as we know them at present, produce new life. Hence there has come into being among biologists a doctrine that all life comes from preexisting life; that no plant or animal appears on this earth except as the result of a process of reproduction carried on by other plants and animals.

Furthermore, there has also become well established the doctrine that "like produces like"; that is, the young will be of the same species and have the same general characteristics as the parent or parents which produced it.

The necessity for reproduction. Plants and animals are living machines. It is important to realize this fact and to realize further that, like other machines, their parts wear out. The worn-out parts are to a certain extent replaceable, just as the worn-out parts of man-made, nonliving machines are replaceable. As a matter of fact, the process of replacement is going on all the time in the tissues of plants and animals. There are, however, definite limits to the amount of repair that can be accomplished. A time comes when replacement is no longer sufficiently effective to keep the machine in working order, and it ceases to run. When a manufactured machine reaches this condition we say it is worn out; when a living machine reaches this condition, it dies. In either case the machine must be replaced by an entirely new one, and the means by which living machines are replaced is the process of reproduction.

There are other causes which destroy the effectiveness of machines besides just the wearing out occasioned by use. For example, accidents may destroy a machine outright or greatly lessen its efficiency all at once. Many kinds of accidents occur to living things, the most frequent of which is the accident of being eaten by some other living thing. This kind of accident may consist in being devoured outright, or it may consist in becoming diseased, for a diseased plant or animal is in most cases merely one whose tissues are being fed upon by another kind of plant or animal of microscopic size, which is present in large numbers. Whatever the cause of the demise of a living machine, whether it be wearing out or an accident, that cause necessitates reproduction.

Young animals originate from parts derived directly from the bodies of their parents. The process of reproduction begins when a part of the living body of the parent animal separates from the rest and embarks on an independent existence. In the simplest cases, which we find represented among the one-celled animals and certain other lowly forms, the body of the parent simply divides into two or more approximately equal parts. Each of these parts is capable, by itself, of growing and developing into a new individual. Each regenerates during its growth all the other parts present in a complete individual. In reproduction of this type as many new individuals are produced as there were parts of the parent, and the identity of the parent is abruptly terminated by the division of its body into young.

Most animals possess specialized reproductive organs. The simple method of reproduction by division, just outlined, is not followed by most animals or plants. They are too complicated to survive a subdivision into parts. Their bodies are such closely knit machines, composed of so many interdependent organs and tissues, that to divide them would have the same disastrous effect that sawing an automobile engine in two would have on its operation. Most animals and plants, therefore, reproduce by some method which does not involve the subdivision of the entire body of the parent, and the consequent loss of parental identity. They accomplish reproduction by means of special reproductive organs, and the parts which become the new individuals are usually single cells which separate from the tissues of these organs. These reproductive cells, upon being separated from the parent body, give rise, by growth and development, to new individuals like the parent. In all these cases the parent continues to live and maintain its identity after the birth of the young, until it becomes worn out or is destroyed by accident.

Reproductive cells fuse in pairs. Reproductive cells usually are differentiated into two sorts: a large, quiescent cell, called the *egg cell*, which usually contains a large supply of stored food; and a small, active cell, called the *sperm cell*, which contains but little stored food. Egg cells care produced in organs called *ovaries* and sperm cells in organs called *testes* (see Fig. 10 for an illustration of the ovaries and testes of a grasshopper). In some kinds of animals, and in many kinds of plants, both ovaries and testes occur in the same individual. In such cases each individual produces both egg cells and sperm cells. Usually, however, one individual possesses only ovaries and is therefore a female, or only testes and is therefore a male. Regardless of whether eggs and sperms are produced by the same parent or by different parents, they are in most cases unable individually to grow into new animals. An egg cell, generally, cannot by itself develop into anything else. The same is true of a sperm cell. Before a new individual can be brought into being, a sperm cell must find an egg cell and the two must merge into a single mass. The behavior of the parent animals which results in bringing eggs and sperms together is called *mating*. The actual merging, or fusing, of the eggs and sperms is called *fertilization*.

REPRODUCTION OF INSECTS

Environmental conditions control reproduction in insects. Being typically terrestrial animals, insects cannot accomplish reproduction so simply as typically aquatic animals do, for the land environment is not so simple as the aquatic environment. For example, when fishes such as Pacific Coast salmon reproduce, the female first lays her eggs in a selected spot; then the male deposits his sperm cells over them. With the liberation of the eggs and sperms the process of reproduction is completed, so far as the adult salmon are concerned. They take no further interest in their young. The sperms, of their own activity, swim through the water, find (or are attracted to) the eggs, and fuse with them. Thus fertilization in the salmon occurs externally. The young which develop from the fertilized eggs are afforded no protection and are left to shift for themselves. This seemingly careless mode of reproduction, as is explained in Chapter XII on "Insect Fitness," is a successful one for truly aquatic animals, for neither the delicate eggs and sperm cells nor the young produced by their fusion are exposed to the great danger that is always faced by a terrestrial animal—the danger of drying out for lack of water. Insects, however, because of the relative dryness of the terrestrial environment, cannot trust to external fertilization (fusion) of their reproductive cells. The only alternative is the fertilization of the egg cells by the sperm cells before the egg cells leave the body of the female parent. In other words, insects must practice *internal fertilization*. This they universally do, a fact which largely determines the structure and arrangement of their reproductive organs.

The sex organs of insects (Fig. 10). The primary sex organs consist, in the female insect, of a pair of *ovaries*, in which the eggs are produced. From these a pair of tubes called the *oviducts*, one leading from each ovary, carry the eggs to the genital openings, from which they may be deposited outside the insect's body. The two oviducts unite a short distance inward from the genital opening to form a common tube known as the *vagina*, which is larger than either oviduct.

In the male, the primary sex organs are a pair of *testes*, in which the sperm cells are produced. A pair of tubular *sperm ducts*, one running from each testis, carry the sperm cells to the genital openings. Like the oviducts, the sperm ducts join before they reach the body surface and form a common tube called the *ejaculatory duct*.

Secondary sex organs also are present in insects. These include the oviducts and the sperm ducts, the vagina, and the ejaculatory duct, already mentioned. In the male insect there is also an elongated, protrusible structure called the *penis*, or *aedeagus*, through which the ejaculatory duct runs and which is used during mating to introduce the sperm cells into the body of the female. Finally, the male insect often possesses one or more pairs of pincer-like *claspers* with which to hold the female during the mating act.

In the female there is often a pouch, called the *bursa copulatrix*, developed in association with the vagina, which receives the penis of the male during mating and into which the sperms are discharged from the penis. In other cases the vagina alone serves to receive the penis. Besides the bursa copulatrix, the female insect often possesses a second pouch-like organ called the *spermatheca*, into which the sperms pass from the bursa copulatrix after mating and in which they may be kept alive and nourished for some time. The sperms are liberated from the spermatheca in small numbers as they are needed. The spermatheca is best developed in the social insects, such as the Honeybee. The queen Honeybee mates but once, yet the sperms received at that time may be kept alive in a usable condition in her spermatheca for as much as five years! In most insects, however, the sperms are not kept for any great length of time. Usually fertilization of the eggs in the body of the female occurs shortly after mating, and all the eggs are laid within a comparatively short time, after which the female dies.

Fig. 55.—Among Insects the Male Is Often Smaller Than the Female, as This Pair of California Timemas Shows.

The male California Timema (*Timema californica*), a somewhat distant relative of the grasshopper and a member of the family of walking-sticks, rides upon the back of the female for hours or even days at the mating period, and during that time transfers sperm cells to the female so that they may fertilize her eggs.

The attraction of the sexes. The sexes of insects are brought together in a variety of ways. With many moths, the males are attracted to the females by a characteristic scent produced by the latter. This scent is the product of special scent glands in the tip of the abdomen. A female moth which is ready to mate protrudes her scent glands, and from them the odoriferous, attractive substance diffuses into the air and is carried away by air currents. Any eligible male moth of the same species which detects this scent becomes agitated and begins a journey "upwind," following the scent until he reaches the female, whereupon mating occurs. Male moths have been reported to travel as much as two miles in search of a female whose scent they had picked up. The sense of smell, by which the males recognize the odor of the female, appears to be located in the antennae. These, in accordance with their use as organs of smell, are large and feathery in many male moths (Figs. 18 and 24). The females of the same species, not having so highly developed a sense of smell, possess much smaller and simpler antennae (Fig. 179).

Sight. Some insects undoubtedly depend on sight to bring the sexes together. This seems to be true with many of our flies and burrowing wasps, in which the compound eyes are larger and better developed in the males than in the females. The males of such wasps emerge earlier in the spring than the females and fly about in the vicinity where the females are due to appear. When the females emerge, the males dart after them and mate with them.

The most striking example of the use of vision to bring the sexes together is probably that of the fireflies. These soft-bodied beetles, as almost everyone knows, produce flashes of light in special organs located in the abdomen. The flashes of light enable the males and females to find each other and mate. Fireflies do not occur in any numbers west of the Rocky Mountains, except perhaps in restricted localities. Some members of the firefly family and of closely related families which are not true fireflies are nevertheless luminous, but lack wings in the female sex. These wingless and luminous females are "glowworms." Several species of glowworms occur in the Far West but are not common. Nonluminous members of the firefly family are common in the West.

Sound. With many insects, such as the grasshoppers, crickets, katydids, and cicadas, sound seems to play a part in bringing the sexes together. At any rate, the males of many species of these insects possess elaborate sound-producing devices (Figs. 94 and 96), and it seems quite likely that the sounds produced by them may have something to do with the attraction of the sexes. This subject is discussed at some length in Chapter XI.

THE PROCESS OF MATING

The mating act. This consists of the actual coupling, or linking together, of the bodies of male and female insects by means of the genital organs (Fig. 56) and in the transfer of the sperm cells from the male to the female during the time the two are linked together. The coupling (technically termed *copulation*) is effected when the penis of the male enters the vagina of the female. If the male possesses clasping organs, these grasp the female, either before actual copulation or at the time of copulation.

Attitudes assumed during mating. With most insects, the male mounts the back of the female and remains there until copulation is completed. The male may mount the female and ride upon her back for some time before copulation occurs. This is illustrated in Fig. 55, which shows a mating pair of California Timemas (*Timema californica*), insects of the family Phasmidae. Among other insects, such as the silk moths, the male and female merely approach each other until they stand side by side and are sufficiently close together to effect copulation. Since copulation sometimes lasts for a period of many minutes or even hours, the original attitude of the sexes is not always maintained until the act is completed. Many stimuli lead to changes in attitude. While still copulating, the insects may wander

Fig. 56.—In Order That Eggs May Be Fertilized, the Female Insect Must Receive Sperm Cells from the Male.

Here is a pair of mating soldier beetles, with the male (the smaller) transferring sperm cells to the female.

about and feed; they may be jarred loose from the object to which they cling and caused to fall to the earth; they may be frightened, or by some other cause induced to fly. The meloid beetles shown in Fig. 56 probably originally assumed the usual position with the male above the female, after the manner of the phasmids already referred to. Yet like many other insects, at the time they were discovered the male and female were facing in opposite directions. When this occurs, the female, being the larger, may drag the attached male about with her. She may even fly, trailing him behind her as so much dead weight. In the spring of the year numerous mating pairs of crane-flies (Fig. 14) may be startled into flight from the grass and weeds of the fields, the female towing the male.

With still other insects, mating normally occurs only during flight, and is so quickly consummated that it is difficult to observe. Several kinds of wasps and bees mate in this fashion. The medium-sized, long-legged black dance-flies of the family Empididae, which are so common in fields and along roadways in the springtime, also mate in the air, but the pairs remain in copulation for some time. If a swarm of these flies "dancing" in the air over a roadway or field be scrutinized, it will be seen to contain many pairs of mating individuals. These dance-flies, which are in part carnivorous, have a curious habit: the male, before mating, captures a smaller insect of some other species and gives it to the female to feed upon during the mating process. Other types of insects which mate or select mates while in flight are May-flies and ants of many species (Fig. 144). The mating of ants and termites is discussed in Chapter XIV.

The most peculiar position assumed by mating insects is that of the dragon-flies (Figs. 1 and 81). In these insects the male has an odd pouch on the undersurface of the second abdominal segment, into which, prior to mating, it discharges its sperms. It does this by bending its abdomen downward into a loop until the genitalia are inserted into the pouch. In coupling with the female, the male first seizes the neck of the female with a pair of claspers at the tip of the abdomen. The two then fly about in tandem fashion, the male in front of the female. Both insects fly; there is no towing and being towed as with the crane-flies. To complete copulation, the female bends her body into a loop below the male and inserts the tip of her abdomen into the pouch to obtain the sperms. Dragon-flies often remain linked in tandem after copulation. In fact, the male, by supporting the female with his claspers, may aid her in depositing eggs. It is no uncommon sight to see a pair of linked dragon-flies hovering low over the surface of a pond and repeatedly dipping to the water, allowing the female to thrust the tip of her abdomen beneath the surface to lay eggs.

Fate of the sexes after mating. The life of the male insect after mating varies in duration according to the species, usually being shorter than that of the female. In some cases, such as that of the Honeybee, it is very short, the mating act practically terminating the male's existence. With other insects, such as the House-fly or the yellowjacket (Fig. 147), the male may live for several weeks after mating. During this time the male House-fly, or yellowjacket, may mate with several other females. In a few cases, the most notable of which are the termites, the male lives for a long time after mating. He shares with his queen the task of founding a new colony and remains with her as a constant companion for the rest of her life, which may be several years.

The duration of the life of the female after mating, like that of the male, varies in different insects. With the tussock-moth (Fig. 179), the female of which is wingless, adult life is extremely short. It lasts just long enough to permit mating and the laying of the eggs. When the female moth emerges from the cocoon her abdomen is distended with eggs which are fully developed and ready for fertilization. Climbing on top of the cocoon from which she has emerged, the female tussock-moth thrusts her scent glands into the air and patiently waits for the male, which is almost certain to appear. Upon the arrival of the male mating takes place, after which the female deposits her eggs, often gluing them to the cocoon beneath her feet. This duty accomplished, she has no further mission in life, and dies.

The females of other insects, such as the House-fly, mosquito, grasshopper, and dragon-fly, live from a few days to many weeks after mating. Some of these lay eggs shortly after mating. With others, the laying of eggs may be delayed several days. Most of the insects in this group, whether or not they deposit eggs immediately after mating, do not lay all their eggs at one time. They lay them in batches at intervals of several days. The House-fly, for example, lays two or three batches of about one hundred and twenty eggs each, separated by intervals of several days.

Among the social insects the period of egg laying is even more prolonged. The queen of a colony of Western Yellowjackets (Fig. 158) lays eggs almost daily over a period of four to six months, laying upward of twenty thousand in all. The queen Honeybee, which lives an average of five years to the wasp's one, lays still more eggs. Cheshire, according to W. M. Wheeler in *Social Life Among the Insects*, estimates that a queen Honeybee may lay as many as one and a half million eggs. The most amazing case of all, however, is that of certain African termites, which have been studied by Mr. Escherich whose observations are given by Wheeler. The queen of one of these termite colonies lays eggs with almost clock-like regularity, one every few seconds, for around ten years! At this rate the queen lays about thirty thousand eggs a day, ten million a year, and one hundred million in her lifetime!

PROTECTION OF THE YOUNG DURING EARLY DEVELOPMENT

Need of safeguards. The young insect, at the moment its life as an individual begins, is nothing more than a single, fertilized egg cell. This one-celled creature, being only a minute speck of living protoplasm, is very delicate and quite unable, unaided, to cope with life in the world in which insects live. If it were released into this world in its primitive, unprotected condition, it would perish within a few minutes. This fate, however, is never visited on the young insect, for during the long evolutionary history of insects through which they became adapted for life on land, there have been developed methods for safeguarding the welfare of the young during its period of infantile delicacy and weakness.

Food and shelter. The young insect, before it can achieve self-reliance, even before it can develop organs which enable it to secure its own food, must be nourished. Therefore food, in the form of yolk, is stored up for the young in the egg. This yolk is mixed in with the substance of the egg, in little droplets, before the egg is fertilized. Enough yolk is supplied by the parent insect to feed the growing young until it develops all its essential organs and is able to forage for itself.

The young insect must also have protection from external influences which would destroy it. To meet this need the egg is provided with a shell by the parent (Figs. 57 and 58). The shell is built around the egg while the egg is still in the oviduct of the female. This shell protects the young insect from animal enemies which would devour it, from disease-producing bacteria and fungi, and from inclement weather. All this preparation is made before the egg is fertilized, even before there is any assurance that a sperm will be available to fuse with the egg. Such preparation is one of the prodigalities of nature, which constantly amaze and delight the observing individual.

When the egg finally slips out of the oviduct into the vagina of the female, it needs only the addition of the sperm to launch it on its career of becoming a new insect—only this last vitalizing influence to set in action all the complex physiological machinery inherent in its protoplasm. Up to the moment of fertilization its potentialities,

Fig. 57.—Insect Eggs Are Provided with Heavy Shells to Protect Them.
These eggs of the buck moth are neatly laid in a mass around a twig. Eggs of other moths are laid in a variety of ways, sometimes singly, but are always glued to some supporting surface.

manifold and complex beyond comprehension, lie dormant, and unless the sperm is added to the egg at the proper moment, they will remain dormant and the egg will slowly die. The question then presents itself: "How does the sperm gain access to the egg to fuse with it and start this chain of activities which will maintain life?" For it will be remembered that the egg is completely surrounded by a shell. Completely? Not quite; for at one definite spot on the egg there remains a tiny pore or a group of pores where the shell is not complete. This spot is the *micropyle.* When an egg, on its way to being laid, passes by the opening of the spermatheca, in which are stored the sperms obtained from the male during mating, a sperm comes out of the spermatheca and passes through the micropyle into the egg to fertilize it. The egg is then laid.

The growth and development of the young insect begins almost immediately after the entry of the sperm through the micropyle. Protected by the enveloping shell, the fertilized egg divides repeatedly to become a many-celled embryo, which gradually takes on the form and proportions of the young insect of the species to which it belongs. The embryo gradually utilizes the food stored as yolk in the protoplasm of the egg, deriving from it the substance and energy needed

FIG. 58.—NEVADA BUCK MOTH CATERPILLARS EMERGE FROM EGGS ON A TWIG AND BEGIN THE SEARCH FOR FOOD.

Fortunately for the caterpillars, the search will not last long; the parent moth laid her eggs on the twigs of the very plant, a species of willow, that is most suited to the needs of the larvæ. In this picture may be seen, in addition to young caterpillars, eggs with unbroken shells, eggs with gaping tops from which the caterpillars have come, and eggs containing caterpillars engaged in chewing their way out of the eggshells.

for the transformation it is undergoing. Finally, having developed organs with which to crawl or walk or run or swim and with which to procure food and oppose enemies, having developed an alimentary canal capable of digesting the materials consumed as food, and a nervous system responsive to external and internal stimulation, the young insect cuts or breaks its way out of the eggshell and begins its active existence (Fig. 58).

But wait! The safeguards placed around the young insect do not end with the supply of yolk enclosed in the egg and the eggshell which covers it during its early development. Still another aid is necessary if the young insect is to survive. When it emerges from its outgrown eggshell as a tiny nymph or larva it must find itself in a suitable habitat. The protection afforded by an eggshell would be of small value if the world into which the young insect makes its debut were an altogether unfriendly one. If a young water-bug on hatching found itself on the parched ground of a dry field, what would be the worth of its preparation for life? If a tiny cabbage-worm found itself, at the moment of hatching, on the rugged and furrowed bark of an oak tree, what would its fate be? Of course, we all know that such things do not happen, at least not normally. The young insects on hatching find themselves in the very habitat to which their every characteristic fits them; but is it not remarkable that this is so, that the parent insect, which, except among the social forms, never sees or knows its young, seeks out the place most suited to the needs of the young and there lays its eggs?

WHERE INSECT EGGS ARE LAID

Egg laying and food supply. The situations in which the eggs of insects are laid are legion, but each situation chosen is related in some way to the life of the insect which chooses it. The adult blow-flies, whose larvae feed on the flesh of various animals, seek out dead carcasses on which to deposit their eggs; or they lay their eggs in the wounds of injured or diseased animals which are yet alive. The House-fly rarely lays its eggs anywhere except on fresh horse manure. Predatory wasps, such as that shown in Fig. 142, lay their eggs on the bodies of other insects which they have captured and paralyzed. Our common mud-dauber wasps (*Pelopaeus cementarius* and *P. servillei*) build mud nests of several cells, store the cells with spiders suitable for consumption by their larvae, and then lay eggs among the spiders, one egg in each cell, after which the cells are sealed. Other species of wasps, and also bees, excavate burrows in the pith of stems. Here they store provisions, here the eggs hatch, and the larvae develop (Fig. 59). Herbivorous insects lay their eggs on the food plant adapted to the needs of their larvae. Among the very curious examples of parental preparation to meet the needs of the young insects is the behavior of the Red-shouldered Leaf-beetle (*Saxinis saucia*), which is native to the Pacific Coast. The adult of this beetle feeds on the leaves of various plants, but the larva lives as a "guest" in the nests of certain seed-collecting ants. It is not safe for the beetle to venture into the ant nests in order to lay its eggs and so it resorts to a trick. It climbs out to the edge of a leaf or the tip of a branch of some plant, raises its abdomen slightly, and slowly lays an egg. The egg is not allowed to drop, however, but is caught and held by the hind feet. The beetle then extrudes, one by one, several peculiar rough brown scales of a waxy substance, produced in glands at the tip of its abdomen. As each of these scales comes forth the beetle presses it against the surface of the egg until it adheres. The egg is then turned a little, while the next scale is being extruded. As a result of the addition of

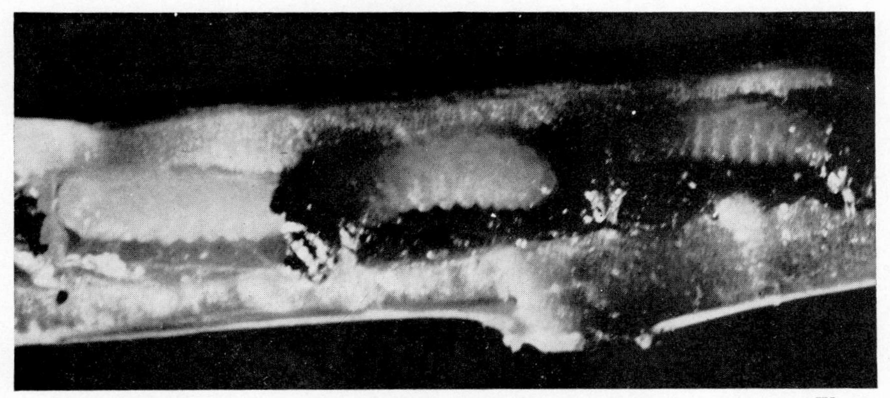

FIG. 59.—THREE LARVAE OF A SPECIES OF SOLITARY BEE, PROTECTED BY THE STEM IN WHICH THEIR HOME HAS BEEN MADE, AWAIT THE RETURN OF SPRING FOR THEIR TRANSFORMATION INTO ADULTHOOD AND WINGED ACTIVITY.

Many species of wild bees of solitary habit use the pithy stems of dead weeds and shrubby plants as sites for their nests. Here, in burrows excavated by the female bees, pollen with perhaps a slight admixture of nectar is stored in small chambers, each containing an egg. The egg hatches to produce a grubby larva, which consumes the stored pollen.

these brown scales the egg comes to resemble a seed. When it is completely covered, the beetle unceremoniously drops the egg to the ground beneath, where it will be found by foraging ants. The rest of the story is not positively known, but presumably the ants, mistaking the egg for a seed, since it resembles other seeds which they collect for food, carry it off to their nest. The egg hatches inside the ant nest, thus liberating the beetle larva in the very surroundings it would choose were it able to make a choice.

Egg laying and protection. The shell around an insect egg protects it against many enemies and adverse influences, but not against all. Many insects increase the protection afforded by the eggshell in various ways. The Green Lacewing-fly (Fig. 115) lays its eggs singly on the top of long, thread-like stalks (Fig. 60). These hold the eggs out of reach of small predatory creatures, such as ladybird beetle larvae, or even the larvae of the lacewings themselves, which might devour

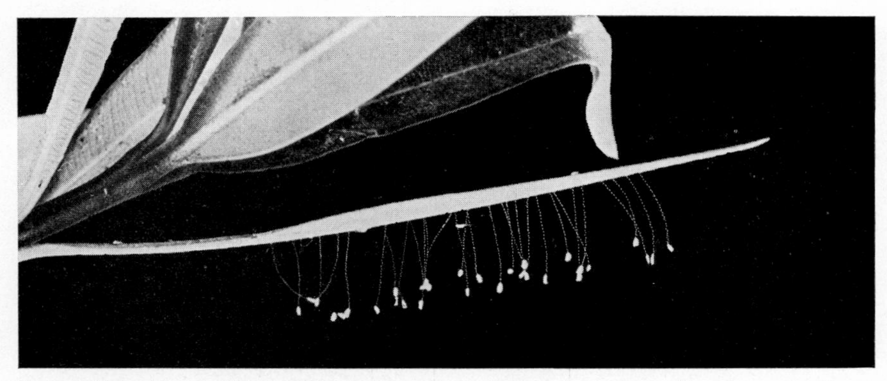

FIG. 60.—THE FIRST TO HATCH WOULD DEVOUR THE REST, SO THE GREEN LACEWING-FLY HANGS HER EGGS ON THREADS.

The young, or larvae, of the lacewing-fly are voracious predators, like all the members of the order Neuroptera, and go far, because of their food habits, in keeping aphids and scale-insects in check. However, they would also eat brothers and sisters yet unhatched if the eggs were not suspended on slender stalks as shown here.

FIG. 61.—ON THE BACK OF THE MALE GIANT WATER-BUG THE FEMALE BUG GLUES HER EGGS.

Since he cannot fly with the eggs on his back, he is forced to stay in the water and so becomes an effective paternal guardian for his unhatched offspring, for they go with him wherever he goes.

them. The female Giant Water-bug glues her eggs to the back of the male (Fig. 61), who carries them until they hatch and thus protects them from enemies which might eat them were they laid in a place which could be safely approached.

Ovipositors. In this connection it will be interesting to examine the accessory sex organs which female insects have developed to aid them in laying their eggs. The abdomen of many female insects bears six processes, arranged in three pairs around the genital opening and serving collectively as a device to guide the eggs as they leave the vagina and to deposit them in the place selected by the female. These

(Photograph by Emily Smith.)

FIG. 62.—THE FEMALE GRASSHOPPER DRILLS WITH HER OVIPOSITOR TO MAKE A HOLE IN THE GROUND FOR HER EGGS.

As the hole is dug, the abdomen sinks into the ground. The grasshopper then lays her eggs in the hole and the soil closes over them as the abdomen is withdrawn. The eggs are thus protected until they hatch.

six processes form a device called the *ovipositor*, a word which means "egg placer." Each single process of the ovipositor is called one of the *valves* of the ovipositor.

In the grasshopper, the ovipositor forms the triangular tip of the abdomen and ends in four pointed, spine-like structures (Fig. 4). The female grasshopper uses her ovipositor as a drill with which to make a hole in the ground in which to lay her eggs. This enables her to insert her abdomen deep into the soil, so the eggs may be deposited well below the surface (Fig. 62). When the grasshopper withdraws her abdomen, the soil closes in over the eggs, completely concealing and protecting them until they hatch.

Certain species of common crane-flies (Fig. 14) of the genus *Tipula*, possess large pointed ovipositors, which in some species are used, like those of grasshoppers, to drill holes. Like the grasshopper, these crane-flies lay their eggs in the ground. After selecting a spot where the eggs are to be laid, the crane-fly hoists her body high into the air, bends her abdomen till it points vertically downward, and then drops her body in such a way that the pointed ovipositor strikes the soil beneath, after the manner of a pick. Repeatedly she strikes the soil, each time dislodging a few grains of soil and throwing them out to one side or in front of her. She may pick away thus with her abdomen for as much as forty minutes before she gets a hole deep enough to satisfy her.

In the saw-flies (Fig. 141), which are the most primitive members of the order Hymenoptera, the valves of the ovipositor are fashioned into tiny saws; with these the female saw-fly literally saws slits or holes to receive her eggs in the leaves and twigs of the plants upon which the saw-fly larvae feed.

In the so-called higher Hymenoptera, especially the bees and wasps, the ovipositor has a double purpose. In addition to being an egg placer, it has become a sting, which may be used to paralyze and kill prey or as an organ of defense. Certain glands associated with the reproductive organs in these insects have become changed into poison glands, and the valves of the ovipositor have become the long, slender lancets which make the punctures into which the poison is poured.

In certain ichneumon wasps (*Megarhyssa*) the valves of the ovipositor are even longer and more slender than in the bees and wasps (Fig. 142). Instead, however, of being used as stings, they are used as probes with which to insert eggs deep into the wood of trees which are infested with the larvae of wood-destroying insects. By some means the female ichneumon wasp of these species locates a point on a tree beneath which the burrow of a wood-boring larva lies. She then probes with her ovipositor until a passageway is found in the form of a minute crack or hole in the wood leading to the insect burrow within. When the burrow is reached an egg is laid. The ichneumon larva which hatches from it crawls along the burrow, finds the borer larva and begins feeding on it. Thus the ichneumon is able successfully to parasitize wood-boring larvae which are seemingly inaccessible.

Primitively, all insects possessed some sort of ovipositor, composed of six valves. During their evolution into their present forms, however, many modern insects have had their ovipositors changed in character. The six valves have been reduced to inconsequential structures and have been replaced by other developments. In the House-fly and its relatives, in place of a six-valved ovipositor there is a long, tapering, tubular device with joints which slip one inside the other, like the parts of an old-fashioned mariner's telescope. This tubular ovipositor is very flexible. It is also sensitive to touch stimuli. With it the fly can feel about for suitable crannies into which to thrust its eggs. Hence we find that the blow-fly which deposits its eggs on the carcass of a dead animal inserts them into the nostrils and ears, beneath the eyelids and the lips, between the teeth, and deep among the hairs which cover the carcass.

PECULIAR METHODS OF REPRODUCTION

Viviparous insects. Most insects lay eggs; that is to say, their young are delivered from the body of the parent while still enclosed in the eggshell and before development has proceeded far enough to be perceptible. Most insects we say, then, are *oviparous*. A few kinds of insects, however, do not bring forth their young until after the eggs have hatched. They deliver their young in an active, advanced state of development. Such insects are termed *viviparous*. The large gray flesh-flies, referred to several times, are the most conspicuous of common insects which are viviparous. With the flesh-flies the eggs hatch at or just before the moment of deposition, and consequently the adult fly deposits squirming larvae on the spot selected. If such a fly be captured and squeezed lightly, it may often be induced to produce larvae. Or if a female flesh-fly be captured and put into a bottle, it will often strew the interior of the bottle with its larvae. There is nothing more amazing than one's first observation of this phenomenon.

Another group of common viviparous insects are the ever-present aphids (Fig. 39), which are to be found on nearly all succulent young vegetation. During the fall of the year oviparous aphids are to be found, but the generations produced during the rest of the year give birth to young by the viviparous method. If colonies of aphids, such as that shown in the figure, be scrutinized carefully, some of the females are almost sure to be found in the very act of giving birth to young. The adult female will have her abdomen tilted upward, and from the opening of the vagina there will be gradually emerging a small but active aphid (Fig. 63). When the young aphid is nearly out, it waves its legs about until they touch the surface of the plant on which its mother stands; then it grips the plant with its own feet,

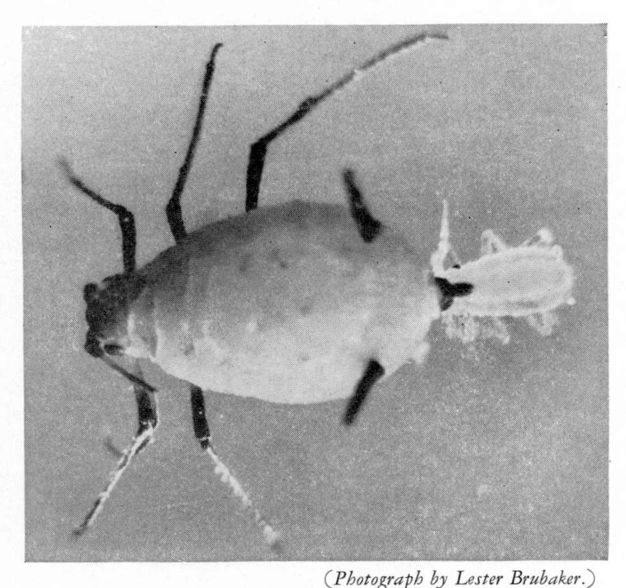

(*Photograph by Lester Brubaker.*)

FIG. 63.—A FEMALE APHID GIVES BIRTH TO ACTIVE YOUNG.

A majcrity of aphids, like the one shown here, are *viviparous*, which is to say that they do not lay eggs but retain the eggs within their bodies until after hatching, and then deliver active young into the world. Most aphids also are *parthenogenetic*, which means that they reproduce without mating and therefore without the fertilization of the eggs. This makes them exceptions to the general rule that mating and fertilization are necessary for reproduction.

pulls itself free, and moves away to begin feeding on the same plant. After an interval of feeding, during which another young grows within the body of the mother, the whole process is repeated.

Still another common, though rarely observed, insect which produces young viviparously is the so-called Sheep-tick. This is not a tick at all, but a peculiarly specialized parasitic fly which sucks the blood of sheep on which it lives. The Sheep-tick produces but few young, and these only one at a time. Each egg hatches in the vagina of the female and the larva is retained there until fully grown. In the meanwhile it is fed by a secretion from glands associated with the reproductive organs of its mother. Finally it is born, being delivered from the mother's body as a fully grown larva, ready to transform into the pupal stage.

Parthenogenesis. In the early part of this chapter it was stated that nearly all young insects result from the fusion of egg cells and sperm cells; that is, they are produced from fertilized eggs. The exceptions which this statement implies are found among several groups of insects, of which one of the best known is the aphid group already discussed. Young aphids, which are delivered to life by the viviparous method, are produced by the method called *parthenogenesis*. This is nothing more than the development of young from unfertilized eggs. Just why it is that certain insects can produce young from unfertilized eggs, whereas all others require the fusion of an egg and a sperm, is as yet an unexplained mystery, though it is a well-demonstrated truth. The great bulk of aphids produced throughout each season of insect activity, generation after generation of them, are parthenogenetically produced. All of these, until the end of the season for aphids draws near, are females. Then an oviparous generation composed of both males and females appears. These mate and the females lay eggs in the usual manner. The eggs do not hatch until the beginning of the following season, at which time they give rise to viviparous females which start the round of parthenogenetic reproduction all over again.

Many species of insects which induce the formation of galls (Fig. 40) on plants are parthenogenetic. The gall-wasps of the genera *Diplolepis* and *Rhodites*, which make galls on wild roses and on oaks, are almost always parthenogenetic. In some of these species many generations have been bred in entomological laboratories without a single male ever having been produced.

The aphids and gall-insects, whenever reproducing by parthenogenesis, nearly always give birth to females only. Among the social insects, however, which usually lay fertilized eggs but are occasionally parthenogenetic, the unfertilized eggs give rise to males only. It seems probable that male Honeybees, called *drones*, and male yellowjackets are always produced by parthenogenesis.

Paedogenesis. A most peculiar kind of parthenogenesis, practiced by a few kinds of insects, is the production of young by larvae as well as by adults. A tiny fly of the family Cecidomyiidae exhibits this kind of reproduction. The larva of this fly forms a sort of gall on the dwarf lupine (*Lupinus nanus*) of the Pacific Coast. Inside these galls the tiny larvae give birth to other larvae before they themselves are fully grown! This type of reproduction is called *paedogenesis*.

Polyembryony. There is another peculiar method of reproduction, *polyembryony*. It is difficult to observe, though it has been demonstrated to exist in a number of kinds of parasitic insects. Polyembryony is exhibited by a minute, wasp-like member of the order Hymenoptera, called *Polygnotus minutus*, which parasitizes the Hessian-fly (*Phytophaga destructor*), a very destructive grain pest. The tiny parasite thrusts its ovipositor into the body of a Hessian-fly larva to lay its eggs. Here, instead of developing directly into larvae, as one would expect them to do, each egg of the parasite develops into a peculiar mass of embryonic cells which divides to form several embryos. During the dividing of the embryos they are fed by nourishment absorbed from the tissues and body fluids of the host. After forming upward of a dozen embryos, the mass of embryonic cells ceases to divide and each embryo develops into a parasitic larva. Thus from each egg laid by the parent parasite as many as a dozen young may develop. An amazing performance, but there are others still more amazing. According to A. D. Imms (*General Textbook of Entomology*), certain parasites of the family Encyrtidae lay eggs which develop by polyembryony into as many as a hundred larvae each!

Though not exactly the same sort of thing, we might say that insects exhibiting polyembryony behave for a time like many very lowly animals, in that they reproduce by simple division into equal parts. Such performances almost lead one to say: "Name the inconceivable and we will find it in the life of some insect."

CHAPTER VIII

HOW INSECTS GET AIR

THE need for air is universal among living things. From the tiniest invisible microbe to the most gigantic whale or the largest tree, all animals and all plants use air. Air is the "breath of life" without which life would not exist. This fact is well known, but the use which living things make of air and the manner in which they secure it are not so well known. For this reason it is advisable to begin our discussion with a consideration of respiration in general, especially as we know it in the vertebrates, and then to discuss our main topic, the respiration of insects.

Only a part of the air is needed. Air is a mixture of several gases, of which oxygen and nitrogen are the most abundant. Oxygen makes up close to one-fifth of the air, and nitrogen about four-fifths. The small remainder consists of carbon dioxide, water vapor, and several other gases in minute amounts. Of all these materials, only the oxygen is used by animals. Oxygen alone makes possible the expenditure of energy by animals. The heat energy with which our bodies are warmed and the mechanical energy expended in every movement we make would not be available if we did not have oxygen to use. Oxygen is the key that unlocks the energy resources in the foods we eat and in the tissues of which our bodies are composed. And since the utilization of energy is a universal accompaniment of life in animals and plants, the need for oxygen obviously is paramount.

The interchange of carbon dioxide and oxygen. When an animal uses oxygen it combines the oxygen taken from the air with some of the food it has eaten, or with some of the substance of its own living tissues. This combining process, which is called *oxidation* and which, chemically, is the same thing as burning, though it occurs at a much lower temperature, results in the liberation of the energy to be used by the animal. It brings about, also, the production of another gas, carbon dioxide, in an amount equal to the amount of oxygen used. The carbon dioxide is of such a nature that it cannot be used by the animal and, indeed, if it were to accumulate in large enough quantities it would cause the animal's death. It is, therefore, eliminated from the animal's body as a waste product. It is given back to the air in exchange for the oxygen taken in. This elimination of the undesirable carbon dioxide is as much a part of an animal's use of air as is the taking in of oxygen. It is this exchange of oxygen and carbon dioxide that constitutes respiration.

Each tissue requires its own oxygen supply. Now, it is not enough that an animal have access to air from which it may extract oxygen and into which it may pour its carbon dioxide. A muscle cell in the tip of an animal's tail or in its stomach wall can make no use of the oxygen in the air that bathes the animal's exterior. Any oxygen which the muscle cell, or any other cell in the animal's body, is to use must be brought from the outside air to the cell itself. The subject of this chapter, "How Insects Get Air," includes therefore not only the means employed by insects to obtain air but also, and more important, the devices for distributing the needed oxygen to every body cell.

The respiration of vertebrates. When a bird, a reptile, or a mammal breathes it alternately draws air into its lungs and expels air from its lungs. During this process the lungs, which are richly supplied with blood, extract oxygen from the air and discharge carbon dioxide into the same air. When the air is expelled from the lungs the carbon dioxide is carried outside the body. We say that birds, reptiles, and mammals are air-breathers because they secure their oxygen directly from the air.

When a fish breathes it gulps water into its mouth and forces the water by means of swallowing movements backward into its pharynx. From the pharynx the water passes outward on either side through a number of slit-like openings in the side walls of the pharynx. These are called *gill slits* because the gills of the fish are found on the walls of the slits. The water flows over the gills as it passes through the gill slits to the outside. The gills are to the fish what the lungs are to a bird, reptile, or mammal. The fish must get its oxygen from the water, since it is unable to secure oxygen from the air. It is the gills, richly supplied with blood, which extract the needed oxygen from the passing water and discharge the carbon dioxide waste into the water. We say that fishes are water-breathers, because they utilize the oxygen that is dissolved in water instead of that in the air.

In all vertebrates, whether air-breathers or water-breathers, the absorbed oxygen is distributed to the tissues which use it in exactly the same manner. The oxygen passes from the air in the lungs, or from the water flowing over the gills as the case may be, into the blood, where it in part dissolves in the blood fluid, as sugar dissolves in water, and in part unites chemically with the red coloring matter of the blood. It is then carried by the blood throughout all the organs and tissues of the body to the individual cells which are to use it. As the cells take out of the blood the needed oxygen they give up to the blood the carbon dioxide for which they have no use. This the blood then carries to the lungs, or to the gills, for elimination.

THE RESPIRATION OF INSECTS

Types of insect respiration. Insects, as a class, include both air-breathing and water-breathing kinds. Whether air-breathing or water-breathing, however, insects differ radically from vertebrates in the manner in which the oxygen they use is distributed. This matter will be discussed a little later. Primitive insects were all air-breathers, and so it will be better to describe the respiratory system of a typical air-breathing insect before discussing that of water-breathing insects.

Insects breathe by means of a system of branching tubes called *tracheae* (Figs. 64 and 68). These ramify throughout the body, carrying air to every organ and tissue. Air-breathing vertebrates have tracheae also, and there is some similarity between the tracheae of insects and those of vertebrates. Both are tubes for the conveyance of air into and out of the body, and both are kept open by ring-like or spiral braces of hard material. The braces in vertebrate tracheae consist of cartilage; those in insect tracheae are cuticular, for the tracheae of insects are lined with a part of the insect's exoskeleton (see Chapter II, "Insect Structures"). This skeletal lining of insect tracheae is provided with spiral thickenings which form the braces. But insect and vertebrate tracheae differ strikingly in several respects. In the first place, they are quite unlike in microscopic structure. More important still, they differ in that vertebrate tracheae extend only a short way into the body, whereas insect tracheae extend throughout the body. In vertebrates the tracheae branch into the bronchial tubes and these branch and rebranch in the lungs, finally ending in numerous little air sacs called *alveoli*. The tracheae and their bronchial branches in vertebrates, therefore, can carry air only as far as the alveoli of the lungs. Insect tracheae, on the contrary, extend to every part of the insect's body, branching and rebranching, to end finally in delicate microscopic tubes called *tracheoles* which penetrate the insect's tissues and carry air to the very cells which are to use it. Insects, therefore, do not have lungs, though in a sense the whole body of an insect is one big lung. Moreover, the blood of the typical insect does not play the important part in the distribution of the oxygen taken from the air that is played by the blood of a vertebrate. Insect blood does aid a little in the dis-

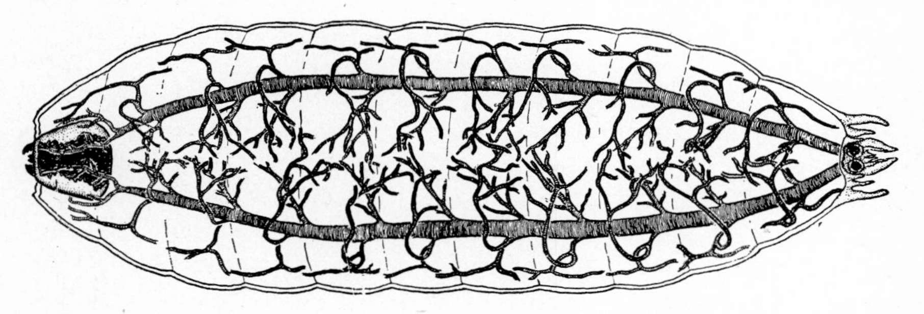

(*Drawing by Tom Rodgers.*)

FIG. 64.—AN INSECT GETS ITS AIR THROUGH A SYSTEM OF TUBES THAT BRANCH THROUGHOUT THE BODY.

The breathing tubes, shown here in a crane-fly larva, are called *tracheae*. The two large ones running lengthwise are *tracheal trunks*. This larva, which lives under conditions that are almost aquatic, takes its air into the body through two spiracles at the tip of the body.

tribution of oxygen, and somewhat more in the elimination of carbon dioxide, but it is not the sole or even the principal distributor of oxygen and collector of carbon dioxide that it is in the blood of a vertebrate.

The tracheal system of an insect. Now let us examine a typical insect, such as a grasshopper, to see how its tracheal system is organized. Along each side of the grasshopper's thorax and abdomen is a series of little holes, one to each segment. These are the *spiracles*, or openings into the tracheal system (Fig. 4). The air inhaled by the grasshopper passes inward through these spiracles; the air exhaled comes out through them. In most insects each spiracle is guarded by a little valve that opens or closes according to need.

Inside the body a short trachea, called the *spiracular trachea*, extends from each spiracle to join a large *tracheal trunk* which runs lengthwise through the body (Fig. 64). There are nearly always two tracheal trunks in an insect's body, one on each side, and in some cases there are four. Several tracheae of small diameter extend crosswise in the insect's body connecting the tracheal trunks. The various tracheae of the tracheal system are thus in communication throughout the body. From the tracheal trunks, from the cross-tracheae connecting the trunks, and from the spiracular tracheae there arise branches which carry air to the body wall, to the muscles, to the nervous system, to the alimentary canal, and to other internal organs. It is these branches which end in the tracheoles.

Certain very lowly insects differ from typical insects in that their tracheae do not form connected systems. In these insects there are tufts of branched tracheae extending inward from each spiracle, but there are no connections between the tracheae arising from the different spiracles.

Certain extremely small insects, such as the minute gray springtails no larger than a pinhead, which live in moist habitats, and certain minute aquatic larvae do not have tracheal systems at all. These insects are so small that they can get enough oxygen through the general surface of the body to supply all their requirements. They have no need of a system of tracheae to distribute air through their bodies.

THE RESPIRATION OF AQUATIC INSECTS

Insects which live in the water fall naturally into two principal classes, according to their method of breathing. There are the incomplete aquatics, which breathe air much as their strictly terrestrial relatives do, and there are the true aquatics, which are water-breathers, getting their air from the water by means of gills, though not exactly as fishes do. Then there are a few kinds intermediate between these two classes, since they breathe air in part, yet have gills with which they extract air from the water (Fig. 65).

Certain aquatic insects, such as the Giant Water-bug (Figs. 21, 61, and 104), the back-swimmers (Fig. 105), and various aquatic beetles (Figs. 76 and 77), inhabit the water in both immature and adult stages. Other kinds, such as the dragon-flies (Figs. 69 and 81), May-flies (Fig. 68), and mosquitoes (Fig. 65), are aquatic only in the larval or nymphal stages. All insects which are aquatic in the adult stage are air-breathers in this stage, though in the nymphal or larval stages some are air-breathers and some are water-breathers.

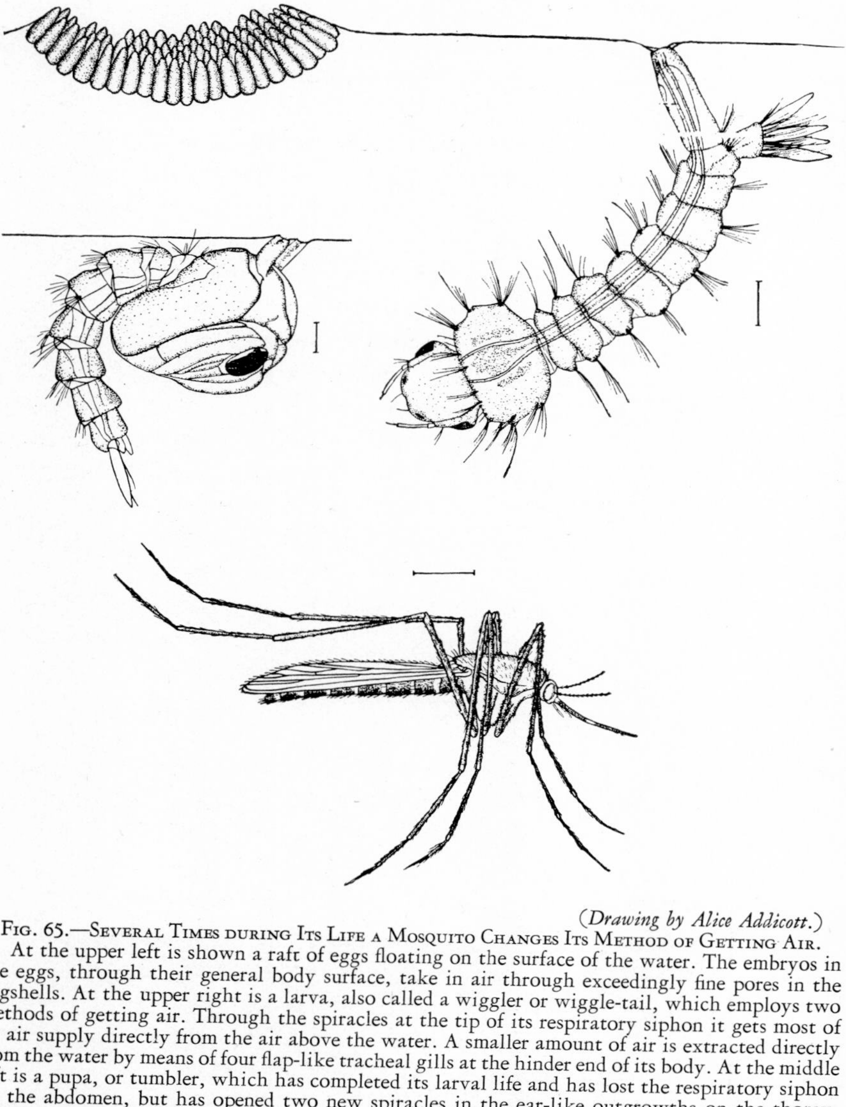

(*Drawing by Alice Addicott.*)

FIG. 65.—SEVERAL TIMES DURING ITS LIFE A MOSQUITO CHANGES ITS METHOD OF GETTING AIR.

At the upper left is shown a raft of eggs floating on the surface of the water. The embryos in the eggs, through their general body surface, take in air through exceedingly fine pores in the eggshells. At the upper right is a larva, also called a wiggler or wiggle-tail, which employs two methods of getting air. Through the spiracles at the tip of its respiratory siphon it gets most of its air supply directly from the air above the water. A smaller amount of air is extracted directly from the water by means of four flap-like tracheal gills at the hinder end of its body. At the middle left is a pupa, or tumbler, which has completed its larval life and has lost the respiratory siphon on the abdomen, but has opened two new spiracles in the ear-like outgrowths on the thorax. Below is the adult mosquito, which uses all its spiracles and thus takes in air through ten pairs of openings, two pairs of which are on the thorax and eight on the abdomen. A knowledge of the breathing habits of mosquitoes in the wiggler and tumbler stages has led to the use of oil on mosquito-breeding water in order to control them.

Adaptations of air-breathing aquatics. Air-breathing aquatic insects must rise to the surface at frequent intervals to secure air. Most of them are, in consequence, active swimmers and divers. Each time they dive they carry with them a store of air to supply them with oxygen during their stay beneath the water. The devices of these insects for obtaining a supply of air and for carrying it about with them are numerous and highly varied in character. They include some of the

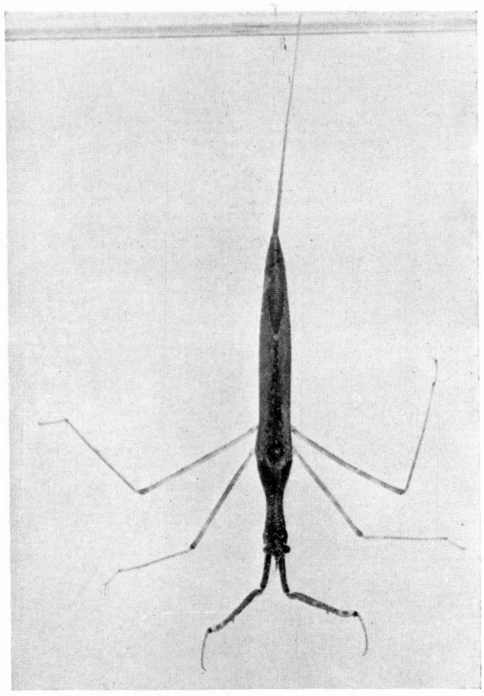

FIG. 66.—*Ranatra*, THE RAPACIOUS WATER-SCORPION, HANGS HEAD DOWNWARD FROM THE SURFACE FILM OF THE WATER WHILE IT BREATHES AIR THROUGH ITS LONG RESPIRATORY SIPHON.
The siphon conducts the air to the one pair of functional spiracles, which open into an air chamber on the back surface of the body beneath the tips of the wings.

most interesting adaptations to aquatic life found among insects, only a few of which can be described here.

Aquatic nymphs and larvae regularly have fewer than the normal number of spiracles. Many of them, in fact, such as the mosquito larva (Fig. 65), horse-fly larva, and crane-fly larva (Figs. 14 and 71), possess only a single pair of functional spiracles, located at the tip of the abdomen. These are periodically thrust into the air at the water surface, thus permitting the air in the tracheae to be renewed. Such larvae generally have tracheal trunks capacious enough to hold a supply of air sufficient to meet their needs for a long time. The absence of spiracles along the sides of the bodies of these larvae is doubtless correlated with the fact that they would be of no use to them. If an aquatic larva did possess the full number of spiracles in normal position it would have to crawl completely out of the water in order to use them—obviously a less efficient method of solving the problem of respiration than that actually employed. Some aquatic larvae, such as the larvae of mosquitoes, and those of syrphid flies belonging to the genus *Eristalis*, not only have their spiracles reduced to a single pair, but have them located at the tip of a tubular extension of the body called the *respiratory siphon*. When securing air these larvae project only the extreme tip of the respiratory siphon above the water surface.

A few species of aquatic adults, the water-scorpion, *Ranatra* (Fig. 66), for example, possess respiratory siphons, but their siphons are quite different in character from those of mosquito and syrphid larvae. The siphon of the water-scorpion consists of two long, slender processes from the tip of the abdomen. These are held together by interlocking hairs along their edges so as to appear as a single structure. The inner surface of each process is grooved throughout its length. When the two processes are held by the interlocking hairs, the grooves meet and thus form a tube through which air can be obtained and conveyed to the spiracles. The functional spiracles also are two in number and located at the tip of the abdomen.

Aquatic adults, in contrast to air-breathing aquatic larvae, usually possess the full number of spiracles in a functional condition. The water-tiger beetles, of the family Dytiscidae (Fig. 76), illustrate this point well. Their spiracles are located much as are the spiracles of other beetles, on the flattened upper surface of the body near the edges, where they are covered and protected by the horny wing covers. The wing covers of these beetles fit closely against the edges of the flattened back and are arched over the middle. They thus enclose a spacious chamber above the back. This chamber is kept filled with air, and since the spiracles open into it, it serves as a reservoir to keep the beetle supplied while beneath the water. When the air in this chamber needs to be renewed, the beetle swims, or rises because of natural buoyancy, to the surface. It then thrusts the tip of its body into the air, and lifts its wing covers a trifle, thus making an opening through which the old air supply may be released and a new one taken into the chamber. Many beetles having this habit not only carry a supply of air in the chamber beneath their wings when they descend beneath the water, but in addition drag after them a bubble of air clinging to the entrance of the air chamber at the tip of the abdomen. Others, such as the water-scavenger beetles of the family Hydrophilidae (Fig. 77), carry air entangled in the microscopic hairs which cover a part of the body surface. In the latter case the air forms a layer

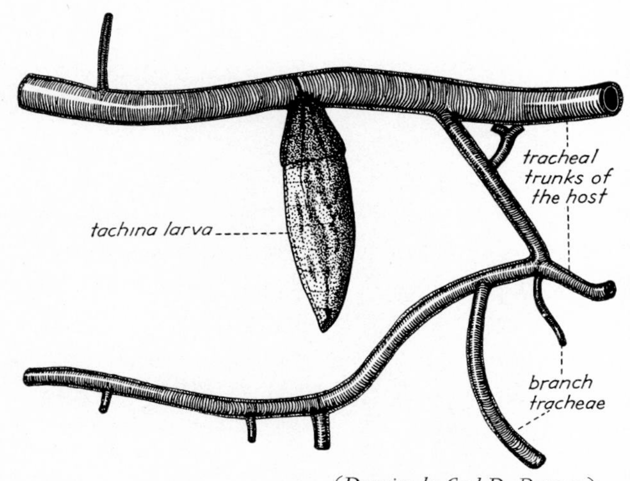

(*Drawing by Carl D. Duncan.*)

Fig. 67.—A Parasitic Tachina Fly Larva, Living in the Blood of a Crane-fly Larva, Solves the Problem of an Air Supply by Tapping the Tracheae of Its Host.

Throughout a considerable portion of its larval existence this tachina larva will remain attached to the tracheal trunk of its host, taking air directly from the tracheae of the latter and, in a sense, using the spiracles of the host in place of its own.

which is in communication with the air chamber beneath the wing covers. When such a beetle is observed beneath the water, the layer of air on its body glistens like silver. The hemipterous insects known as back-swimmers (Fig. 105) also carry air entangled in the body hairs.

A few air-breathing aquatics, most of them beetle larvae of the family Chrysomelidae, do not ascend to the surface periodically to renew their air supply. Instead, they have "learned" that the stems and roots of aquatic plants contain passages that are filled with air and that these passages can be punctured and the air secured. These insects, therefore, obtain their air supply from aquatic plants instead of from the water surface.

The larvae of certain parasitic insects such as tachina flies (Fig. 67) solve the problem of an air supply in much the same manner as these chrysomelid beetle larvae. Living immersed in the body fluids of the insect which they parasitize, these tachina larvae are as truly aquatic as if they lived in a lake or stream, except that there is no surface

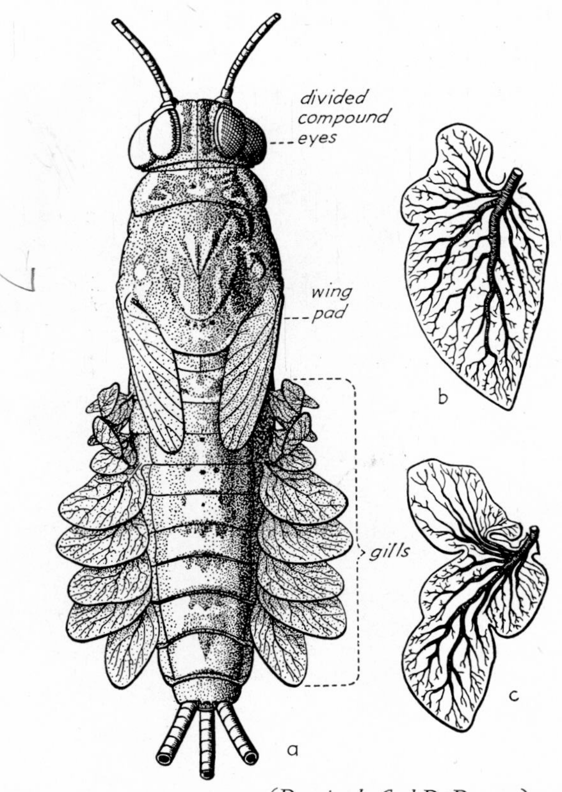

(*Drawing by Carl D. Duncan.*)

FIG. 68.—ALONG THE SIDES OF THE ABDOMEN OF A MAY-FLY NAIAD, LEAF-LIKE TRACHEAL GILLS TAKE AIR FROM THE WATER IN WHICH THE NAIAD LIVES.

This beautifully mottled May-fly naiad, like all other kinds of naiads, is completely aquatic; thus it has no use for spiracles, since it gets its air supply from the water as does a fish. At frequent intervals and for some moments at a time the leaf-like gills are rapidly vibrated so as to set a current of water moving across them, in this way bringing a fresh supply of oxygen. Individual gills are shown at the right.

available through which to renew their supply of air. This would be a well-nigh insurmountable handicap were it not for the fact that the host, being also an insect, possesses tracheae. The parasite larvae, then, attach themselves to the tracheal trunks of the host and secure the needed air from them.

Adaptations of water-breathing aquatics. Water-breathing aquatics get their oxygen supply from the water in one of two ways. Either they breathe through the general surface of their bodies, taking in oxygen at any point and giving off carbon dioxide in the same way, or they possess special structures known as *gills* (Figs. 65, 68, and 69) by means of which breathing is carried on. Very minute aquatic larvae

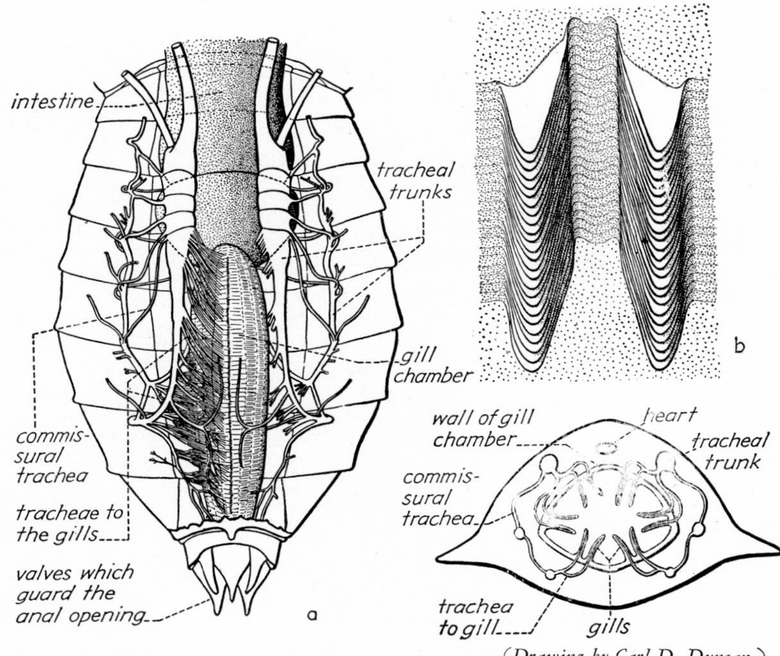

(*Drawing by Carl D. Duncan.*)

Fig. 69.—Water Drawn Rhythmically through the Anal Opening into an Abdominal Respiratory Chamber and Then Forced Out Bathes Numerous Internal Gills and Thus Supplies the Oxygen Need of This Dragon-fly Naiad.

A large part of the abdomen (*a*) is occupied by the enlarged rectum which serves as a respiratory chamber. Numerous gills (*b*) project from the walls into the interior of the chamber where they are bathed by the water taken in; *b* shows only a few of the gills, which are distributed in twelve longitudinal rows. Below *b* is represented a cross section of the abdomen. The respiratory chamber serves also as a locomotor organ, as is explained in the legend for Fig. 80.

(and a few larger kinds, such as some species of "bloodworms," which are larvae of flies of the family Chironomidae, and the so-called *phantom larvae* of the genus *Corethra*, which is variously treated as belonging to the mosquito family or as constituting a separate family) breathe wholly or in large part through their general body surfaces. These larvae have much reduced tracheal systems and no functional spiracles (some have no tracheae even), and therefore the blood serves to distribute the oxygen and collect the carbon dioxide as it does in vertebrates. Most water-breathing aquatics, however, possess gills of some sort. Gills are hollow outgrowths from the body wall, adapted for extracting oxygen from water. They are of two types: tracheal gills, which contain branches from the tracheal system, and blood gills, which do not contain tracheae. Tracheal gills are much more common than blood gills. Many insects possess only tracheal gills or only blood gills, but some insects, such as certain "bloodworms," possess both kinds. Tracheal gills often are leaf-like structures (Fig. 68), though they may be tubular (Fig. 132). They are attached to the body at various places. The oxygen dissolved in the water passes through the wall of the gill into the tracheae inside the gill, and thence into the general tracheal system. In a sense, therefore, tracheal gills take the place of spiracles. May-fly naiads (Fig. 68) have two rows of tracheal gills, one on each side of the abdomen. These gills not only absorb oxygen from the water, but they vibrate as if they were fins and thus keep the water moving over them, bringing a fresh supply of oxygen. Damsel-fly naiads have three large tracheal gills at the tip of the abdomen. These gills also have a double function, for the damsel-fly uses them as oars to scull itself through the water in a clumsy fashion. Dragon-fly naiads have numerous tracheal gills projecting into the rectum which is enormously enlarged (Fig. 69). The water from which the dragon-fly naiad extracts its air supply is alternately drawn into and forced out of this rectal gill chamber through the anal opening (Fig. 80). (See also page 154.) Mosquito larvae, in addition to their respiratory siphon, have a group of four tracheal gills on the last segment of the abdomen, close to the siphon (Fig. 65).

Blood gills may be leaf-like, sac-like, thread-like, or feathery, but in any case they contain no tracheae. They contain only blood. The oxygen which they absorb from the water, therefore, is taken up and distributed by the blood instead of by tracheae. Blood gills are of much less frequent occurrence than tracheal gills. The larvae of caddis-flies (Fig. 132) and midges have blood gills. Blood gills may be attached to almost any part of the thorax or the abdomen.

The foregoing discussion does not by any means exhaust the subject of the breathing of insects. It merely presents a sample of the multitudinous devices employed by insects for securing their share of the oxygen so necessary for life.

CHAPTER IX

HOW INSECTS MOVE

INSECTS inhabit the earth more completely than any other class of animals. They walk and run upon its surface, they burrow into the soil which covers its land areas, they dive and swim through its waters, and they fly through its atmosphere. In achieving this diversity of action they have developed almost every conceivable type of locomotor mechanism known in the animate world. Certain physical factors, however, consequent on the small size of insects, have limited the exact manner in which many of these locomotor mechanisms have been utilized. Insects fly, though few if any of them soar like hawks; of all birds their flight is most like that of hummingbirds (Fig. 162). Insects walk and run, but in most cases not as vertebrates walk and run. The swimming of insects has much in common with the swimming of vertebrates, but insects have developed far more varied mechanisms with which to swim than vertebrates have. In creeping and crawling, insect larvae, especially certain fly larvae, have developed modes of progression entirely unknown among vertebrates, though employed by worms.

An understanding of insect movement may at first seem difficult to acquire, for it demands the mastery of certain mechanical principles, but once appreciated it will add to the study of insects a fascination that will richly compensate for the effort expended. The difficulty involved, as is so often the case, is more apparent than real, for the necessary understanding can be acquired step by step. Each step by itself is relatively simple, and each is related logically to the preceding one, so that, as one progresses, the insect is revealed as one of nature's truly marvelous mechanisms, the study of which is a never-ending delight.

HOW MOVEMENT IS ACCOMPLISHED

Muscles. Strange as it may seem in the face of the extreme diversity of insect activities, there is only one way in which insects, or any other of the higher animals, can accomplish movement, and that is by the pulling of muscles (Fig. 12). Everyone knows that when a muscle acts, or as we say contracts, it shortens and thickens. The shortening exerts a pull in the direction of the shortening. At the same time the

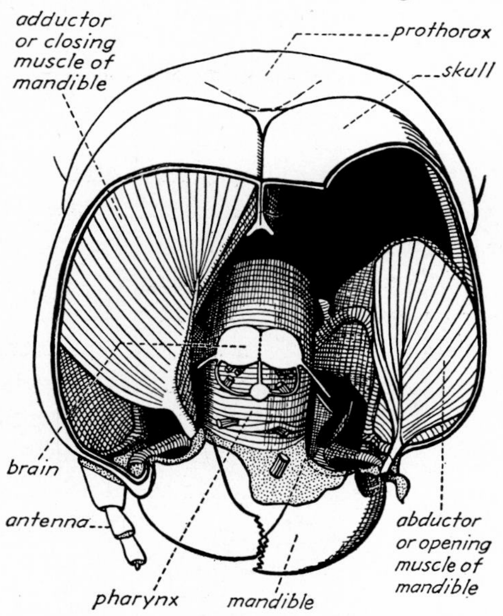

(*Drawing by Carl D. Duncan.*)

FIG. 70.—INSECT MUSCLES WORK IN PAIRED SETS.

The head of a sphinx caterpillar with part of the head wall cut away in front shows the sets of opposing muscles that operate the mandibles—two to each set and one set to each mandible. In each set a comparatively small muscle, known as the *abductor muscle*, opens the mandibles so that a bite may be taken; and a much larger and more powerful muscle, called the *adductor muscle*, closes the mandible against the opposite mandible as the bite is taken.

thickening exerts a push at right angles to the pull. This push may be easily demonstrated by the use of the biceps muscle. If a rubber band is placed around the muscle when a weight is being lifted, the rubber band will be stretched by the outward pushing of the muscle as it thickens. If a string is used in place of a rubber band it may be broken. For reasons which need not be explained here, the pulling effect of a muscle may be more economically used than the pushing effect. Hence, in the make-up of animals, muscles are always placed so that their pull is used rather than their push.

Muscles work in paired sets. Since only the pull of muscles is made use of, it is necessary, except in certain special cases, for muscles to work against each other in pairs or paired sets. For example, to clench our fists we use one set of muscles; to open our fists we must use another set. In the same manner, when a caterpillar takes a bite out of a leaf, there is one set of muscles to open its jaws so that they may be placed about the leaf's edge and another set to close the jaws when the bite is taken (Fig. 70). There is one set of muscles to lift the wings of a flying wasp and another set to pull them down. When a grasshopper jumps, one set of muscles pulls its jumping legs into position and an opposing set gives the kick which hurls the grasshopper through the air.

The opposing sets of muscles may be readily observed in action in certain kinds of living insects. If a young May-fly naiad (Fig. 68) of one of the transparent species be mounted on a slide or placed in a small dish of water and examined with a microscope, the muscles which move its leg joints and antennae may be seen. A mosquito larva (Fig. 65) shows certain of the muscles which move the head and mouth parts. Such insects and many other transparent kinds may be found in every locality and are well worth observing.

HOW MUSCLE PULL IS MADE USE OF BY INSECTS

Although every movement made by insects is accomplished by muscle pull, there are but two common methods of making muscle pull effective: syringe action and lever action. But there are many variations of these methods. The nature of the methods may best be made clear by the use of examples.

Syringe action. Everyone is familiar with the action of a syringe. If a syringe is filled with water or some other fluid and the bulb squeezed, the water is forced outward through the tube of the syringe; and it exerts considerable force as it goes. The force exerted by the outward rushing water may be made use of in a variety of ways. There are many mechanical toys in which the motive power is obtained from some sort of syringe-like device. In all insects and other higher animals syringe action is made use of in passing food along the alimentary canal and in forcing blood through the circulatory system. In addition to this usage, many insect larvae and many worms use syringe action in accomplishing locomotion.

If a transparent insect larva of small size, such as the larva of a midge (a fly of the family Chironomidae), a phantom larva, or a mosquito larva, is watched with a microscope, waves of contraction may at times be seen to pass along its alimentary canal. Each wave appears as a sudden narrowing or constriction of the canal, and the narrowing moves from one end of the canal toward the other. As the constriction moves, it is often possible to see that some of the contents of the canal are forced along by the constriction, much as water is

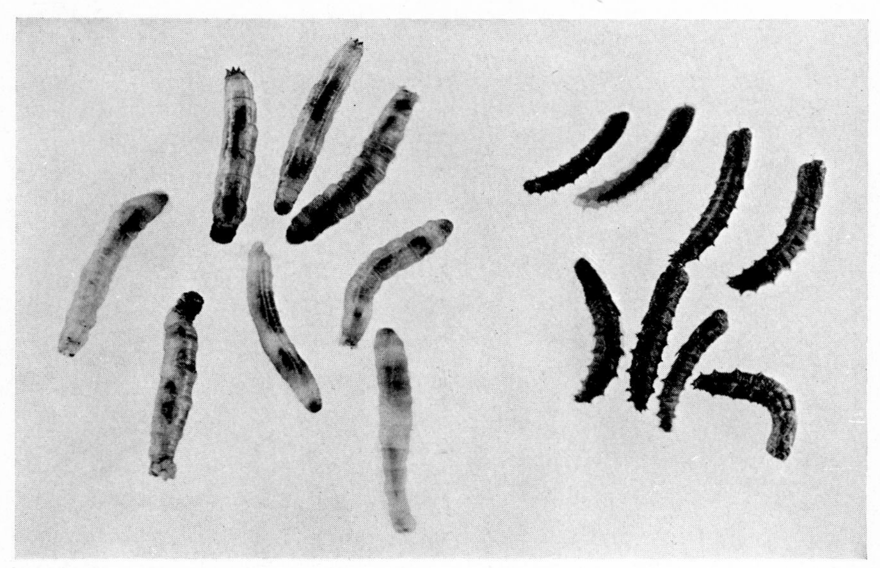

Fig. 71.—Crane-flies as Larvae Have No Legs, but Progress by Telescopic Locomotion.
In telescopic locomotion the body of the larva acts like a two-way syringe. The movement is brought about by the alternate contraction of sets of longitudinal and circular muscles. This type of movement forces these larvae through the damp decaying vegetable matter in which they live. In the figure the darker objects on the right are crane-fly pupae. (See also Fig. 14.)

forced through the tube of a syringe. This action, called *peristalsis*, is a kind of syringe action.

Peristalsis occurs because the digestive canal is encircled by rings of muscles which contract, one after another, making the constriction which travels in wave-like fashion along the canal. The contraction of each circular muscle squeezes the food in the canal and the succession of squeezes forces the food along.

In the same larvae peristalsis may be observed in the heart, which is a transparent tube lying just beneath the body wall along the back of the larva (Fig. 10). The waves of peristalsis in the heart always move toward the head and, since they move much more rapidly than the waves in the alimentary canal, they are usually called *pulsations*. Blood, and not food, is the material forced along by this peristalsis.

Many insect larvae, such as the fly larvae which live in mud or burrow through the soft tissues of plants or the carcasses of dead animals and certain beetle larvae which burrow in wood, crawl by a

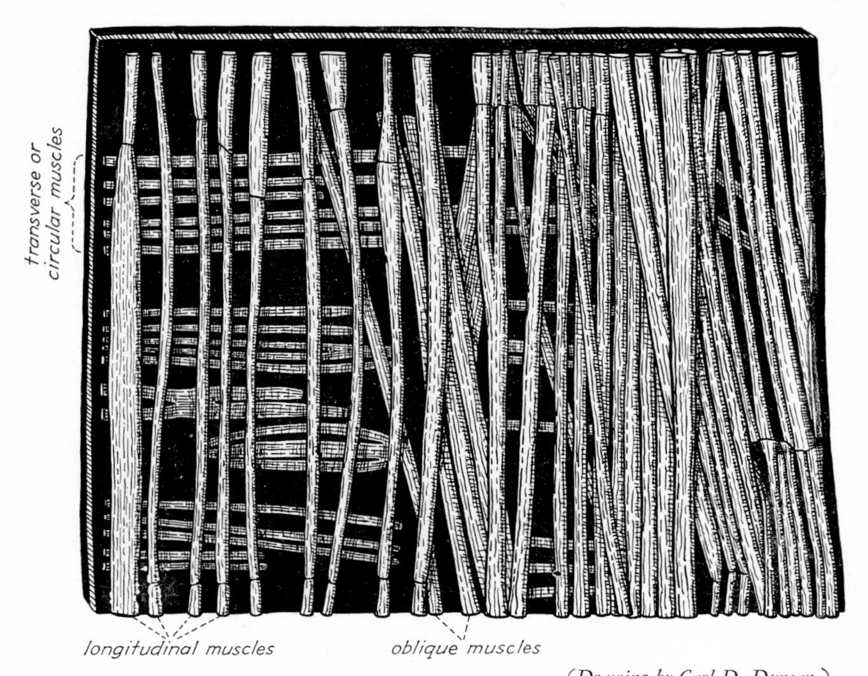

(*Drawing by Carl D. Duncan.*)

FIG. 72.—PART OF THE MUSCLES USED BY A CRANE-FLY FOR ACCOMPLISHING TELESCOPIC LOCOMOTION. In this drawing showing part of the body wall of a crane-fly larva, cut open and laid flat, the muscles that run crosswise are the circular muscles (circular in form in an unopened larva); the others are the longitudinal muscles. With the circular muscles the larva squeezes its body fluids and tissues, making the body narrower and pushing the head end forward. With the longitudinal muscles the larva pulls up its back end the same distance that the head was moved forward.

method of locomotion that is called *telescopic locomotion* and is accomplished by a kind of syringe action similar to peristalsis.

Crane-fly larvae (Fig. 71) give a perfect demonstration of telescopic locomotion. They may be dug out of the mud along the edge of a stream or pond in the spring. They also occur in accumulations of decaying litter in the crotches of trees and beneath loose bark on dead trees or rotting logs. Horse-fly larvae, also found in mud or sand near water, are equally good for this purpose.

When the crane-fly larva or the horse-fly larva is first placed on a dish or piece of glass for observation, it contracts all its muscles and becomes short and plump. In a few moments, however, it relaxes and begins to crawl. At this time its body may be seen to become narrower and to lengthen. The narrowing and lengthening are due to the contraction of numerous circular muscles in the body wall of the larva (Fig. 72). These contractions squeeze the body fluids and internal organs, forcing them against the ends of the body and therefore causing it to lengthen. During the lengthening, the hind part of the larva

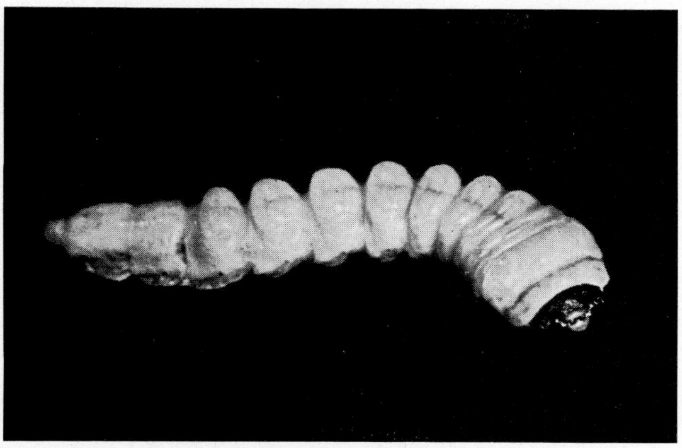

Fig. 73.—The Larva of the Pine Sawyer Moves through Its Wood Burrows by Telescopic Locomotion.

The Pine Sawyer is a large beetle (Fig. 74) that lives as a larva in wood, through which it tunnels with chisel-like mandibles. Since it has no legs, it moves through these tunnels with a telescopic action, and uses the projections on the sides of its abdomen to grip the walls as it moves along.

remains in one spot and the head is thrust forward into new territory. All the lengthening thus contributes to forward progression.

In order to hold the new ground gained, the crane-fly larva presses its head against the surface over which it is crawling, or the mud through which it crawls. It then draws the hinder part of its body forward by contracting its longitudinal muscles. The manner in which this is done is somewhat complicated, but it is essentially as follows: The muscles in the last few segments are contracted first. This moves the posterior end forward a short distance, shortens the segments involved, forces a large part of the body liquids and internal organs in these segments forward into the more anterior segments, and produces a slackened zone in the body wall which is thrown into a series of transverse wrinkles. The forward movement of body liquids into the anterior segments causes the body to thicken once more, restoring to it the plumpness which characterized it at first. Immediately after the hind end of the body is pulled forward, the longitudinal muscles of the other segments contract in rapid succession, beginning with the muscles of the segment in front of the slackened zone. As the longitudinal muscles in front of the slackened zone contract, those behind it relax. The result is that the slackened zone of the body wall is moved forward around the body liquids and internal organs, much as a slackened zone in the finger of a glove is slipped along around one's finger as the glove is being put on. As soon as the slackened zone reaches the front end of the larva, forward progression is again possible, for the slack in the body wall permits the head to be pushed forward once more.

The proof that the body liquids surge forward when squeezed by the circular muscles is easy to secure. The internal organs may be watched through the transparent wall of the larva. These occupy only a part of the large body cavity and practically float in the fluid (in this case the blood) which fills the rest of the cavity. The internal organs are but loosely held in place by strands of connective tissue and by branches of the tracheae, so that when the body liquids are forced forward by the squeezing of the circular muscles, the internal organs are swept along with them, much as seaweed is swept along by sea water as it surges into and out of a tide pool. What an extraordinary experience telescopic locomotion must be! It was in part the appearance of the internal organs sliding back and forth inside the body wall that suggested the name *telescopic* for the kind of locomotion possessed by the crane-fly larva. The movement of these organs suggested an old-fashioned telescope in which the smaller parts slide inside the larger ones when the telescope is put away.

It will be interesting now to examine another larva which exhibits telescopic locomotion and to learn how its structure and behavior differ from those of the crane-fly larva. The round-headed borer (Fig. 73) is such a larva. This larva has broad protuberances, called *locomotor tubercles*, along the sides of its abdomen, and it can protrude or withdraw them at will. At the beginning of forward movement the larva thrusts out the tubercles in the hindmost segments, pressing them against the walls of the burrow through which it is crawling. The remainder of its tubercles it withdraws to the level of the general surface of its body. As soon as the advance of the head end into the new territory is completed, the larva thrusts out the tubercles in the forward part of its abdomen and withdraws those in the slackened zone produced by the contraction of the longitudinal muscles. It thus gets a forward grip on its surroundings while the hindmost part is being drawn forward by the longitudinal muscles. As the zone of slack in the body wall is moved forward, the tubercles in the segments in front of this zone are successively pulled in and those in the segments behind the zone are successively thrust out. Thus there are never any tubercles protruding from the part that is moving.

Lever action. Nearly all movements not accomplished by syringe action are accomplished by the use of levers. Now, in many of its characteristics, a lever is the exact opposite of the body liquids used in syringe action. A lever is a relatively rigid structure of constant shape, instead of a nonrigid fluid the shape of which changes with every change in the shape of its surroundings. A lever does not surge and flow; it moves by rotating about a fixed point called the *fulcrum*. Let us examine a well-known lever in the human body to get an understanding of what levers are and how they are used. The bones of the human foot act as a lever, as do most of our bones. When we rise on our toes, the point of contact between our toes and the ground is the fulcrum of our foot lever. The large muscle in the calf of the leg pulls upward on the heel, which is the back end of the foot lever, and lifts the weight of our body, which rests on the foot lever at the ankle joint.

The use of levers in connection with muscles makes it possible to accomplish some tasks which otherwise would be very difficult; for by them we often can lift large weights or move large objects with only a small force. Also, levers enable us to change a powerful, slow-moving force into a much more rapid-moving though less powerful force. Still other advantages are gained by the use of levers, but they need not be discussed here.

In the locomotion of insects and other animals, syringe action is useful only for worm-like progression. Locomotion by running, swimming, or flying requires the use of levers. Body movements, also, often require the use of levers. In this connection it should be recalled that the body covering of an insect is its skeleton. On the body the parts of the skeleton have the form of more or less flat plates, or of ring-like segments; the skeleton of the legs and antennae consists of tube-like pieces connected by movable joints. Nearly all of these parts function as levers. Thus when the head of an insect is turned from side to side, or is raised or lowered, it acts as a lever; the wings act as levers in the achievement of flight; every leg and every segment of a leg is a lever; the jaws and other mouth parts are levers (Fig. 70), and so are the antennae and their segments. Even the ring-like subdivisions of the abdomen act as levers. The muscles of the insect constitute a complicated and beautifully coordinated system for operating these numerous levers, so as to accomplish the manifold movements of which the insect is capable.

Combinations of syringe action and lever action. Most adult insects, and many larvae, depend entirely on the action of levers for all movements except those of the heart and the alimentary canal. Certain larvae, such as the fly larvae and the round-headed borers already mentioned, use only syringe action in their locomotion. Others, such as the caterpillars (Figs. 33, 38, and 136), use both syringe action and lever action in their crawling. The lever action is not, however, of so simple a character as that used by adult insects and vertebrates.

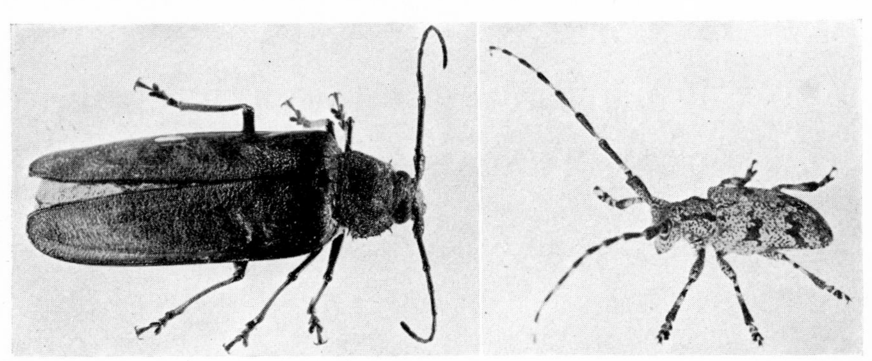

Fig. 74.—Long-horned Beetles Have the Sturdy, Jointed Legs of Insects That Move Freely on the Surface of Objects.

Like nearly all beetles, they have delicate hind or under wings that are used in flight (Fig. 130), and these are protected by shield-like upper wings called *elytra*. The beetle on the left is the Pine Sawyer (*Ergates spiculatus*) and the other is the Spotted Tree Borer (*Synaphoeta guexi*). Their larvae burrow in wood (Fig. 73).

ADAPTATION IN INSECT MOVEMENT

The movements of any insect, especially those of locomotion, must be adapted to the conditions of its environment. The horse-fly larva, crawling through mud in search of worms or insect larvae on which to feed, would find legs or wings worse than useless. They would be so much in the way that the mere possession of them would be a severe handicap. If the round-headed borer (Fig. 73) possessed well-developed walking legs, it would have to cut a much larger burrow in which to live, a procedure that would obviously be costly because of the large amount of labor involved. On the other hand, to a free-ranging insect, legs or wings are of great importance, for they help it in clinging to its food plants, in fleeing from enemies, and in seeking mates. Obviously, too, the kinds of movement and locomotion displayed by an aquatic insect of necessity differ from those displayed by a terrestrial species. We may group the methods of insect movement and locomotion into certain definite types in accordance with the kinds of environment inhabited.

TERRESTRIAL LOCOMOTION

For present purposes, terrestrial locomotion is thought of as the locomotion of all insects which move in contact with the soil or some other solid or nonelastic substance. It, thus, includes even the locomotion of those aquatic insects which walk or pull themselves over the bottoms of ponds and streams. The telescopic locomotion of burrowing larvae, which has already been discussed, is also a kind of terrestrial locomotion.

Most terrestrial locomotion consists of walking or running, but the walking and running of insects is accomplished in a manner somewhat different from that employed by large vertebrates, such as dogs, cattle, man, and other mammals. The difference is not due to the fact that insects have a different skeletal organization, nor to any essential difference in the nature of insect and vertebrate muscle; it is due solely to the fact that insects are small and vertebrates are large.

When a person walks, as anyone can determine for himself, he leans forward and begins to fall, but before he really falls he swings one of his legs forward and catches himself. This method of walking, therefore, characteristic not only of man but of most other walking vertebrates, is accomplished by partial falling and recovery, repeated over and over. It is a method, however, that is practicable only to relatively large animals whose weight is great in proportion to body surface and who, therefore, encounter but little air resistance as they move. The body weight of insects is small, but the body surface in proportion to weight is great. Air resistance and other factors of too complex a nature to be discussed here tend to slow down the movement of insects and prevent the small weight of their bodies from being effective in a fall-and-recovery type of locomotion. And so we find that the walking and running of insects is accomplished in another manner.

The walking and running of insects. The system of walking used by insects and related animals may be characterized as a push-and-pull system in which the weight of the animal plays only a negligible part. If the legs of a beetle, a wasp, or any other insect be examined closely it will be seen that each "tarsus," or foot, is tipped with a pair of claws which are usually curved or hooked (Figs. 109, 112, and 130). On the undersurface of the feet of some insects there are also small pads, often covered with minute hairs which produce an adhesive secretion. Usually there are spines on the legs, the largest of them at the junction of the feet with the legs in positions corresponding roughly with the ankle and wrist joints of human beings (Figs. 109 and 158). When an insect walks over a horizontal or an inclined surface it behaves much as a large animal does when climbing. It hooks its tarsal claws over little irregularities in the soil or vegetation and thrusts its spines into little holes, or catches them against little projections, and thus gets a firm hold. It then pulls with its front legs and pushes with its hind legs, while its middle legs act as pivots for its body. Thus by a sort of push-and-pull action it moves forward at a speed and with a stability impossible for so small a creature if the fall-and-recovery method of walking were used.

When vertebrates run, they use both the push-and-pull method of locomotion employed by insects and the fall-and-recovery method of their own walking. This is a matter of common knowledge and is necessary because more force is needed to accomplish high speed in running than is supplied by the weight of the body in a mere fall-and-recovery method of locomotion. And see how vertebrates are equipped to accomplish push-and-pull locomotion in their running! It is for this purpose that they have claws and hoofs (though claws and hoofs are used for other purposes also), and it is for this purpose that spikes are built into the soles of the shoes worn by athletes.

AQUATIC LOCOMOTION

Insects living in intimate relationship with water fall naturally into three classes: the surface-dwellers, which are not truly aquatic but merely walk or glide over the water surface; the incompletely aquatic forms, which spend most of their time submerged and are therefore aquatic in so far as most of their activities are concerned, but are, nevertheless, air-breathers; and the truly aquatic species, which not only move about beneath the water surface but secure their oxygen from the water by means of gills, after the manner of fishes. The methods of locomotion employed by the members of these groups differ according to the differences in their habits and the degree to which they are aquatic.

The locomotion of surface-dwellers. In their manner of locomotion, surface-dwelling insects do not differ essentially from terrestrial forms. They use a typical push-and-pull method of locomotion dependent on lever action. The only significant difference between them and terrestrial forms is that they have developed a means of walking on water without getting wet, whereas most typically terrestrial animals are unable to do this.

The explanation of the ability to walk or run on water surfaces is the same in all cases. It depends on two things. First, the surface layer of all bodies of water constitutes an elastic film or membrane with many of the properties of a stretched sheet of rubber. This water film possesses considerable strength, which can be measured directly, and it will support any object the weight of which is less than the strength of the film itself, provided the object is protected in some manner from becoming wet. Second, the insects and spiders in question possess the needed protection against wetting. Their feet, and often their entire bodies, are covered with fine hairs or a layer of oil. The hairs prevent wetting by holding a layer of air between the water film and the body of the insect; the oil prevents wetting because it will not mix with water.

Surface-dwellers are supported by the surface film on which they stand, but, though they do not break the film, they do make depressions or dents in it. Thus each foot of a surface-dwelling insect rests in a depression, and these depressions act as the irregularities which make a push-and-pull method of locomotion effective. With the surface-dweller, however, the push is more important than the pull. At each step, or advance, the surface-dwelling insect pushes or gives a vigorous kick against the slanting surface of the depressions in which its feet rest. There is no group of surface-dwelling insects in which this fact is more apparent than the water-striders, or "skaters," as they are often called (Fig. 181).

The incomplete aquatics. The incompletely aquatic insects, most of them active swimmers and divers, differ from the completely aquatic species, not only in their mode of respiration, as already noted, but in other respects. For example, most air-breathing aquatics, such as the numerous water-beetles (Figs. 76 and 77), the Giant Water-bugs (Figs. 21, 61, and 104), the water-boatmen (Fig. 75), and the back-swimmers (Fig. 105), have a specific gravity less than that of water. By this we mean that the body of a diving insect weighs less than an equal bulk of water. The result is that any diver will float or rise to

Fig. 75.—The Water-boatmen Row with Their Hair-fringed, Oar-like, Third Pair of Legs. Since the oars are worked together, these insects move through the water, as do most incomplete aquatics, by little spurts. Like all incomplete aquatics, Water-boatmen rise to the surface unless they cling to the stones or to each other to remain below, as the picture shows. As occasion demands, and as the spirit moves them, adult Water-boatmen crawl out of the water, spread four well-built wings, and fly to new pastures. Most of these flights take place at night, as a result of which great numbers are attracted to electric lights and to their doom.

the surface, unless it keeps itself beneath the water by actively swimming or by clinging to submerged plants, stones, or other objects.

The low specific gravity of diving insects is undoubtedly an adaptation to enable them to rise to the surface easily and frequently to secure the air needed for respiration. For an air-breathing diver to possess a specific gravity greater than that of water would be a severe handicap. Those air-breathing aquatics which have eliminated the necessity for coming to the surface by securing air from aquatic plants (see page 133) can stay beneath the water indefinitely. They do not need to be able to move about quickly in the water. In consequence, many of these air-breathers are not true divers, but are creeping forms of sluggish behavior exhibiting typical push-and-pull locomotion like that of terrestrial species, or telescopic locomotion like that of mud-dwellers.

All true diving insects swim by using their legs or other body appendages as means of propulsion. In most species the legs are modified to serve as oars. They are often greatly elongated, as in the water-boatmen (Fig. 75), the back-swimmers (Fig. 105), the Giant

(*Photograph by Lester Brubaker.*)

FIG. 76.—NOT ONLY IS THE THIRD PAIR OF LEGS IN THE PREDACIOUS DIVING-BEETLE MODIFIED TO SERVE AS OARS BUT THE WHOLE BODY IS REMARKABLY STREAMLINED FOR RAPID PASSAGE THROUGH THE WATER.

To carry out the-streamline idea, the beetle's hard shell is smooth, hairless, and unwettable. Since the oars need to work in one plane only, the first leg segment, or coxa, which provides for rotation of the leg in walking insects, is greatly flattened and consolidated with the wall of the thorax. The antennae fold back into grooves behind the eyes.

Water-bugs (Figs. 21, 61, and 104), and the diving-beetles (Figs. 76 and 77). They are also frequently flattened so as to present a broader surface to the water as they beat against it, and they may be fringed with hairs. The majority of diving insects work their oar-like swimming legs in unison, much as a person rows a boat by pulling on both oars at once. The result is that the insects move by a series of spurts, often at a surprisingly high speed. The water-scavenger beetles, or hydrophilids (Fig. 77), however, are peculiar in that they use their legs alternately. As a consequence, they swim more smoothly, though less rapidly.

The complete aquatics. These insects, which are the gill-breathing aquatics, universally have a specific gravity greater than that of water. This fact gives them several advantages not possessed by diving species. For example, they do not need to expend the large amount of energy that must be expended by diving species in just getting below the water surface. Their modes of locomotion, in consequence, may be more varied and more economically effected.

FIG. 77.—WATER-SCAVENGER BEETLES MOVE SMOOTHLY, FOR THEY WORK THEIR SWIMMING LEGS ALTERNATELY.

These insects are not so highly specialized for aquatic life as are the predacious diving-beetles. They have, however, a smooth exoskeleton, and like all incomplete aquatics must come to the surface of the water for air, which they take in along the sides of their elytra, or upper wings. They also carry a film of air under their streamlined bodies.

In most cases at least, gill-breathing insects do not use their legs as swimming organs, and the use of other vibratory appendages is the exception rather than the rule. The abdomens of some gill-breathers, however, such as those of May-fly naiads (Fig. 68), have on them leaf-like gills which vibrate rapidly. Just what part, if any, these gills play in swimming is uncertain, since most of the energy expended is obviously derived from undulatory movements of the abdomen, comparable to those of a fish, except that they are up-and-down movements rather than side-to-side movements. The principal function of the gill vibration is to keep a current of water moving over them, thus ensuring a continually renewed supply of oxygen.

Gill-breathing insects usually propel themselves by means of general body movements. These movements are of various types, and according to the manner in which they are effected they may be characterized as wriggling, sculling, or undulating. Damsel-fly naiads bend their bodies from side to side in an awkward sort of sculling movement, which drives them slowly through the water. The three large leaf-like gills at the tip of the abdomen of the damsel-fly naiad doubtless act as fins and make the sculling more effective than it otherwise would be.

FIG. 78.—THIS BIG WESTERN DOBSON LARVA IS VERY AGILE AND AS FIERCE AS IT LOOKS. The larvae of complete aquatics, as shown by this dobson larva, often are not highly specialized for aquatic locomotion. With their thoracic legs dobson larvae crawl over submerged objects to find their food of worms and juicy larvae. When danger threatens, they beat the water violently with their abdomens, and dart backward, crawfish fashion, into nearby holes. Incidentally, though predacious water-beetles and water-scavenger beetles are aquatic both as larvae and as adults, dobson larvae must come from the water to pupate, for the gauzy-winged adults cannot swim.

The most effective swimming by gill-breathing insects is accomplished by wriggling movements such as those made by mosquito larvae (Fig. 65) or by the so-called *bloodworms*, the larvae of midges. The midges constitute a family of flies, known as the *Chironomidae*, which are related to the mosquitoes. Midges are among the most abundant of insects, and their larvae may be found in almost every body of water except the most temporary. In wriggling, the body of the larva is bent violently and suddenly, first one way and then another. At each bending the body of the larva beats against the water and is carried forward a short distance. The action is remotely similar to the swimming of a one-armed man, but it is proportionately much more violent and powerful. Mosquito larvae bend much less than do the midge larvae. The latter sometimes form complete figure-eight loops, with the ends of their bodies crossed.

Mosquito larvae and "bloodworms" travel freely in any direction through open water by wriggling. Other gill-breathers depend on wriggling only to escape from enemies. The Western Dobson larva

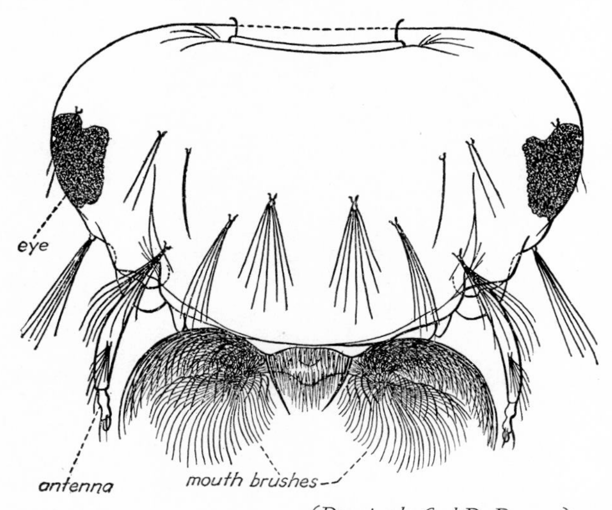

(*Drawing by Carl D. Duncan.*)

FIG. 79.—THE MOUTH PARTS OF A MOSQUITO LARVA ARE ADORNED WITH DENSE MOUTH BRUSHES WITH WHICH TO COMB FOOD FROM THE WATER OR TO SWIM, AS OCCASION DEMANDS.

These magnificent mustachios are at one and the same time veritable "soup strainers," with which the mosquito larva sweeps microscopic plants, animals, and debris into its mouth, and "propellers" of the tractor type, for by rapidly extending and spreading its mouth brushes, then drawing them inward through its mouth, the larva can feed itself or travel, as it chooses.

(Fig. 78) belongs to the latter group. In its ordinary exploring activity this dobson creeps rather slowly and leisurely over submerged leaves and sticks or stones on the bottom of the streams it inhabits. When disturbed, however, it darts rapidly backward in a sort of wriggling movement in which the abdomen beats the water violently in an up-and-down direction.

In addition to wriggling, which they use for all rapid locomotion, mosquito larvae make use of another and more extraordinary means of propulsion. Each larva bears on its mouth parts a pair of dense mouth brushes (Fig. 79), like great mustachios, composed of beautifully curved and exquisitely shaped setae (hairs) (Fig. 5*h*). When feeding, the larva "combs" the water around itself with these brushes, thrusting out and spreading the setae to their utmost, then drawing them into its mouth, straining out of the water as it does so the microscopic plants, animals, and vegetable debris which constitute its food. Thus the mouth brushes are not only mustachios, but veritable "soup strainers" as well. Occasionally, while hanging suspended from the surface film or drifting through open water, the larva speeds up the action of its mouth brushes, whereupon they become "propellers" drawing it forward at a slow but steady rate.

In their more ordinary and leisurely wanderings in their watery world, dragon-fly naiads (Fig. 80) walk about over the bottoms of ponds and streams or over aquatic vegetation, using a typical push-and-pull method of locomotion. Some kinds burrow through sand and mud, advancing slowly and using their legs to force themselves along. When disturbed, the dragon-fly naiad folds its legs against its sides, or at least brings them in close to its body, and advances rapidly by a succession of spurts, in the accomplishment of which the legs play no part. There is no apparent mechanism by which this peculiar locomotion is accomplished, but if we watch a naiad for a little while we discover the mechanism. Whenever the naiad "takes off" from the bottom of the pool or stream in which it lives, or comes near any silt-covered object, a little cloud of mud or sand is blown up behind it. Obviously this is caused by the squirting of water. A little further observation discloses the fact that the rectum of the naiad is enlarged to form a chamber (Fig. 69) from which water is forcibly ejected by the action of circular muscles in the wall of the chamber. In the intervals between ejections, the chamber is opened, whereupon it fills with water. Here we have a perfect example of a syringe used as a locomotor organ! At each ejection of water from the syringe the naiad is driven through the water, rocket-like, in one of the spurts of movement already described.

AERIAL LOCOMOTION

All truly aerial locomotion, whether of insects or of other animals, consists of flying. To be sure, there are other means of progression through the air, but none of them is very effective. Animals, such as the so-called *flying squirrels* and *flying fishes*, travel through the air, sometimes for considerable distances, but they do not truly fly; they merely coast or glide. The exertion which propels them is completed before they take "flight," and when the impetus of this initial exertion is expended the animals must come to earth. Insects, on the contrary, like birds and bats, actually fly. They are carried through the air by the beating of their wings against the air, and their flight can be maintained as long as the muscles responsible for it can be kept working.

(*Photograph by Lester Brubaker.*)

FIG. 80.—THE ELABORATE ABDOMINAL GILL BASKET OF THE DRAGON-FLY NAIAD FUNCTIONS BOTH IN RESPIRATION AND IN LOCOMOTION.

Water drawn through the anal opening into the highly modified rectum supplies the oxygen. Water forcibly ejected from the gill chamber by the action of powerful abdominal muscles drives the naiad, rocket-like, in a series of rapid spurts through the water. (See also Fig. 69.)

The flying of most insects is not like the flying of most birds, though it is similar to that of hummingbirds (Fig. 162). In most bird flight the beating of the wings is fairly slow, slow enough to be followed by the human eye; whereas in most insect flight the beating is so rapid that the wings are visible only as a blur. In bird flight, too, there is generally more or less coasting or soaring interspersed with the active flying. That is not the case with most insects. Certain butterflies and moths and the larger dragon-flies do some coasting, but few, if any, insects soar.

These differences between the flight of birds and that of insects are largely unavoidable consequences of their differences in size. The rapid wing action of insects is practically impossible for larger animals, such as most birds, because of mechanical reasons which need not be explained in detail here. These same mechanical reasons completely prevent flight by any of the very large animals. It is no accident that elephants do not fly. They couldn't fly, even if they had wings.

Despite the differences between their modes of flight, there is one respect in which insects and birds (and bats as well) are alike, and in which they differ from most of the flying machines constructed by man. In the insects, the birds, and the bats, the parts which support the body in the air are the same as those which exert the force that propels the body forward. The wings do both. This is not true of airplanes, with the exception of the autogiro, for the wings of an airplane serve only to support the plane, while the propeller drives it forward. The propeller is a kind of wheel, and nowhere in the animal kingdom is the exact counterpart of a wheel to be found. The wheel, the most effective mechanism in existence, has never been "invented" by nature. Perhaps this is because the existence and use of a wheel demands the complete separation of parts in the engine of which it is a part, and complete separation of moving parts of the sort required in a wheel is not possible in animal bodies.

The small size of insects compensates for their inability to produce and use propellers, however, for small bodies may be moved much more readily than large ones. Flying insects have developed amazing versatility in their aerial movements. It is only necessary to watch one of the more specialized of the flies (Fig. 177), wild bees (Fig. 161), wasps (Fig. 147), or moths (Fig. 162), in flight to be moved to wonder and admiration. At one moment it will be poised in one spot, motionless except for its whirring wings; in another moment it will dart away at such breath-taking speed that the eye can hardly follow it. Some of these flying marvels can fly upward or downward, forward, backward, or sideways, and can spin round and round in spirals, loops, and rotations so complicated that the flight of a stunting airplane is tame by comparison.

Not all insects are so versatile as the flies, bees, and wasps; nor do all other insects fly in the same manner. There are many variations in both the method of flying and the machinery of flying. As is true of other insect parts and behavior, all these variations have been brought about by the modification and specialization of a simple primitive type of machinery: the primitive type of insect wing, together with the body parts which support and move the wing.

Specializations for efficiency in flying. Neither the body form nor the shape and construction of the wings of primitive insects was conducive to efficient flying. In those insects, therefore, which have adopted the air as their special domain—the dragon-flies (Fig. 1), true flies (Fig. 177), wasps (Figs. 142 and 147), and bees (Fig. 161)—

FIG. 81.—THE WINGS OF A DRAGON-FLY ILLUSTRATE FLIGHT, THE MOST HIGHLY DEVELOPED OF INSECT MOVEMENTS.

This is the Ten-spot Dragon-fly (*Libellula pulchella*), and though its wings, like those of all dragon-flies, are somewhat primitive in possessing veins that form a network, still it is an efficient and skillful flier. The ability to fly has gone far toward making insects a dominant group in the world of animals.

both body and wings have been changed in form. The dragon-flies have changed less than the others, and as a consequence, though powerful, speedy, and agile fliers, capable of flying either forward or backward, they have not achieved quite the versatility of certain flies and bees. The dizzy gyrations exhibited by many flies and bees during mating, or by some of the predatory wasps in their struggles with captured prey, have no counterpart in the flying of dragon-flies. Dragon-flies fly mostly on the level, alternately speeding on rapidly vibrating wings and coasting on relatively quiet wings.

Bees, wasps, and flies, on the other hand, exhibit two striking modifications which increase their speed and flexibility in flying. Their bodies exhibit the well-known streamline form to cut down air resistance, and their wings are either reduced to a single pair, as in the flies (Figs. 14 and 177), or the hind wings are much reduced and are linked to the forewings with hooks (Fig. 5*i*), so the two pairs act as a single pair, as in wasps and bees. Flight accomplished by a single pair of wings is apparently more economical and efficient than flight accomplished by two pairs of wings placed one behind the other. Furthermore, both the individual wings of flies and the linked wings of wasps and bees are slender compared with the wings of most insects, being narrowed at their attachment and rounded at the tips. The narrowing at the base provides great flexibility and permits their being moved through a wider angle than would otherwise be possible. It also permits them to be tilted so as to cut the air at various angles. This narrowing, together with their shape, makes them the nearest approach to propeller blades that is found in the animal kingdom.

The subject of insect movement should not be brought to a close without once more calling attention to the amazing transformation which a highly specialized insect, such as a fly, experiences during its lifetime. The transformation in locomotion and locomotor machinery is just as profound and as nearly incomprehensible as the transformation in form and in feeding habits. In passing from the larval state to adult conditions the fly changes from a cylindrical, footless, headless maggot, progressing more or less slowly through mud or decaying organic matter by means of telescopic locomotion, to a brilliant, scintillating, complicated flying mechanism of unparalleled versatility!

CHAPTER X

HOW INSECTS ARE PROTECTED

ALL animals, and of course that includes insects, must do four things to continue to exist: they must get air, they must get food, they must reproduce themselves, and they must be protected. Other portions of this book are devoted to the matters of air getting, food getting, and reproduction. Here will be considered briefly some of the devices and some of the activities by means of which insects are protected from their enemies.

All animals have enemies. This is one of the inexorable laws of Nature. At first thought, to human beings, this fact would seem to make of Nature a cruel "creature" and not the gentle, kindly "individual" we have always thought her. Yet when it is pointed out that animals are successful chiefly because of their enemies, Nature is seen once more as a great benefactor.

If it were not for enemies that continuously weed out the weak and the unfit, any group of animals would rapidly degenerate until they would become depauperate or would suffer extermination as a result of their own accumulated inertia. And because of this, when the active enemies of any group of animals are removed, these animals eventually begin to decline because the weak, diseased, and unfit among them are left to propagate their kind. Again, if they were even for a time able to succeed without enemies, animals would so increase in numbers that they themselves would become their own enemies; and so, under natural conditions, would crowd out their own kind through lack of space or lack of food. Thus the circle of enemies that surrounds all living things has become one of the highly important factors in the balance of nature. Without it there would be no balance. And the human being presents no exception to this great rule.

Insect enemies fall into two great classes: passive enemies, such as adverse conditions of temperature and water, and scarcity of food; and active enemies, such as other animals that feed upon them or diseases that afflict them. The active enemies, again, are of two types: the various diseases and internal parasites; and the external enemies, the "predators," that capture and devour. Against all these enemies, especially if they are of frequent occurrence in the life of the insect, there usually is some method of protection. Means of protection against passive enemies are not impressive or startling. Likewise, means of protection against disease and internal parasites are usually intangible. This chapter, therefore, proposes to outline some of the means that insects employ in protecting themselves against

FIG. 82.—THE WOOLLY BEAR IS PROTECTED BY ITS SPINES.
Spines are only one type of protective covering that prevents many insects from furnishing tasty bites for birds or other enemies. The woolly bear is the larva of the Acraea Moth (Fig. 163).

their active enemies, those enemies that, for the most part, are predators and are intent upon securing an insect meal.

Protection by locomotion. First and foremost among methods employed by insects in their self-preservation against active enemies, against predators, is the use of legs and wings. Legs and wings serve insects in several capacities, carrying them to more or better food supplies, helping them to find mates, and aiding them in distributing their eggs; but they are frequently highly developed in order to carry insects away from their enemies. The significance of the wings in this capacity is impressed on everyone who has tried to catch a butterfly or has tried to swat a fly. The significance of legs in this respect is impressed on one who has tried to catch a grasshopper or a cricket. To the natural enemies of insects, legs and wings are even more impressive, since for birds or other animals they bring about frequent disappointments in the search for insect meals.

Protective coverings. Running and flying are among the most primitive of all methods whereby insects protect themselves. A more advanced method is the use of protective coverings. Such protective coverings may have been supplied by Nature through some process of natural selection during the ages. The hard outer skeleton and hard upper wings (elytra) of beetles, effective protection from many ene-

FIG. 83.—THE INTERESTING LITTLE TREE-LIKE SPINES ON THE LARVA OF THE NEVADA BUCK MOTH SERVE TO PROTECT IT.

mies which do not relish a meal of armor plate, doubtless developed in this manner.

Other protective coverings which Nature has supplied are irritating coats of rough or prickly hairs or spines. The tufts of hair-like spines on the woolly bear caterpillar are protective (Fig. 82), for they make woolly bears undesirable food for nearly all birds. Such protective coverings are present on many species of caterpillars. The Christmas-tree coverings of the larvae of the buck moth (Fig. 83) are not only rough; they are poisonous and leave a stinging rash wherever they come in contact with tender portions of the human skin. They undoubtedly have the same effect on the mouth lining of a bird or mammal.

Another type of protective covering is that which an insect actively adds to itself. Caddis-fly larvae, which live on the bottom of streams and would be good food for dragon-fly naiads and water-bugs, gather up sticks or stones and build about their soft bodies elaborate little "houses" (Fig. 133). For each species of caddis-fly there is a definite plan of architecture. Some build their houses entirely of small twigs laid lengthwise; others lay the twigs crosswise as they are laid in log cabins; still others use small pebbles and make a house that resembles, in its architecture, a cobblestone chimney. When a caddis-fly larva must move from one place to the next, it thrusts its head and legs from the front end of its house and moves ahead, dragging the house after it. When danger threatens, it pulls its head and legs back into the house. Even the American Dipper or Water Ouzel, that remarkable little bird that gets its food from the bottom of flowing streams, has difficulty in breaking open the house of a caddis-fly larva.

Another striking covering made by an insect, that apparently serves its greatest function as a protective device, is the frothy mass secreted by spittle-bugs (Fig. 84). These bugs thrust their proboscis into the stem of a plant and while they suck up the sap they extrude liquid from their posterior end and work it into a froth by a telescoping action of the abdomen, until the mass completely conceals them.

Protection through combat. In any group of animals some are able to protect themselves, in part, through actual combat, to fight back when an active enemy threatens. Among insects there are active warriors that use their mouth parts in fighting; there are those that sting; and, most astonishing of all, there are those that bombard their foes with poisonous gases.

The youthful insect collector will be astonished, for instance, at the fighting spirit and pugnacity of a Jerusalem Cricket (Fig. 107). When teased, it will squeak with leg strokes along its abdomen and open big powerful mandibles to tear its tormentor apart. That same youthful collector is sure to learn, perhaps to his intense discomfort, that water-bugs and back-swimmers will use their piercing and sucking beaks to defend themselves (Figs. 104 and 105). Their bites under such circumstances are as effective as well-placed stings.

An effective sting is a well-known characteristic of some insects. One should point out here, however, that stings are used by yellow-jackets, wasps, and bees only as protection for themselves or for their nests. None of these insects goes about stinging merely as a pastime; no insect will sting unless there is some real or apparent cause for it. Stings are used also to paralyze other insects or spiders that are used as a food supply for the young of the wasps or bees (see the chapter on "Insect Foods and Feeding Habits"), but that is another

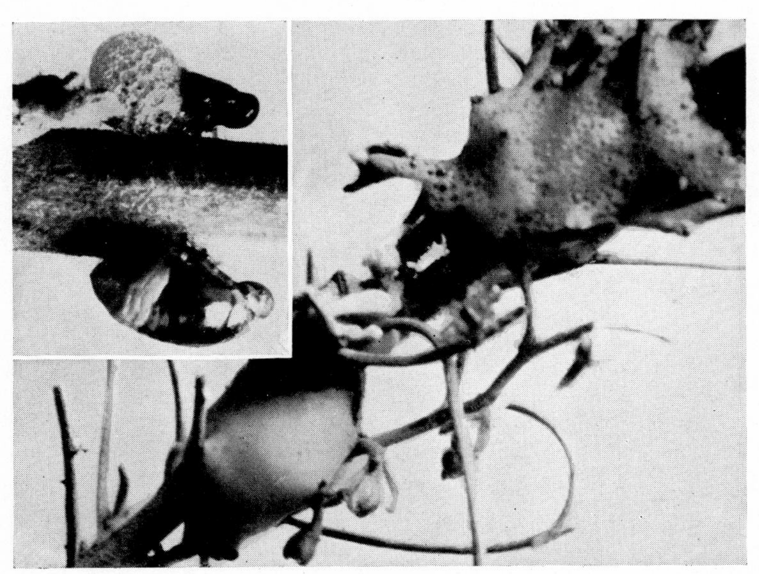

FIG. 84.—THE SPITTLE MASSES OF THE SPITTLE-BUGS APPEAR TO SERVE AS A PROTECTIVE COVERING FOR THE INSECTS THAT PRODUCE THEM.
The mass seems not only to resist drying but also to conceal the bug from enemies.

story. Here stings are considered only as an effective means of protection against enemies.

Gas warfare was used by human beings for the first time in the World War a quarter of a century ago, but certain insects have been using gas warfare for countless ages! Unlike ruthless human beings, however, insects use gases and chemicals only in defensive combat, never in offensive. Many insects are repugnant to other animals because of bad odors or bad taste and so are protected from most of their enemies. This is true of the stink-bugs and several species of beetles. But it is a passive protection, and as such is considered under a separate heading. Those insects, on the other hand, that discharge bad odors or poisonous chemicals when they are defending themselves are far more unusual than those that merely carry about with themselves a bad taste, and far more striking in their methods of defense.

FIG. 85.—WHEN ENEMIES THREATEN, THIS DARKLING-BEETLE STANDS ON ITS HEAD AND EMITS A STREAM OF POISON GAS FROM THE END OF ITS ABDOMEN.

There are several bombarding beetles and other insects that protect themselves by gas defense. This beetle (the Dentate Eleodes, *Eleodes dentipes*) will hold this pose for several minutes while the air about becomes filled with the bad odor of its gas.

Turn over a rock on a dry California hill. Sooner or later you will discover a big shiny black beetle (Fig. 85). It will be *Eleodes*, a darkling-beetle, belonging to the family Tenebrionidae. If sufficiently startled by your rock turning, it will hoist its abdomen high in the air and discharge odorous chemicals to keep away all enemies, meanwhile walking stiff-legged and slow. Pick up that beetle and your hands, by their persistent odor, will remind you for a long time thereafter of the strange abilities of that insect.

Even more astonishing is the performance of the bombardier beetles belonging to the ground-beetle family (Carabidae). These trim little beetles, with their tan or rust-colored "chests" and lustrous blue-black elytra, are found commonly between or under cobblestones along creek and river margins. When disturbed, the bombardier beetles literally shoot "poison gas" at the disturber. An audible report and a visible puff of vapor accompany each discharge. Bombardier beetles are widely distributed in this country and in Europe.

This defensive gas warfare among insects is most highly developed among certain of the formic ants. These ants also are widely distributed, both here and abroad. In the chaparral of California, for instance, an ant of this group builds the nests typical of the group by gathering together large mounds of leaves and twigs (Fig. 101). These nests are defended by the ant with a chemical warfare that will rout all ordinary foes. Suppose you tap such a nest with your boot or a stick. Furiously the defending ants rush out with their big mandibles widely agape. These same mandibles are set violently into the invader by some of the defenders while others face the enemy, prop themselves up, curl their abdomens forward between their legs, and fire away with minute jets of poisonous spray (Fig. 86).

Larvae of certain species of the genus *Papilio*, such as the swallowtail, the life history of which is discussed in Chapter IV, also protect themselves by bombarding with odorous chemicals. When disturbed, the caterpillars of these species evert from the first segment of the thorax two brilliantly colored orange-red sacs which scent the air for several minutes with a pungent odor (Fig. 32). The sacs, or osmeteria, are quickly retracted into their pockets after the contents have been thrown into the air.

Protection by the possession of poisonous or distasteful parts. Many insects, especially beetles, true bugs, and caterpillars, enjoy a high degree of immunity from enemies because they are repugnant to creatures which otherwise would eat them. The poisonous, irritating, or distasteful substances to which certain insects owe their repugnance are produced by special stink glands. There are few persons who have not, at some time or other eaten, or rejected as unfit to eat, a raspberry with an odor strongly reminiscent of an irritated stink-bug. These

FIG. 86.—THESE FORMIC ANTS ARE BOMBARDING WITH GAS AN ENEMY THAT HAS THREATENED THEIR NEST.
They face the enemy, curl forward the abdomen, and from it shoot tiny jets of formic acid.

bugs, members of the hemipterous family, Pentatomidae, produce their vile-tasting and vile-smelling protective secretion in glands on the thorax.

In the blister-beetles and oil-beetles, members of the family Meloidae, the protective substance is an irritant poison which appears to be contained in the blood. An oil-beetle stiffens its body when picked up, bends its legs, and leaks big drops of irritating yellow blood from pores in its "knee joints." Some ladybird beetles do likewise though the liquid they produce is not irritating.

Other insects seem to have the objectionable material generally distributed throughout their bodies. This appears to be true of lady-

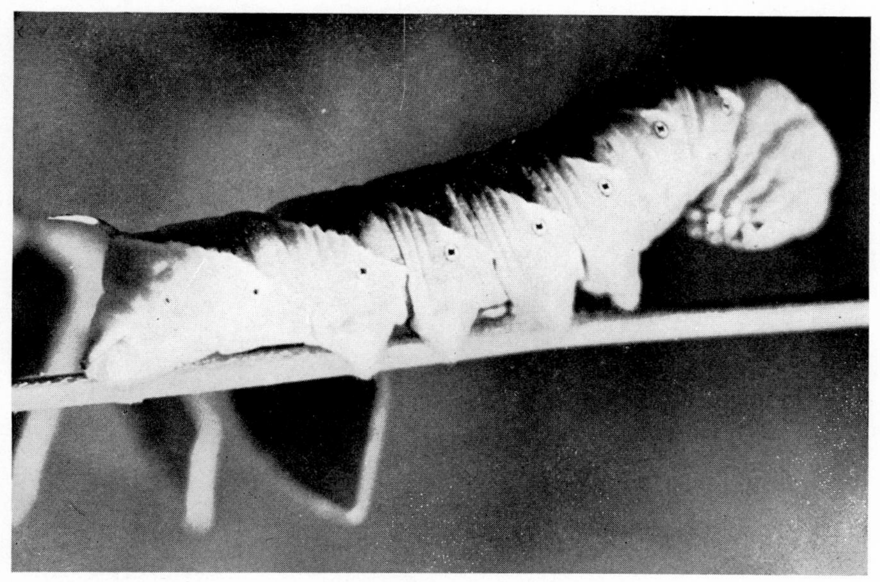

Fig. 87.—Sphinx Caterpillars Attempt to Protect Themselves by Assuming as a Bluff the Famous Sphinx Pose.

The caterpillar here is the larva of the Tomato Sphinx Moth and, like other sphinx caterpillars, lifts its front end and curls the head under when enemies annoy. Because of this pose, presumed to resemble that of the Egyptian Sphinx, the members of an entire family are called sphinx moths.

bird beetles generally, and it is true of certain caterpillars also. The caterpillars of the Monarch Butterfly, for example (Fig. 136), which look good to eat, actually seem to be downright distasteful, for they are regularly shunned by birds.

Protection by bluff or intimidation. Most insects which will enter into active combat with their enemies also use that well-known means of self-protection, the bluff. In fact, most animals that will fight for their safety, bluff first. If this bluff, or intimidation, does not work, then they will fight with tooth and claw, with sting or gas. There is another group of insects, however, that neither would nor could fight in the last extremity, but which still use a most effective bluff.

The larvae of many moths and butterflies, for instance, make good food for many species of birds. Most of these larvae have a coloration that serves to conceal them, but many also are capable of an intimidation display, or bluff. The caterpillars of the family of

FIG. 88.—THE LEAF-GREEN COLOR OF THE FORK-TAILED BUSH KATYDID GIVES IT THE PROTECTION THAT COMES THROUGH COLOR RESEMBLANCE.

Here is the case of an insect that secures protection through a color resembling that of its environment.

sphinx moths (Sphingidae) have earned their name of "sphinx" by their habit of rearing up their front ends, drawing in their heads, and thus assuming a threatening attitude that slightly suggests the pose of the Egyptian Sphinx (Fig. 87). Other caterpillars have harmless "horns" and protuberances on their heads or anterior ends, and these they swing violently back and forth when danger threatens.

Protective coloration. There are few animals, indeed, without a coloration that will serve to assist in concealing them, and hence

Fig. 89.—With Its Pattern of Lights and Shadows the Tobacco Sphinx Moth Merges into the Bark on Which It Rests.

The concealment is brought about, not by colors that are exactly like those of the object that serves as a home, but by a picture pattern that matches the lights and shadows there.

serve in protecting them. But protection through color is utilized more fully by some animals than by others. So far is this phase of protection carried that many insects rely on it altogether; and amazingly, since the usual major phase of protective coloration is countershading that gives to animals white underparts and dark upper parts, the back-swimmer that lives a life upside down, still presents this type of coloration by having its back light and its under surfaces dark (Fig. 105).

There is but little doubt that the leaf-green color of long-horned grasshoppers and katydids has been evolved through the ages by a natural selection which kept in existence those forms that were more protectively colored than others. When one examines a Fork-tailed Bush Katydid (Fig. 88) or the true Katydid (Fig. 97) on a stem, surrounded by green leaves, and notes that the color of the katydid's wings and body makes it almost indistinguishable from the leaves among which it sits, the great protective value of that type of coloration is immediately obvious.

One of the most remarkable cases of protection through coloration is that of the Tomato-worm Moth, or Tobacco Sphinx Moth (*Protoparce quinquemaculata*), which, as an adult moth, has a pattern that resembles to a striking degree the markings on an old weathered board or the furrows and ridges of tree bark. When this moth remains quietly upon such a favorite resting place, its picture pattern almost completely conceals it (Fig. 89).

Mimicry. In this account of the means and devices utilized by insects in protecting themselves, the most remarkable of all has been reserved for the last. It probably represents the highest specialization in this great field. If, in protecting itself, an insect resembles some definite object that will mislead an enemy, because the object resembled is not good to eat or is dangerous, then that phase of protection is called *mimicry*. Protective coloration is, to be sure, a mild phase of mimicry, though colors can be concealing without actually making an insect look like another object. Mimicry will be restricted here to those cases in which an insect actually resembles something that it is not.

Mimicry can be active or passive. There is the notable case of the Viceroy Butterfly, a butterfly that is good to eat from the standpoint of birds, but which so closely resembles the Monarch Butterfly, an insect that birds shun, that it is protected by its mimicry. This is

Fig. 90.—A Striking Method of Protection Is Shown by the Walking-stick.
Its long legs, long antennae, and slender body make the walking-stick difficult to distinguish from the stems among which it quietly lives.

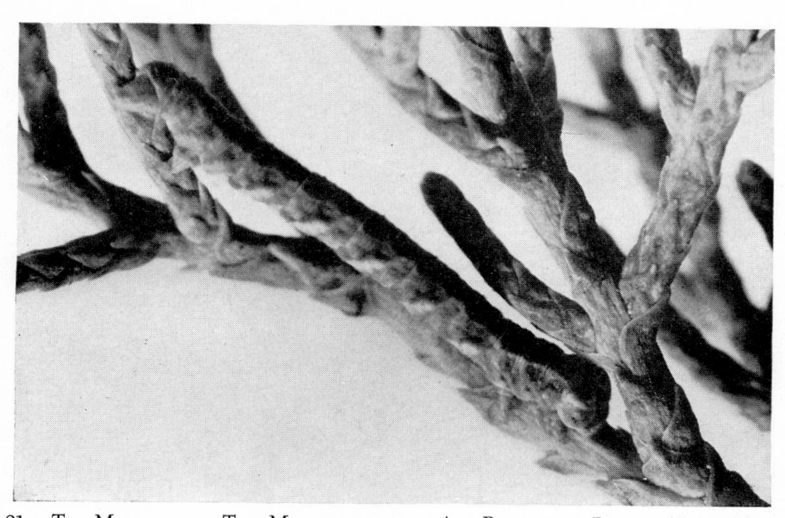

Fig. 91.—The Markings of This Measuring-worm Are Protective Because They Look Like the Scales of the Cypress on Which the Worm Lives.
Some measuring-worms pose so as to imitate stems (Fig. 92), but here is a measuring-worm that has the markings of the stems among which it lives.

passive mimicry, for Nature has brought about this protection without any active cooperation on the part of the butterfly.

Perhaps the best known of all cases of passive mimicry is possessed by those astonishing insects, the walking-sticks, which really look so much like sticks or stems that one has difficulty in distinguishing all their parts from the twigs and stems among which they live (Fig. 90). Reference will shortly be made to active mimicry among

FIG. 92.—TWO MEASURING-WORMS UPON THIS BRANCH ARE PROTECTING THEMSELVES BY IMITATING STEMS.

Look carefully! That big twig on the right and that other on the left are not twigs, but motionless measuring-worms! Here, indeed, is the highest art of self-defense. For many minutes or hours these "twigs" are stiff and lifeless; then at last they slowly bend, come to life, and go looping along in measuring-worm fashion.

certain of the measuring-worms, but a measuring-worm that presents an excellent type of passive mimicry is shown in Fig. 91.

Active mimicry is best and most amazingly displayed by those insects which can assume quickly a guise that is quite unlike their usual appearance. Certain large measuring-worms, of the family Geometridae, have the ability, when danger threatens, to stiffen themselves out at angles to the stem upon which they have been feeding or crawling, and thereafter for several minutes or hours to resemble perfectly bare and lifeless twigs (Fig. 92). These indeed have reached the highest level in the art of self-defense!

In conclusion and summary a small outline of this interesting subject is here given:

A. Protection by locomotion
  1. Running
  2. Flying

B. Protection through coverings
  1. Armored parts
  2. Supplementary coverings, such as "houses"

C. Protection by the possession of poisonous or distasteful parts
  1. Secretions of stink glands
  2. Poisonous or irritating blood
  3. General distastefulness

D. Protection through fighting or combat
  1. Biting
  2. Stinging
  3. Bombardment with chemicals and bad odors

E. Protection through bluff or intimidation

F. Protection through coloration

G. Protection through mimicry
  1. Passive
  2. Active

CHAPTER XI

INSECT VOICES

Did you ever watch a Snowy Tree Cricket sing? Did you ever, with a flashlight, trace a loud "click, click, click, click" to its source and find the Angular-winged Katydid, an insect with wings like a leaf? Have you ever with care, caution, and patience worked your light along the sidewalk edge to discover a male Black Cricket singing "chee, chee, chee" to a near-by female? Did you know that some insects sing in chorus?

Purpose of insect voices. Insect voices, like the songs of birds, are restricted largely to the males. It would appear, then, that insect voices, like the songs of birds, are frequently related to the courtship of insects. That is generally but not always true. Courtship is the most important function of insect voices, and is most pronounced in the males, though a few females, such as the female Fork-tailed Bush Katydid (Fig. 88), produce sound. Also, insect voices have a relationship to protective behavior, and in some are used only as a part of protective display. Thus the squeaking of the West Coast Ten-lined June-beetle, Prionus Beetle, and Jerusalem Cricket are part of the grand bluff that these insects present when they are teased or frightened. There are, furthermore, a few insect sounds, such as the hum of wings, that are incidental to the insects' activities and are not deliberately made, as are the sounds produced for courtship or for defense.

The insects that produce sound. Though the air seems fairly to throb with insect sounds on a warm summer night, still the number of singing species is not large. In fact, insect sounds of any sort are relatively few in number. The hum produced by rapidly vibrating wings occurs widely, but it is, as has been noted, an accidental voice. Deliberate sound making is most highly developed among the Orthoptera, those straight-winged insects, the grasshoppers, katydids, and crickets. Hardly less impressive are the voices possessed by the cicadas, or harvest-flies, of the order Homoptera. Sounds that bluff are largely restricted to the Coleoptera, the order of beetles, and the Hemiptera, the order of true bugs.

Insects, generally, do not make sounds with vocal chords, as you or I do. They have no such structures. Their sounds are produced by wings, by legs, by sliding or telescoping one part of the body into another, or by special sounding drum devices. In an exceedingly small number of cases true vocal sounds are produced by forcing air through the spiracles. One very large grasshopper, *Taeniopoda picticornis*(?), of the lubber type which inhabits western Texas, makes a spewing sound by forcing a mixture of air and watery liquid out of the second pair of thoracic spiracles whenever it is disturbed. Certain flies and bees are credited by some biologists with making sounds with their spiracles. To make clearer some of these methods, a few examples will be given. Since insect voices are produced for different reasons, they will be divided into humming, bluffing, and courtship voices.

Humming sounds. No one who has lain awake trying to swat that mosquito with the irritating hum will deny that mosquitoes have a voice. The hum of a mosquito is produced by the wings, and perhaps is merely an incident related to the rate of wingbeat. Perhaps, too, it may have a function; the suggestion has been made that the antennae of the male mosquito are tuned to the particular pitch that the beat of the female's wings produces, and he is thus enabled to find her.

Bees and flies hum as they fly or merely by vibrating their wings when not in flight. This, too, is probably merely an incident related to the rate of the wingbeat. It is a matter of interest, though, because the tones produced by the different species of flies are in some cases sufficiently defined to be identified. The House-fly hums in the key of F in the middle octave, but the Bluebottle-flies, much larger, with a slower wingbeat, hum in a distinctly lower key. Incidentally, it is amazing to note that the key of F in the middle octave requires a wingbeat of 345 times per second—20,700 times a minute![1] Though the number of wing vibrations can be judged by the pitch they register, actual counts have been made by allowing the wing to mark

[1] John Henry Comstock, *Introduction to Entomology*, The Comstock Publishing Company, Ithaca, N. Y., 1925, pp. 80–81.

upon a revolving smoked drum. Similarly, the hum of a bee may register different notes because of variations in the rate of wingbeat. These variations reflect the nervous condition of the bee, and an attentive ear can thus tell much of the temper of the hive as can the other bees. For instance, bees have a distinct "contented" hum as they work; they have a distinct "angry" hum when they have been disturbed; and, it is said, they have a hum that denotes a queenless colony.

Bluffing sounds. The Jerusalem Cricket is a grand bluffer (Fig. 107). All that is necessary to get a display from this big fellow is to tease it a bit. The cricket will face its tormentor and then move the hind or third pair of legs and rub them vigorously up and down against the abdomen. The roughened areas produce a sound like that caused by rubbing two pieces of sandpaper together. Occasionally the procedure is varied. The cricket holds its legs steady while it jerks the abdomen up and down between them. Again it bends its legs inward so that they rub against its abdomen while the cricket runs away. When the West Coast Ten-lined June-beetle (Fig. 130) is held it produces a pronounced squeaking by pulling and rubbing the terminal segments of the abdomen under the hard upper wings. Many beetles are capable of this type of squeaking under similar circumstances.

The most astonishing bluffing display of all is produced by big long-horn beetles of the genus *Prionus*. When next one of these beetles blunders into your room, or is found in May or June stranded beneath a light, pick it up and carry it to a table. Gently prod it with your finger or a pencil. It will soon cease its attempts to escape and face you with an amazing show. The hind, or last, legs are brought up alternately and rapidly against the margins of the hard upper wings. With each movement a sharp scratching sound is produced. Spines, minute ridges, or sharp edges on the legs of these beetles, rub against the wings and produce the scratching sounds, while the long legs go up and down with such rapidity that they give the impression of wheels revolving.

Courtship sounds. The insect sounds that have a relation to courtship are by far the most numerous. These sounds are restricted almost entirely to the males. Here are the true songsters among the insects, for though of real music there is none, still the "intent" is that of the serenader. The best known of these songsters, the possessor of the insect voice of legend and story, is the Field Cricket, more popularly known as the Black Cricket (Fig. 93). This insect is heard from coast to coast in North America. It was a near relative of the Black Cricket that inspired *The Cricket on the Hearth*. In the Far West, the Field Cricket is responsible for the first insect voice of the

FIG. 93.—THE FIELD CRICKET FIDDLER IN THE CENTER WAS PLAYING WHEN WE FOUND HIM. He makes his "chee, chee, chee" with his wings, and it is noticeable that his wings are of a structure unlike those of the female with him. The Field Cricket (*Gryllus assimilis*) is also called Black Cricket, and the whereabouts of the adult male is usually made known by his persistent voice.

season. Indeed, the Field Cricket in this region is singing before the winter rains have ceased; and a few, from sheltered niches, may sing throughout the winter. All through the summer and into the fall they continue to sing, joining their songs to those of the Snowy Tree Cricket that does not begin to sing until late June. The Field Crickets may be heard throughout most of the nation, even in the deserts. At Palm Springs, in the Coachella Valley, we once listened to a Field Cricket, and the song seemed loud beyond all proper proportions. Investigation showed the songster wedged into a crevice in a Blue Gum tree, where the cavity behind acted as a vast sounding box for the small black fiddler.

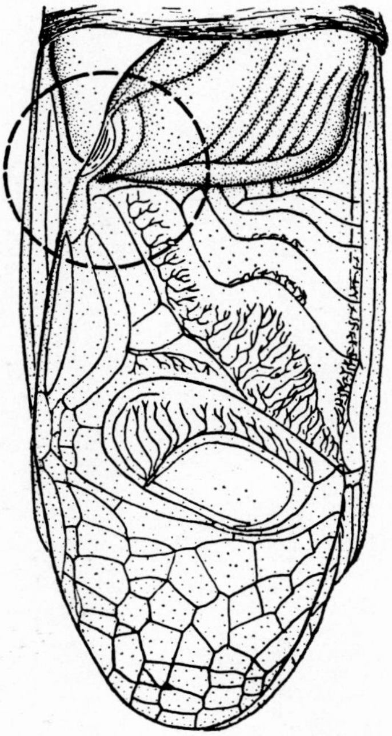

(*Drawing by Tom Rodgers.*)
FIG. 94.—THE FIELD CRICKET PULLS A SCRAPER OF ONE WING OVER A FILE OF THE OTHER.
The scraper is a semicircular notch in the area that is encircled by a broken line in the figure; the file is a series of tiny teeth on the heavy vein that leads away from it across the wing. The remainders of the wings act as sounding boards.

The Field Cricket sings with its upper wings. For this purpose it has special devices on these wings. On the inner margin of each upper wing and near the base is a hardened area called the *scraper* (Fig. 94). Extending away from this scraper along a thickened vein is a series of minute projections like those on a rasp, the so-called *file*. The cricket raises its upper wings, spreads them, and then moves them in and out, drawing the scraper of one over the file of the other. Both wings are supplied with scraper and file so that the wings can take turns—the one that now scrapes can change position and become the one that is scraped, and vice versa. The basal ends also of these upper wings are thickened and so act as amplifiers when set into vibration as the scraper passes over the file.

The song of the Field Cricket is unmistakable. It is the loud, clear "chee, chee, chee, chee" that is so pronounced on spring evenings. To watch a Field Cricket sing, go out with a flashlight and cautiously approach the direction of the notes. As soon as he is disturbed he will stop. Wait then until the song is resumed. Advance again. Thus by a series of cautious advances and pauses you will finally have your light upon the soloist. Note then the action of the wings. His ladylove may be near. You will know her because, since she does not sing, her wings are not thickened as are those of the serenader, and she has, in addition, a long ovipositor (Fig. 93).

By early summer the attentive ear will note that a new insect song has joined the "chee, chee, chee" of the Field Cricket. At that time the Snowy Tree Cricket tunes its fiddle. The voices of the Snowys increase in number as summer advances, and by August a welling chorus comes up from every garden.

The Snowy Tree Cricket is a fascinating insect; green in color, but so pale and transparent of wing that it seems as ephemeral as a

FIG. 95.—THE "CHUR, CHUR, CHUR" THAT COMES FROM GARDEN SHRUBS AND FLOWERS IS THE SONG OF THE SNOWY TREE CRICKET.

Throughout the summer and until the heavy frosts of autumn, the Snowy Tree Cricket sings during the long night hours. Usually there are several of these pale and transparent fiddlers, and, instead of solo music, a chorus wells up from each garden.

skiff of snow (Fig. 95). Its wings have the same file-and-scraper device as the wings of the Field Cricket, except that the scraper of the right wing is not so highly developed as that of the left, so that the scraper of the left only is used over the file of the right (Fig. 96). The Snowy Tree Cricket does more than merely lift its upper wings; it elevates them until they stand at right angles to the body and then pulls

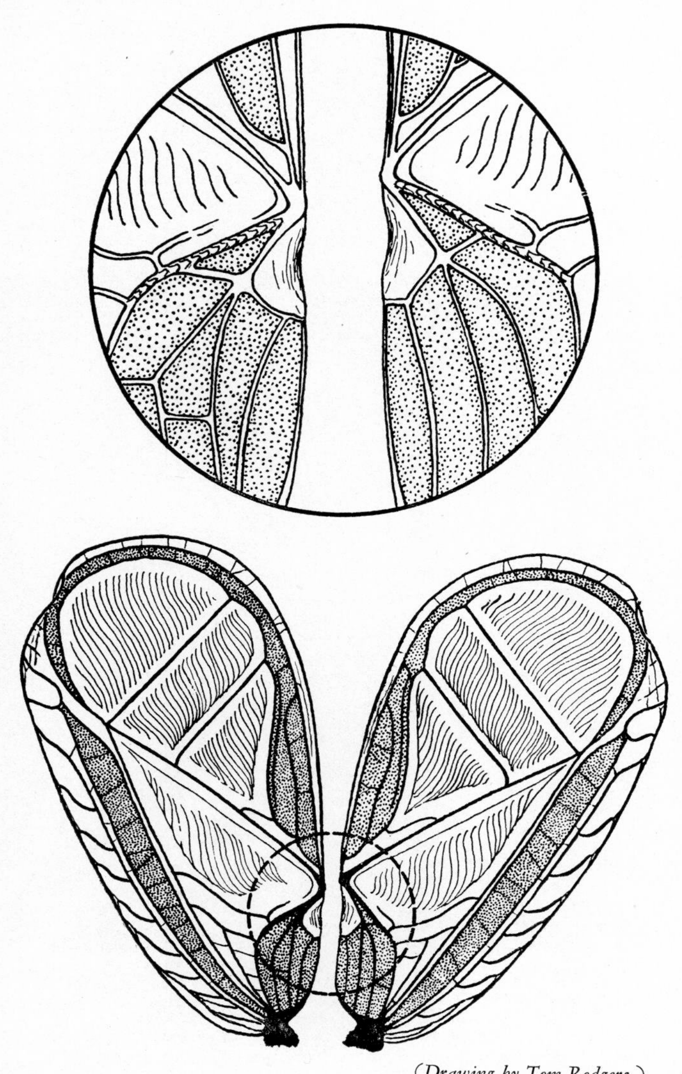

(*Drawing by Tom Rodgers.*)

FIG. 96.—THE SNOWY TREE CRICKET SINGS WITH THE SCRAPERS AND FILES AT THE BASE OF ITS WINGS.
In the upper drawing, the margins of the semilunar transparent areas are the scrapers; the files are formed by the projections on the rasping veins. The scraper of one wing is drawn over the file of the other, the wings being pulled rapidly back and forth to make the "chur, chur, chur." The lower drawing gives a general view of the entire wing surface and shows the big amplifying area which comprises nearly all the rest of the wing surface.

them out and in, scraper over file, to make its "chur, chur, chur, chur."

In the Far West the Snowy Tree Cricket is first heard in early summer, and not until the coldest winter weather comes is it hushed. It is now Thanksgiving Eve in central California, and in the quiet distance a Snowy Tree Cricket may be heard. Last year one sang in late November, and two years ago it was January 4 before the last Snowy's bow and fiddle were put away. When finally their songs cease, six months will pass before Snowy Tree Crickets sing again. Then the songs will be of another generation, one that has come from eggs that were laid in the autumn and hatched after winter's rains.

It has been said that the song of the Snowy Tree Cricket sounds like "chur, chur, chur, chur, chur, chur." When there are two Snowys not far from each other, their songs assume the same tempo: a note of one is followed immediately by a note of the neighbor. They will thus keep time singing throughout the night. If there are many of these crickets in one locality, they will produce a monotonous chorus.

The temperature greatly influences the rate of utterance of the Snowy Tree Cricket. The early summer evening is warm, and then the "chur, churs" are uttered about as rapidly as a human being can repeat them with ease. When the cool of morning has come, the rate will have dropped, sometimes to one-fifth this speed. Now, with the notes uttered more slowly, one may detect that each "chur" is made up of about five parts, parts which cannot be detected when the notes are rapidly given. Each of these parts perhaps represents the passage of the scraper over the file. Slowly, indeed, does the cricket sing in the frosty early winter evenings, and toward morning the songs cease altogether. That aged fiddler that carried on into January's chill drew his last bow like the cold and tired musician that he was. His notes no longer sang a brisk "chur, chur," but each quavered out into "ch-ch-ch-ch-ur, ch-ch-ch-ch-ur" as his last song was forever done.

Field Crickets are usually on the ground and Snowy Tree Crickets in low garden plants. At night in the West, as summer advances, from the shrubs and from the trees another note is heard. This one is exasperating for the insect hunter, and is not repeated regularly, but only now and then. It is like "tzit, it, it" or merely "tzit." This is the voice made by the Fork-tailed Bush Katydid (Fig. 88), another night voice that is made with wings. Its wings are not so highly modified, so its voice is not developed to the extent of Field or Snowy Tree Crickets.

In the San Joaquin Valley and through the Middle West a loud "click, click, click" like the tick of a grandfather clock, but rapidly repeated, will lead you to the Angular-winged Katydid and to one of the greatest surprises of your investigating life, for this katydid has upper wings that look like green leaves.

The crickets and katydids described in the preceding paragraphs are the common songsters of garden, orchard, and park in the Far West. The grass-brown hills and wooded mountains of the western summer have another. This is one of the shield-backed grasshoppers. These grasshoppers are given this name because the plate that covers the first segment of the thorax is extended back over the remainder of the thorax and onto the abdomen like a large shield. Most of the shield-backs have wings so short that they do not project beyond the back end of the shield and are, of course, useless as flying structures. But, if they cannot support the shield-back in flight, still they can produce music. To the shield-back and its short wings you must attribute most of the insect music you hear at night in wooded regions, hills, and mountains. If you are driving at night over mountain roads during late June, July, August, or September, stop the motor for a moment. Almost certainly there will be, near at hand, the "p-zee, p-zee, p-zee, p-zee," loud, fast, and monotonous, of a shield-backed grasshopper.

Though the Far West has several interesting singing insects that are at their best at night, it is in the Middle West and Southeastern United States that the greatest volume arises from the nocturnal insect songsters. The Field Cricket and the Snowy Tree Cricket are there, but the greatest volume of song comes from the members of the long-horned grasshopper family. From the cornfields and the weed patches of these regions there wells forth a veritable din produced by several species of these insects. Throughout the day they are heard, and at night also if the weather is warm.

Where the deciduous forests occur in Southeastern United States, from central Iowa south and east, one also hears the true Katydid (Fig. 97). It produces such a loud and emphatic voice that it requires only a little imagination to believe that the insect is saying "Katy did—didn't!" The true Katydids sing only at night.

All the insects mentioned up to this point are at their musical best at night. But insect sounds, though most noticeable in the quiet that prevails after sundown, are not restricted to this part of the day. A few are at their best in the light and heat of a brilliant sun. This is true of that gay bearer of castanets, the Carolina or Black-winged Locust, and several of his relatives, such as the locust shown in Fig. 107. When at rest these insects are drab grasshoppers that love the heat and dust of unsurfaced roads or the soil of any bare field. Their colors harmonize with these surroundings and here their "music" may be heard. This is always delivered in the air as the grasshopper vaults from one dusty spot to another. Often the grasshopper will

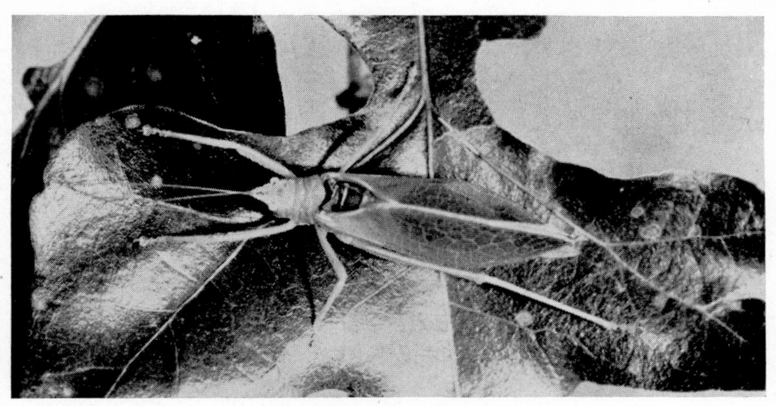

Fig. 97.—This Insect Says "Katydid" with Its Wings.
The portion of the upper wing that is modified to make the sound can be seen as a triangular area on the upper surface of this true Katydid's wings.

leap up and hover in the air above a particular spot while his castanets play a lively tune. Search below will sometimes reveal the reason for this attention in the person of a quiet female grasshopper.

Drab these grasshoppers may be upon the ground, but color flashes as they unfold their underwings. These underwings may be black and white, blue or yellow, or even brilliant red. It is the beat of these wings against the leathery upper wings that produces the castanet-like clatter.

The most noticeable of all daytime performers, however, are not grasshoppers, but the harvest-flies, or cicadas (Fig. 98). These queer insects have the most remarkable of all musical instruments. On the undersurface of most male cicadas there is a pair of plates behind the last pair of legs. These extend back from the thorax over the base of the abdomen. Each conceals a pair of cavities in the abdomen. The paired cavities beneath each plate lie one toward the side of the abdomen and one toward the undersurface. The cavity on the

FIG. 98.—CICADAS MAKE THE MOST PRONOUNCED OF DAYTIME INSECT SONGS.
With an amazing and complicated apparatus these insects fill the warm days of spring and summer with high-pitched buzzing songs.

side is supplied with a *timbal* membrane; the cavity toward the undersurface has a *folded* membrane, below which is a *mirror* membrane. When the muscles contract, these membranes are pulled down; when the muscles relax, the membranes spring back. This action produces sound. The folded and mirror membranes serve to reflect and intensify the sound in the chamber in which they lie. The cicada may also raise and lower the plates to increase or subdue the volume of sound.

In California lowlands there is a common cicada that comes into voice in early May. This means that its long nymphal life underground has ended, that the nymph has crawled from its burrow and split its old skin for the adult to come forth (Fig. 19). The song of this cicada is a high-pitched buzz, "so piercing shrill it almost stings." It continues to sing in the quiet heat until August comes.

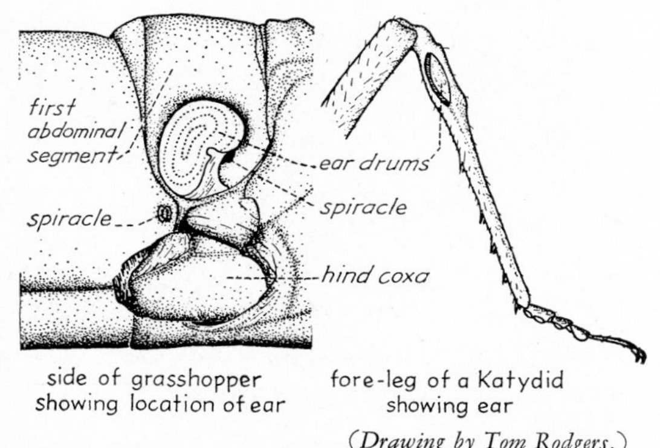

(*Drawing by Tom Rodgers.*)

FIG. 99.—INSECTS MAY HEAR WITH EARS IN THEIR ABDOMENS OR IN THEIR LEGS. The ear of a grasshopper (left) is located in the first segment of the abdomen. The drawing at the right shows an ear in the foreleg of a katydid.

One of the California cicadas has disdained the marvelous song box of its relatives and has gone back to producing sounds with its wings. This cicada has greatly thickened veins that form the forward margins of the front wings. It whacks these veins together *beneath its abdomen!* The result is a loud "click, click, click, click." Slowly wind a cheap watch and you have it exactly, only you must exaggerate the watch sound about tenfold. This *watch-winding cicada*, as we call it, begins to be heard in late March and doesn't leave off until June has come.

Though cicadas occur in the Far West, it is in the warmth of the Middle West and southeastern United States that the largest number of species occur. In the Middle West, for instance, we expect August to bring one that sings all day long from the cottonwoods, and when evening comes another cicada sings a serenade to the setting sun.

Insect ears. There would be no point to insect voices if insects did not have ears to hear. It can be proved that many insects are sensitive to sound, but only a few have special hearing devices. Some of those without such special devices may receive sound vibrations with their antennae. This appears to be true of male mosquitoes with big brushy antennae bearing special receptor organs tuned to catch the hum of the female. The larvae of certain long-horn beetles have hearing organs beneath translucent patches of skin on the wall of thorax and abdomen.

The locusts, or short-horned grasshoppers, have big eardrums on the first segment of the abdomen just above the hind legs (Fig. 99). So, also, do the owlet moths, the adults of our common cutworms. One of these structures is a typical eardrum, or *tympanum*, with a special nerve to pick up the vibrations. Crickets and katydids, though they have no ears in the wall of the abdomen, are not to be outdone, for they have an ear in each front leg (Fig. 99) just below the knee.

SUMMARY

A. Insect groups which produce sound

1. Many species of the order Orthoptera: grasshoppers, crickets, and katydids
2. The cicadas of the order Homoptera
3. A few beetles
4. A few true bugs
5. Flies, gnats, and mosquitoes
6. Bees and ants

B. The methods of producing sound

1. The hum of flight (bees, mosquitoes, midges, flies)
2. True vocal sounds
3. By rubbing or rasping of surfaces
    - *a*. By rubbing wings together (crickets, katydids, certain grasshoppers)
    - *b*. By striking wings together (locusts among the grasshoppers, certain cicadas)
    - *c*. By rubbing legs against body or wings (Jerusalem Cricket, California Prionus)
    - *d*. By telescoping or rubbing one portion of the body into or against another (June-beetles)

   4. By rapidly vibrating a membrane by means of a muscle (most cicadas)

C. The functions of insect sounds

   1. For protection or a reaction to fear (bluff of California Prionus, squeaking of captive June-beetles)
   2. Incidental to flight (hum of flies and bees, which, though incidental, may still carry various meanings)
   3. Courtship (attraction of mates or warning to other males of the same species; the hum of female mosquito; display before females of locusts, grasshoppers, crickets, and katydids)

CHAPTER XII

INSECT FITNESS

EVERYONE is acquainted with the bees and butterflies which throng our gardens and visit the wild flowers of the open fields; we all know the dragon-flies which speed on vibrating wings above streams and ponds; we know the "skaters" which dart over the surface of these same streams and ponds. We are familiar with the various caterpillars, "worms," and other "bugs," which devour our crops; we know the flies and mosquitoes which we try to screen out of our houses, and the bedbugs, fleas, and lice from which we strive to keep ourselves and our pets free. And knowing these creatures, we confidently believe that we know something about insects; but how meager is our knowledge when compared with the whole!

These insects we know are only a minute fraction of the staggering total of insect life, only the few whose activities obtrude themselves on our attention so forcibly that we cannot possibly escape noticing them. The remainder, the overwhelming majority of insects, most of us cannot even imagine. Yet insects are the most abundant and, aside from the one-celled organisms, the most ever-present of living things. With the exception of the open seas, the coldest parts of the ice-bound polar regions and mountaintops, and the hottest, driest parts of deserts, there is hardly a square yard of the earth's surface that does not provide shelter and a livelihood for a number of insects.

The ever-presence of insects. Insects are everywhere! The leaves of herbs, trees, and shrubs, from the time the buds unfold until the leaves have fallen and crumbled into dust, are fed upon by an ever-changing succession of insect species (Figs. 31, 38, 83, and 136). That layer of green slime which you see on the sides of horse troughs, or on the surface of rock outcrops over which water trickles, is the home of several kinds of insects. The brown ooze at the bottom of every stream, pond, and roadside puddle, unless it be of the most temporary character, supports an insect population. Every handful of last year's grass and weeds, every fungus growth, save the most minute, is inhabited by insects and eaten by them. The carcass of every dead animal teems with insect scavengers. Every live rabbit, mouse, squirrel, or larger mammal, as well as every bird that delights us with its color and song or its interesting habits, supports from one to ten kinds of insect parasites, often in numerous company (Fig. 122). Every spadeful of soil from field or forest contains insects in some stage of their life cycle. Every handful of moss on rock surface, fence post, or tree trunk harbors insects. Even the dung left in the dark recesses of caves by prowling animals or dropped into the crannies of rocky islands by the sea birds which rest on the islands has its insect population.

Insects are everywhere! They are so abundant that it is almost impossible, even in our metropolitan cities, except in winter, for a person to go from his home to school, to church, or to his place of business without coming into close proximity, if not actual contact, with at least one insect. Why, then, do so many of the insects escape our notice?

The unobtrusiveness of insects. Chiefly the small size and unobtrusive habits of most insects account for the general lack of acquaintance with them. Another factor contributing to the general ignorance of insect life is the extreme interest of man in himself, which keeps him so absorbed in his own immediate affairs that he remains profoundly ignorant of his surroundings. Only in comparatively recent times has man learned to look beyond himself at the world about him. Were insects larger, even as large as mice and sparrows, they would be the most familiar of animals.

Dominance of insects. In scientific literature insects are often referred to as the dominant form of animal life in the present age; and well do they justify the title. An explanation of the dominance of insects, which is the purpose of this chapter, is to be found in their peculiar fitness for terrestrial life.

PRIMARY ADAPTATIONS TO TERRESTRIAL LIFE

In the first place, insects are sufficiently complex to live on land remote from water. They have "solved" the three great problems which must be solved by all organisms which live on land. All three of these problems arise out of the universal need of all living things for water.

Protection from drying. The living part of every plant or animal must be saturated with water at all times if the activities of life are to be carried on. Life can be maintained temporarily in certain forms of plant and animal life, such as seeds and some eggs, in a state of comparative dryness, but for plants and animals in general to dry out is to die. We, ourselves, all know the distress of thirst, and how necessary it is to drink large quantities of water to replace that lost in perspiration and excretion. The first requirement of terrestrial life, then, is protection from drying out.

General protection from drying out is afforded to insects by the nature of their skeleton. Composed as it is largely of horn-like chitin, which often is almost impervious to water, and covering the entire body, it is an excellent protection against the loss of water. Still it is not perfect, for though the thicker and more horny parts probably allow no water at all to escape, the thinner and more membranous parts, necessary to provide flexibility in the joints and between segments, are not so efficient a protection. Much water is lost through these membranous parts.

In certain insects the skeleton is largely membranous, and as a result these insects lead a much more precarious existence than do their harder shelled relatives. Examples of such delicate species are the adult stone-flies (Figs. 16 and 119), the plant-lice (Fig. 39), and the smaller leaf-hoppers. In order to survive, such insects find it necessary to live either in a habitat where the air is humid, and in which the danger of drying up is not great, or in a habitat where an abundance of water is available for drinking to replace that lost by evaporation. The adult stone-flies choose the former kind of habitat, the plant-lice and leaf-hoppers the latter. Stone-flies live in damp places close to streams and lakes, being rarely found far from the water's edge, and preferring shade to sunshine. Plant-lice and leaf-hoppers live mostly on succulent green vegetation, from which they suck enormous quantities of watery sap.

Respiratory organs adapted for breathing air. There is one part of the insect's anatomy to which a simple skeletal covering cannot give the needed protection against drying out; not that a skeletal covering would be inadequate, but because this part cannot be so covered and still function. The part in question is the respiratory system, or at least that portion of it through which oxygen is absorbed and carbon dioxide given off. To absorb oxygen, a tissue must be delicate and it must be exposed to the air. But it also must be kept moist, for only through moist surfaces is oxygen absorbed readily by living substance. The second problem, therefore, of any animal that is to live on land is the problem of finding some means of exposing moist respiratory tissue to relatively dry air and yet protect the tissue from any rapid drying out.

Most land animals, as everyone knows, meet the respiratory problem by enclosing their respiratory tissue in a pair of elaborate pockets, called lungs, within the body. Instead of lungs, as was explained in Chapter VIII, insects develop an extensive system of breathing tubes, the tracheae (Fig. 64). Without these tracheae, insects, like earthworms and sow-bugs, would be restricted to wet or at least damp habitats.

Internal fertilization. Effective means of protecting the body from drying out and at the same time of providing for the exposure of moist respiratory membranes to the air do not, however, completely fit an animal for terrestrial life. The perpetuation of a species depends not only on the success of the individual, but also on the success of its reproductive processes in bringing new individuals into being. Now, it is almost universally true, as was made clear in Chapter VII, that each new individual comes into being through the union of two single cells, the egg cell, produced by the female parent, and the sperm cell, produced by the male parent. This union of egg cell and sperm cell is termed *fertilization.*

The eggs and sperms are naked cells and, therefore, very delicate. It is necessary that they be delicate, for otherwise they would not be able to merge in the fertilization process. But this delicacy subjects them to many dangers. Only a momentary exposure to the dry air of a typical land environment would kill them. For this reason some special protection against drying out must be provided for terrestrial life.

Insects and other completely terrestrial animals have solved the problem of protection for their eggs and sperms by developing internal fertilization. The sperm cells produced by the male are introduced into the body of the female (Fig. 56) and there they fertilize the eggs before these are laid. Thus neither the sperms nor the eggs, prior to fertilization, are exposed to the air. Then, with insects, before the fertilized eggs leave the body of the female they are covered with a tough or hard, resistant shell, which protects the developing young within until they are ready to come forth and wrest a living from their environment with their own resources (Fig. 58).

Primitive animals, which are all aquatic, and those which are only semiterrestrial, such as the frogs, toads, and salamanders, rarely exhibit internal fertilization. They do not need to, for their reproduction is carried out in the water, where there is no danger of drying out. These animals merely discharge their eggs and sperms into the water. Fertilization occurs outside the body of the parents.

THE SOURCES OF INSECT FITNESS

Fitness due to small size. The small size of insects confers on them a great many advantages not possessed by larger organisms, and in so doing contributes to their fitness.

The quantity of food needed to nourish a small body is itself small. Insects, therefore, are able to utilize small stores of food which would be totally inadequate for a larger animal. Several caterpillars, for example, can complete their entire growth and development from birth to maturity on a quantity of leaves which would not sustain a rabbit for one day. The various species of leaf-mining insects (Fig. 100) present a still more striking illustration of this principle. Leaf-miners are often so small that several can complete their development within the tissues of a single leaf without consuming more than a fraction of it.

Because of the small food requirement of insects, enormous populations may develop whenever food is plentiful. It is not at all uncommon for a large oak tree to support a population of a million insects at one time, and soil insects, in a rich forest loam, may occur to the number of fifty million to the acre. This abundance reduces the danger of extinction to which insects, as well as all other animals, are subject. No matter how severe the calamity which befalls the insects of a given locality, there are certain to be a few in some cranny or sheltered place which escape and perpetuate the species. This fact makes the extermination of an insect pest by man practically impossible. There is no known method by which all the numerous members of an insect population may be found and killed.

A small animal can complete its development in a shorter period of time than a large one. Hence insects, because of their small size, are able to grow from egg to maturity in only a fraction of the time required by most vertebrates. They benefit from this in two important ways.

Several generations of insects can develop in a single season if food and the other requirements of life are available. This, together with the fact that insects generally produce large numbers of young (Figs. 57, 61, and 65), makes it possible for them to recover quickly

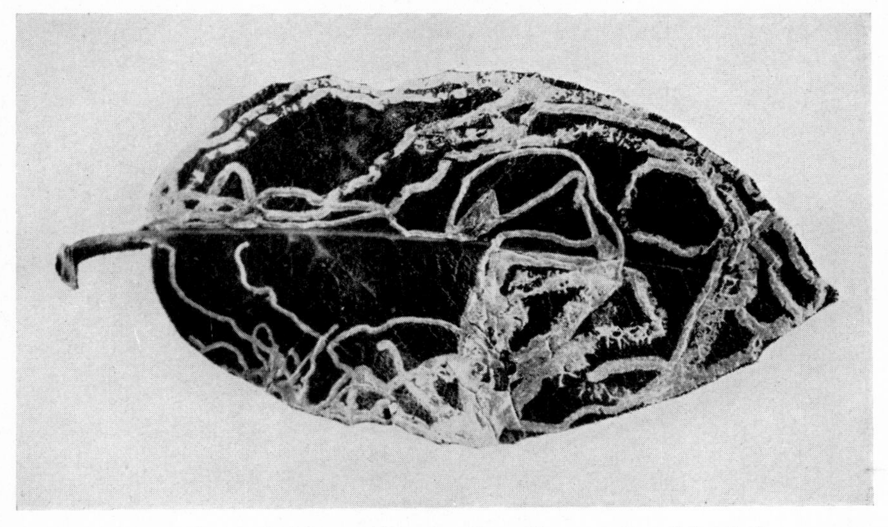

Fig. 100.—Insects Can Be So Minute That All Their Growing Days May Be Spent in the Tissues of a Leaf.

These insect mines in a manzanita leaf were in the tissues between the upper and lower surfaces. More than that, they were cut in the tissues of just one side of the leaf! As the insect larvae grew, they left wider and wider trails, but always their homes were bounded by the walls of the leaf.

from the effects of epidemic diseases or other calamities. It also makes it possible for insects to take advantage quickly of unusual opportunities, such as a suddenly increased food supply. For example, it has been computed that from a single pair of Vedalia Ladybird Beetles (*Rodolia cardinalis*), if all circumstances were favorable to their multiplication, a population of twenty-two trillion beetles could be produced in six months' time! This is approximately twenty-two thousand times as many beetles as there have been minutes of time since the birth of Christ! Such incomprehensibly great numbers of insects never actually develop, of course, because crowding, food shortage, and enemies halt the increase; but the potentialities are there, and in these potentialities lies the explanation of the insect's ability to take advantage of every opportunity that comes its way.

The other benefit enjoyed by insects as a result of their short life cycle is their ability to take advantage of food supplies and of favorable living conditions which are seasonal in character or of only short duration. Flesh-flies and carrion-beetles are able to develop to

FIG. 101.—THE STRENGTH OF ANTS IS SUCH THAT THEY WERE ABLE TO CONSTRUCT THIS PILE OF STICKS.

These mound-building ants, a species of *Formica*, are common in brushy and wooded regions. With the strength due to small size and the advantage of numbers, the ants pile up large mounds of twigs and gravel, in which to excavate the galleries of their home.

maturity in the carcasses of dead animals before bacteria bring about their decomposition. Mosquitoes are able to pass from egg to adult in the mere cupful of water which collects in a hoofprint made by a cow, providing the water remains in the hoofprint for as long as two weeks. There are minute gall-making wasps which parasitize the staminate (male) flowers of oak trees and are able to complete their entire development during the short blooming season of the oaks.

Everyone is acquainted with the remarkable jumping ability of fleas. Everyone, too, has at some time or other marveled at the seemingly great strength of ants, which can carry or drag objects much larger than themselves (Fig. 101). Nearly everyone has concluded that such small creatures are prodigiously strong in comparison with human beings and large animals. Yet this is not so.

The apparently great strength of insects as compared with that of vertebrates does not represent an actual superiority in muscular equipment. In fact, it has been shown that, muscle fiber for muscle fiber, insects are really a little weaker than vertebrates. If this be true, what is there to account for the ability of insects to move relatively large objects and to perform other remarkable feats of strength? Well, strange as it may seem, the answer is that insects can perform remarkable feats of strength because they are small. But how can small size increase the apparent strength of animals? Let us see.

To solve this problem, it will be necessary to turn our attention away from insects for a moment and consider certain well-known mechanical matters. If we suspend a hundred-pound ball by means of a quarter-inch rope, we commonly say that the rope is supporting a weight of one hundred pounds (Fig. 102*a*). And this is true for the end of the rope to which the ball is attached. The upper end of the rope, however, the end farthest from the ball, is supporting not only the weight of the ball but the weight of the rope as well. Furthermore, if a long rope is used, the upper end will have to support more weight than if a short rope is used (Fig. 102*b*), and only a little imagination is needed to show that if a sufficiently long rope is used, the ball will have to be taken off or replaced by a smaller one, else the rope will break, for the combined weight of rope and ball will exceed the strength of the rope. From this we can conclude that the longer the rope the smaller the weight that can be suspended at the lower end of it; or, stated in another way, the weight which a given rope can support is equal to its total strength minus its own weight.

Let us now consider a second proposition. If we use four quarter-inch ropes of a certain length, they will together support four times as much weight as one quarter-inch rope of the same length (Fig. 102*a* and *c*, *b* and *d*). This will be true whether the ropes are long or short; the important thing is that they be of the same length. The same result will follow if we use a single large rope equivalent in thickness to four quarter-inch ropes (Fig. 102*e* and *f*). Observe incidentally that such a large rope is not four times as thick as a single rope, but only twice as thick.

Thus we recognize that the strength of a rope varies with the thickness. (To be precise it varies directly as the square of the diameter varies.) The strength of a large rope is equal to the combined strength of the number of small ropes to which it is equivalent. The conclusion of the preceding paragraph concerning the length of a

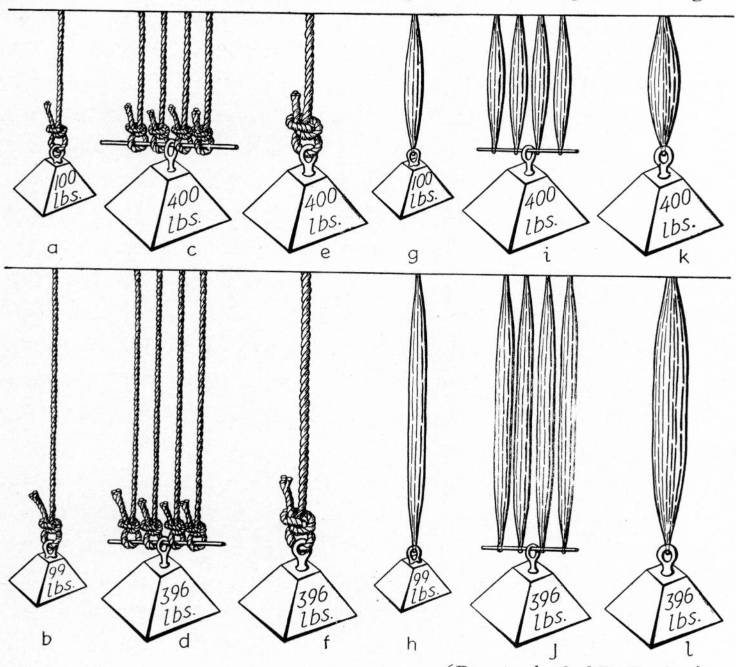

(*Drawing by Carl D. Duncan.*)

FIG. 102.—THE STRENGTH OF ROPES AND OF MUSCLES VARIES WITH THICKNESS, NOT WITH TOTAL SIZE.

Common experience tells us that, if one rope or one muscle (*a* and *g* of the figure) can support a maximum weight of one hundred pounds, four ropes or four muscles of the same size (*c* and *i*) will be able to support a maximum weight of four hundred pounds. Similarly, a single large rope or single large muscle (*e* and *k*) that is equivalent to four of the smaller ones, will be able to support four hundred pounds also. But a series of ropes or muscles (*b*, *d*, *f*, *h*, *j*, and *l*) equal in diameters, respectively, to those of the first series, but longer, will be able to support, not one hundred pounds or four hundred pounds as the case may be, but one hundred pounds or four hundred pounds *minus* the weight of the extra lengths of rope or muscles.

rope and the load that it can support applies also when several small ropes or when single large ropes are used. Let us now apply our conclusions concerning the strength of ropes to propositions concerning muscles, for the same relationships exist with them (Fig. 102*g* to *l*).

The muscles of large animals, such as man, are much stronger than those of insects because they are much thicker. But the muscles of large animals are also much longer than those of insects and therefore weigh much more in proportion to their strength. And not only is this true, but the weight of all the other parts of the body, much of which is supported by the muscles, is proportionately much greater in a large animal than in an insect. Moreover, a large animal must maintain a considerable reserve of strength not ordinarily needed, in order to keep the parts of its body in proper balance and to control their momentum when they are in motion. The useful strength of a large animal, therefore, that available for carrying loads or doing other work, is equal only to the total strength of its muscles minus most of the weight of the muscles and other body parts, and minus the reserve that must be maintained for the handling of the problems of balance and momentum. Hence the useful strength of a large animal is far less, proportionately, than that of an insect. In fact, a large animal is able to use only a small fraction of its total strength for the accomplishment of work. Insects, on the other hand, since their muscles are short and their weight almost negligible, can use nearly all their total strength for the accomplishment of work. It is for this reason that they appear so disproportionately strong.

Thus, by virtue of the apparently great strength borne of small size, insects can accomplish a relatively tremendous amount of work. Let us consider for a moment the activities of the Thread-waisted Sand Wasp shown in Fig. 142. During the course of a single afternoon this wasp may dig a burrow four inches long, find and paralyze a caterpillar considerably larger than itself, drag the caterpillar to the burrow and down to the bottom of it, lay an egg on the caterpillar, and then refill the burrow. To perform a comparable task, a man would have to dig a hole in the ground three feet in diameter and about eighteen feet long, hunt and kill an animal the size of a pony, drag the quarry for perhaps a quarter of a mile over rough ground strewn with boulders or covered with brush, draw the beast to the bottom of the hole, and then refill the hole. And that would be quite an afternoon's work! Yet if a man were as small as the wasp in question, and as well adapted to the task, and other things were in proportion, the man could accomplish this task more easily than the wasp, because the man's muscles in such a case would be stronger than those of the wasp.

Not only is the apparent strength of insects made possible by their small size, but their extreme agility is also due to this cause; and agility as a factor in determining fitness for existence is of no slight significance. The rapid running of a cockroach and the complicated actions of flying insects enable them to hide or flee from danger in but a fraction of the time required by a larger animal. This is true because it is easier to move and to change the course of small bodies rapidly than it is to move or change the course of large ones.

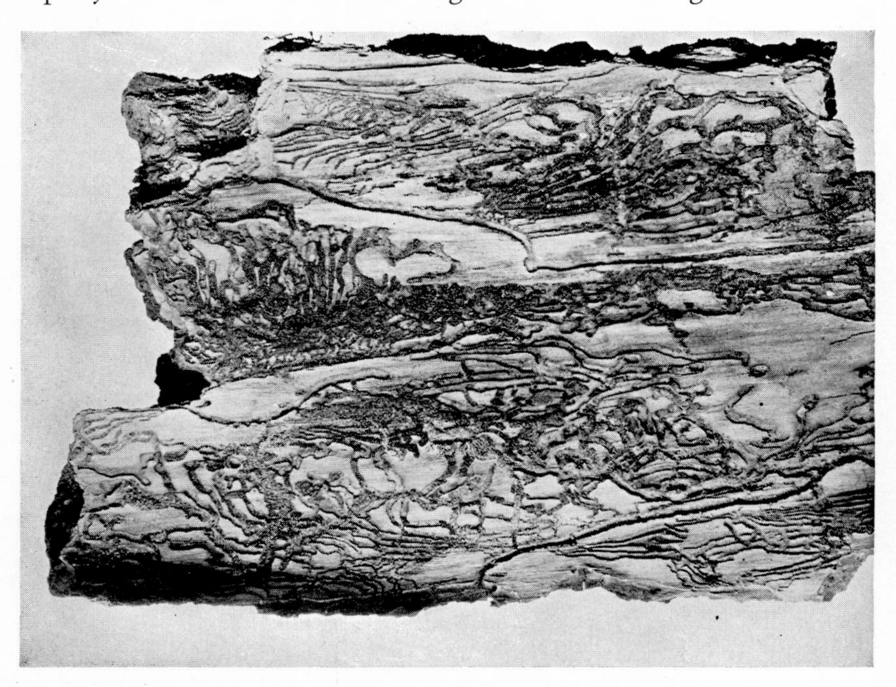

Fig. 103.—These Galleries of the Bark-beetle Constitute but One of Myriad Insect Homes. In making this kind of home, the bark-beetles (family Scolytidae) frequently destroy the cambium zone between wood and bark, and the tree dies. Especially is this true of the conifers of the Western states, when these trees have lost vigor as a result of a long period of drought.

In still another way are insects benefited by their small size. Being small, as was noted in Chapter IX, an insect possesses a body surface quite large in proportion to its bulk. This means that a moving insect encounters a proportionately great resistance from the air, as a result of which movement is impeded. As a consequence, an insect is never even so much as injured by a fall, no matter from how great a height. Nor are insects injured by collisions except at high speeds, speeds much greater than those which they, themselves, are capable of producing. For example, flying insects do not often spatter an automobile windshield unless the automobile is traveling in excess of thirty miles an hour. Other small animals, of course, enjoy the same benefits resulting from small size. This explains why nestling birds often are uninjured in a fall from their nest.

(*Photograph by Lester Brubaker.*)

FIG. 104.—THE FITNESS OF THIS GIANT WATER-BUG LIES IN ITS ADAPTATIONS TO LIFE AS A PREDATOR IN THE WATER.

Coloring that simulates perfectly the mud, leaves, and stones among which it lives; large efficient compound eyes that enable it quickly to recognize prey or enemies; smooth streamlined contours that allow it to slip easily through the water; flattened hind legs to make swimming easy; and powerful front legs shaped somewhat like a pair of ice tongs: these are the most obvious adaptations which fit this bug, *Abedus*, for life in the world beneath the water surface.

Fitness due to adaptability. For reasons which remain a mystery, insects appear to be more adaptable than almost any other group of animals. Something in their make-up has made it possible for them to evolve more rapidly and to produce more variations than other groups of animals have done. For example, in spite of their long evolutionary history, the frogs and salamanders are still restricted to a moist or wet habitat, whereas insects have "learned" to inhabit water, land, and air. Whereas the fishes have perfected but two principal types of locomotion, though with several minor modifications, aquatic insects have developed at least four distinct types of

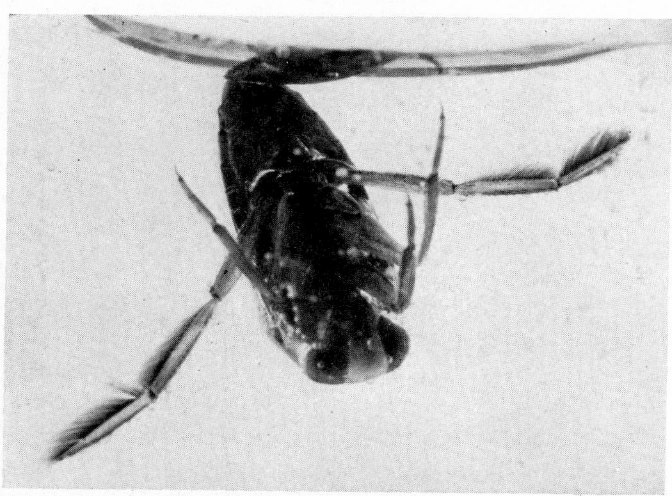

Fig. 105.—The Back-swimmer Is a Topsy-turvy Bug. It Swims in an Upside-down Position, Making It Easy to Approach Its Prey from Beneath; Yet, Out of the Water, It Flies Right Side Up Like Any Other Insect.

The back-swimmer is darker on the under (ventral) side than on the upper (dorsal). Most insects follow the law of protective coloration by being darker on the upper side than on the under. Since most insects move with the back side up this countershading effaces them and protects them from their enemies. But the back-swimmer swims upside down so it also reverses the coloring. When the back-swimmer finds it necessary to seek another watery home, it comes to the surface, where it gives a quick flip with its paddle-like hind legs and turns over. The wings are spread a little to dry and then the back-swimmer takes off in sudden flight.

locomotion, each of which presents large numbers of minor variations. If an insect lives aboveground and is active, it usually possesses well-developed, functional wings; if it lives belowground or in some other concealed habitat wherein flight is impossible, it may completely lack wings (Fig. 107); and so it goes. No other group of animals exhibits so wide a range of adaptability as do insects; and no other group is quite so successful.

As a result of this adaptability, there is not a habitat on land or in fresh water which does not have its insect inhabitants (Figs. 103–106). Insects exhibit thousands of adaptive modifications fitting them for life in these habitats (Figs. 104–107). If the food of an insect is abundant but not very nutritious, as in the case of the wood-eating beetles (Figs. 25, 73, and 106), the life cycle is lengthened, thus permitting the insect to consume enough food to ensure its development. If the environmental conditions for which an insect is adapted are of short duration, the rate of development is speeded up and the life cycle is shortened (Figs. 174 and 177), so development can be

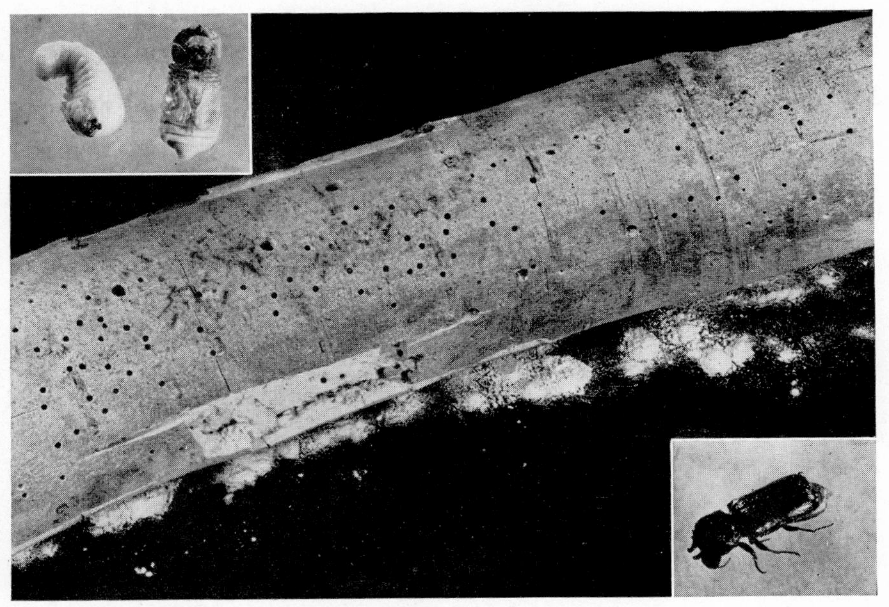

Fig. 106.—Powder-post Beetles Get Water Where There Is No Free Water.
The larva of this beetle (upper left), family Bostrichidae, is plump and juicy though it has lived its life in a branch of dead desert ironwood in the Colorado Desert. Most of the water that makes it juicy is the water of metabolism, the water that results when certain foods are digested within the animal's body. All animals produce it to some extent and most waste it, but desert animals conserve it. Beside the larva is a pupa of the beetle, and in the lower right is the adult. It is the magic of adaptation that makes it possible for these insects to find shelter, protection from enemies, food, and water in the dry, sun-baked wood of the desert.

completed before the favorable conditions change. If the food of an insect is available only at long intervals, the insect becomes dormant during the intervening periods and springs into activity when food is again available.

If water is extremely scarce, as it is in the habitats of certain desert-dwelling darkling-beetles, the cuticle is greatly thickened and hardened, forming a heavy impenetrable armor through which water cannot pass. In these beetles, also, all body parts fit closely together when not in actual use so that no membranous areas are exposed. The mouth parts fold into the muzzle of the head and the head is withdrawn into the prothorax. These beetles also extract every vestige of removable water from the indigestible food remnants in their intestine so that the refuse which they eject as fecal pellets is practically bone-dry.

Other insects of dry habitats meet their water problem in a markedly different way. Such are termite species (Figs. 112 and 160) which live in relatively dry wood, and powder-post beetles (Fig. 106) which live in and feed upon still drier wood. Powder-post beetles originally were native to dry or desert regions wherein it is their function to decompose the branches and trunks of dead desert trees and shrubs, many of which are extremely hard. These beetles are now found in many other regions living in and feeding upon cured hardwoods in the form of tool handles, furniture, floors, and cabinet-work. Such insects, in the larval and pupal stages at least, always possess soft, juicy bodies containing an ample supply of water, no matter how dry their surroundings. They appear to secure much of their water from the wood which they eat, for in the digestion of wood water may be produced as a by-product.

Perhaps the most amazing example of an insect adapting itself to periodic changes in the environment was reported a few years ago by Professor G. F. Ferris, of Stanford University. It seems there is a scale-insect known as *Margarodes vitium* which feeds on the roots of plants occurring in the arid regions of Chile, in South America. The immature individuals of this scale-insect are enclosed in hard cases or cysts made of secretions from their own bodies. On attaining maturity, the insects emerge from the cysts. Emergence occurs, however, only during the season of the rains which come at long intervals. These rains may be several years apart, so the insects may have to wait that long before they can emerge. About the year 1900 specimens of the immature scale-insects, enclosed in their cysts, were secured by a collector, later to be deposited in the collection of Stanford University. On opening these cysts in 1917, Professor Ferris found that one of the scale-insects was still alive. It had waited over seventeen years for a rain to make possible a completion of its development!

Fitness due to general features of physical structure. The physical build of insects makes them especially well fitted for life. The position of the insect skeleton on the outside of the body makes it an effective mechanical protection to all the soft tissues and internal organs. Not one of them is exposed to direct injury or infection, as are the soft tissues of many other animals. There are, to be sure, parts of the insect skeleton which are thin and membranous and which, therefore, offer less protection than the harder and tougher portions, but these thin parts, which are necessary to permit freedom of movement, are generally covered by the overlapping edges of the harder

FIG. 107.—THIS GRASSHOPPER AND JERUSALEM CRICKET ARE RELATIVES, YET ADAPTATION HAS FITTED THEM FOR DIFFERENT HABITATS.

The grasshopper (*Trimerotropis*), a denizen of the open fields, has a proportionately light body, slender fore and middle legs used only for support and in walking, powerful hind legs for catapulting it into the air, and broad membranous wings to sustain it in flight. The Jerusalem Cricket (*Stenopelmatus longispina*), a dweller beneath the soil by day, often a surface prowler by night, has no need of body lightness, but it makes full use of its powerful head, with mouth parts formed beneath like the blade of a thick hoe, and of its six sturdy legs, all equipped with strong spines, for it uses both head and legs in digging the burrows in which it lives.

parts of the skeleton. For all practical purposes, an insect, thanks to the nature of its skeleton, presents an almost invulnerable exterior.

The protective nature of the insect skeleton is further increased in two ways. In the first place, it is often so smooth and slippery that an enemy (except a large animal) seeking to seize an insect has small opportunity to secure a firm grip; jaws and claws slip off more often than they take hold. In the second place, since nearly every part of the surface of an insect's body is curved, every part of the insect skeleton constitutes an arch, which is well known to be one of the strongest types of construction. The force of every blow struck against the body of an insect is met by a skeletal arch rendering many blows ineffective. The insect is thus spared many injuries to which it otherwise would be subject.

Fitness due to instinctive persistence. Lastly, as Metcalf and Flint point out in their book, *Fundamentals of Insect Life*, the persistence of insects in their reactions to various stimuli is an important factor in their success on earth. No matter how many times an irritated dozer slaps at an offending fly, the fly returns to pester him. In regions where ants are common, it often seems that no matter what safeguards are thrown around food supplies, sooner or later the ants reach them. Insect activities are controlled by instinctive urges which are relentless. Hence, in the face of an opposition or danger that would drive a vertebrate into hiding or cause it to flee in fright to another territory, the insect usually persists until it accomplishes what it is attempting to do or is killed in the attempt. And for every insect that fails or is killed in its attempt to find food or to mate there is another to take its place; for, thanks to the small size of insects and their rapid rate of reproduction, there are so many insects that enough always succeed in reproducing to perpetuate the race and maintain the population. It is no wonder that insects dominate the world of life on this earth of ours.

CHAPTER XIII

INSECT ORDERS

EVERYONE has noticed that insects fall into distinctive groups but all may not have realized that those groups are named; they are called *orders*. Thus, if one speaks of a "beetle," he is mentioning an order. If one says "moths and butterflies," he is naming an order. The words *true bugs* describe an order. That person who has, or may develop, an interest in insects will want to know what it is that makes a beetle, that makes a true bug, that distinguishes moths and butterflies from all other insects. With just a little attention, it is possible to learn to place nearly all insects in their proper orders. When that is accomplished, the first great step in knowing insects has been taken.

First, in any listing of insect orders, one will note the arrangement. This proceeds from the primitive to the specialized. What makes a simple insect? What, a complex? If an insect has no wings and gives evidence that its ancestors never had wings, that is evidence of primitiveness or simplicity. If an insect makes no conspicuous body change in growing up, that, too, is evidence of primitiveness. An insect that makes no provision for its young, other than the mere laying of eggs near food material, is primitive in this respect. Conversely, an insect that produces wings is advanced over one that has no wings except in those cases in which the wings have been acquired and then lost. The more distinct and numerous the body changes—gradual, incomplete, and complete metamorphosis—the higher the insect is placed. Finally, if an insect has wings and elaborate body changes and makes elaborate provision for its young, it is considered to have specialized above all others. In the arrangement of orders, note how this specialization advances.

Thysanura, the tassel-tails or bristle-tails (Figs. 108 and 170). It is an unusual home that does not have a Silverfish. But then most homes do have a Silverfish. From some fireplace crevice, some pantry niche, some wallpaper seam, some bookshelf, one may be seen to creep forth as nighttime comes. In the niches of the pantry the Silverfish finds waste bits of flour or bread or sugar for its food. The wallpaper seam lets the Silverfish get beneath the paper where wallpaper paste yields up its tasty sugars and starches. In a pile of books or magazines the Silverfish may find a home too, there to eat the glue of bindings. A Silverfish or two can do no great amount of harm, and they rarely occur in numbers. When they do become abundant, however, they

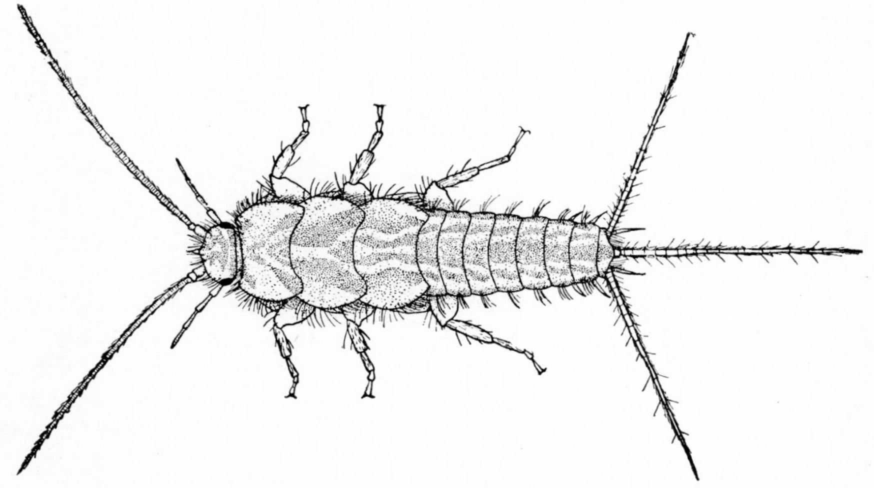

(*Drawing by Alice Addicott.*)

FIG. 108.—THE SILVERFISH, A MEMBER OF THE ORDER THYSANURA.
The projections from the tail end of the body explain the name Thysanura, which means "tassel tails." Thysanurans change only in size as they grow; so young and old look alike.

may be very troublesome. Try to catch a Silverfish. Only nimble fingers can ever close about it, and more than likely when they do they will come away with tiny silvery scales but no Silverfish.

Silverfish relatives can be found under loose bark on trees, under nearly all stones in dry fields, and under piles of dry leaves. One never need mistake them for anything else, for from the tail end long prongs extend (the "tassel-tails," or *cerci*), and their slender bodies glide so swiftly over any surface that only the skillful will ever capture them.

Orthoptera, the straight wings (Figs. 2, 4, 20, 55, 62, 88, 90, 95–97, 107, 109–111, and 164). If there were no grasshoppers, crickets, or cockroaches, the agriculturist would be saved from some serious pests, but there then would be no katydids, no cricket songs, in fact, very

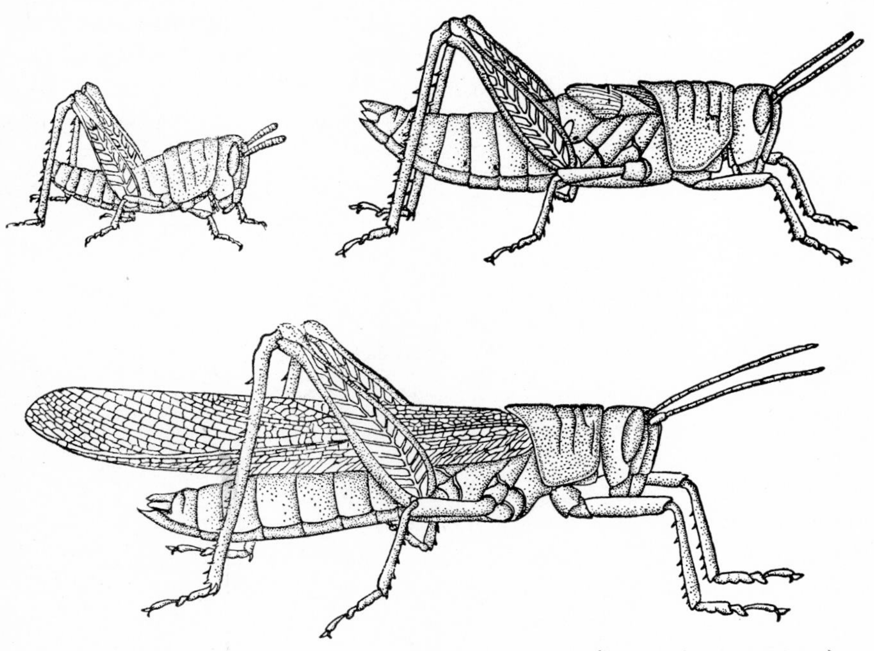

(*Drawing by Alice Addicott.*)

FIG. 109.—THESE ARE GROWTH STAGES IN THE LIFE OF A GRASSHOPPER, A MEMBER OF THE ORDER ORTHOPTERA.

Grasshoppers and other Orthopterans change, as they grow, chiefly by the addition of wings, which appear first as little pads.

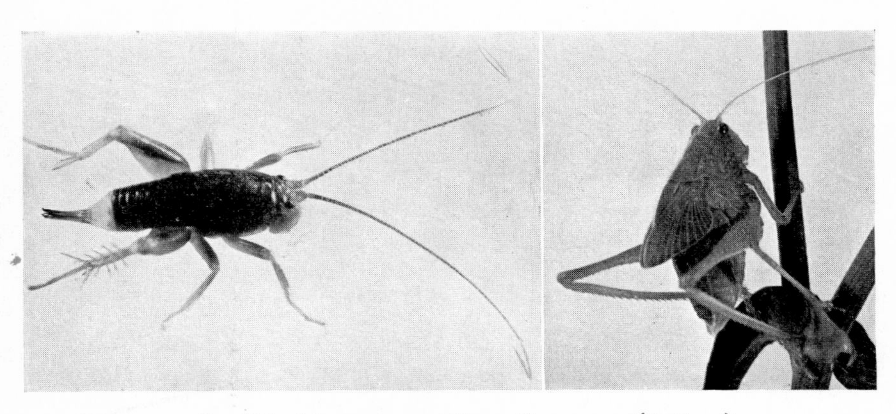

FIG. 110.—MEMBERS OF THE ORDER ORTHOPTERA (*Continued*).

On the left is a California Camel Cricket, which never has wings; on the right is a nymph, or young katydid, with wing pads.

little insect music; and many birds would be hard put to it for food. Moths and butterflies may be the loveliest of insects, beetles may be the most obvious and most blundering, flies and bees the most skillful fliers, but the straight wings are the most romantic. Perhaps it is

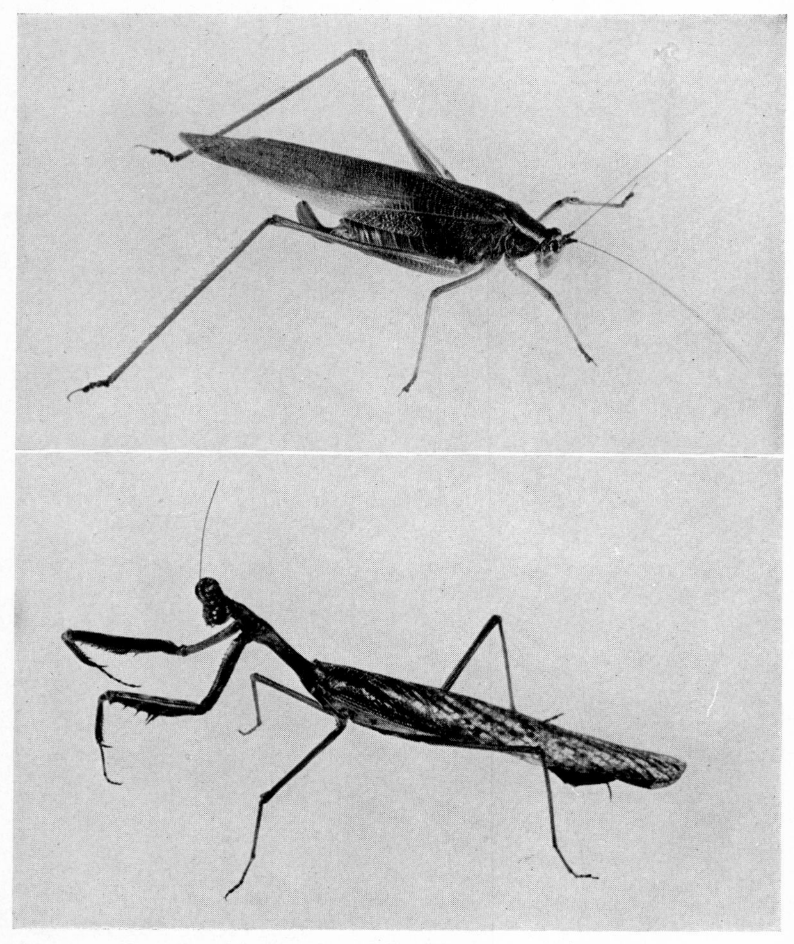

FIG. 111.—MEMBERS OF THE ORDER ORTHOPTERA (*Continued*).
The upper is a female Fork-tailed Bush Katydid; the lower is a praying mantis.

because they are so varied; but we think it is because they have the most musicians.

If straight wings are grown up, and if, grown up, they have wings, then there is no trouble at all in naming them to order. The upper wings are long and straight and leathery. The membranous lower wings are long and straight also and lie under the upper wings when at rest, neatly folded in "plaits" like a fan. The fans spread out when straight wings fly. But straight wings may not be grown up, and then there are no wings at all, or maybe only little pads that show the growing wings; or possibly there may never be any wings. How shall one know straight wings then? Almost always one can guess from its form that it is a grasshopper or a cricket, wings or no wings, for even that big bully, the blundering, wingless Jerusalem Cricket, is obviously a member of this order, even if someone does call it *Potato Bug*.

It is always true that the young insects with gradual metamorphosis, such as straight wings, look like their parents. But here is a process of elimination in naming an insect to order that may be used with any stranger that comes to hand. Suppose you have picked up a young cricket but do not know it. You do know that it was under a board in the back yard, that its mouth is obviously formed for chewing (it has no lapping tongue, no beak for piercing and sucking, no long tube for siphoning), that there are tiny wing pads showing, that it is about Honeybee size. With this information, gathered by just looking, you are prepared—after a study of the table of insect orders at the end of this chapter—to name your insect to order by the eliminating process.

First, those wing pads prove that it is an insect with gradual metamorphosis, for the caterpillars, grubs, or maggots of insects with complete metamorphosis never show external wing pads. Second, the chewing mouth eliminates true bugs and the Homoptera. The place where you found it eliminates nearly all orders of parasites. Its size eliminates several orders of small insects. There is left only the straight wings, and so your insect must be a member of this order. Turn to the Orthoptera in any insect book and there you may be able to trace it to family.

Of course, not all insects are so simple, and many are so small that only an enlarging lens will show enough to permit the eliminating process. Nevertheless, this is the method all insect students employ, though often they do so subconsciously.

Isoptera, the termites (incorrectly called white ants) (Figs. 41, 112, 113, 159, 160, and 189). Perhaps, if you have never really looked for insects, the "white ants" you have seen weren't white at all, but dark brown. And perhaps you thought they were true ants because they were swarming out of the ground on wings. Termites, however, are nearly always white or cream or gray in color, and they are not true

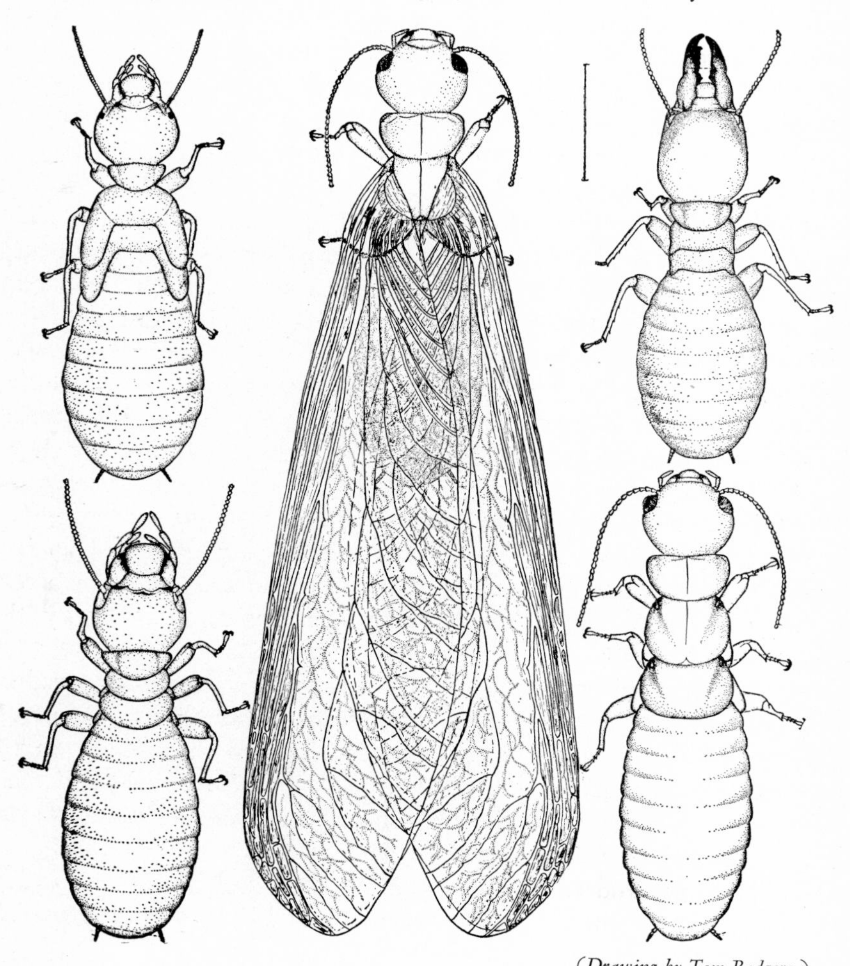

(*Drawing by Tom Rodgers.*)

FIG. 112.—CASTES IN A COLONY OF TERMITES, MEMBERS OF THE ORDER ISOPTERA. The termites, though sometimes incorrectly called white ants, are not true ants because they have a different method of growing up and do not have the thin waist of true ants. Upper left, a king or a queen that possesses eyes, but with wing pads that never grow larger; lower left, a blind worker; center, a queen or king possessing wings with which to fly away on a dispersal flight, after which it will mate and establish a new colony; upper right, a blind soldier with great mandibles for fighting; lower right, a king or queen that has taken the dispersal flight and then broken off its own wings, only stumps being left to show their original positions.

ants. True ants have waists, very narrow waists, and termites have no waists at all, for their pursy abdomens join broadly to the thorax.

This matter of waists or no waists will at once distinguish true ants from termites. Then, too, the termite method of growing up is quite different from the growing up of true ants; the young of termites look like the adults, for they develop with gradual metamorphosis. The young of true ants go through a complete metamorphosis, or life history, that begins with a little, white, legless, helpless grub,

FIG. 113.—DISCARDED WINGS OF TERMITE KINGS AND QUEENS.
After a rain the dark-winged queens and kings of a termite colony swarm out into the air on a dispersal flight, after which they mate. They fly but once and for a short distance only. Quickly they settle to the ground, spread their wings, and rub them off. Then the wings, lavish structures that serve but once, may be caught by a heedless wind and swirled into piles and windrows.

changes to a pupa, and then becomes an active six-legged, thin-waisted adult. In addition, true ants are almost never white, and termites almost always are.

Termites live on wood almost exclusively. The wood is nearly always dead wood, but because it may be the sills of a house basement, their feeding habits sometimes make them a serious problem to homeowners. They bore tunnels through this wood; and if in their movements they must pass from one log to another, they avoid the risk of going into the dry air by building a tunnel of sawdust or earth from one feeding station to the other.

FIG. 114.—MEMBERS OF THE ORDER NEUROPTERA.
The upper Neuropteran is a rubber-neck bug, one of the snake-flies. Its larvae live beneath the bark of trees and in ground litter where they feed on other insects. The lower is the Western Dobson that, while a larva, lives as a water demon in swift brooks. (See Fig. 78.)

Neuroptera, the nerve wings (Figs. 17, 54, 78, 114–117, and 180). This is an order of insect demons and dragons. Most of these insects,

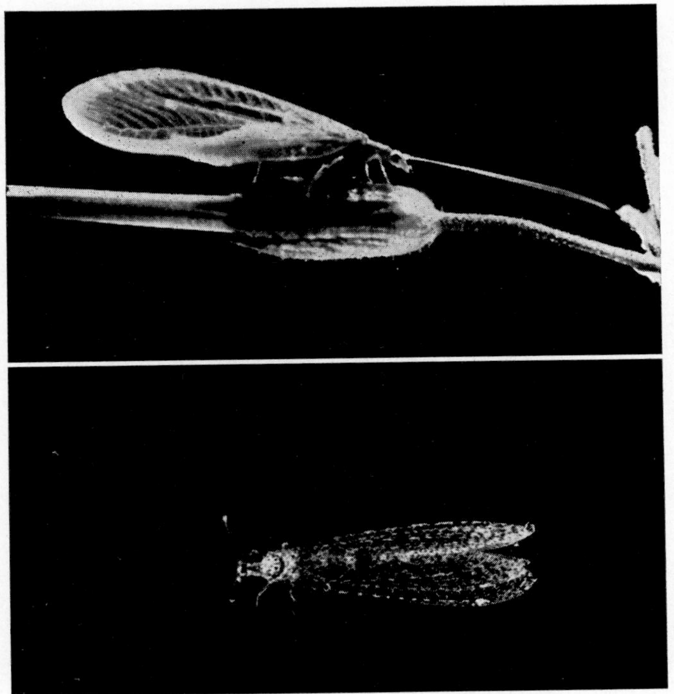

FIG. 115.—MEMBERS OF THE ORDER NEUROPTERA (*Continued*).

The upper is the Green Lacewing-fly. Its larvae spend their growing days eating plant-lice, or aphids. For a picture of its eggs see Fig. 60. The lower is the ant-lion, or doodle-bug, grown-up. For the larva and pupa of the ant-lion, see Figs. 116 and 180.

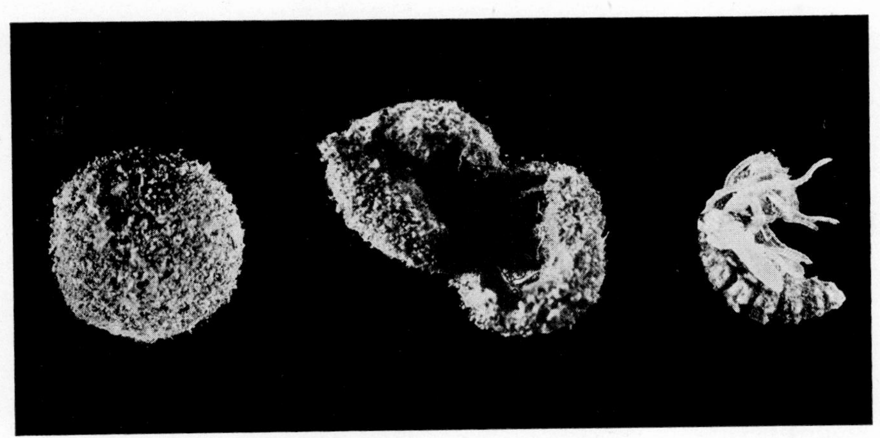

FIG. 116.—TWO COCOONS AND A PUPA OF THE DOODLE-BUG, OR ANT-LION, A MEMBER OF THE ORDER NEUROPTERA.

Like all Neuropterans, the ant-lion has four stages in its life history: the egg, larva (in this case the doodle-bug), pupa, and adult.

grown up, are so seemingly delicate, so ephemeral with their gauzy, lacy wings (the fine veins give them their name), so airy in flight, that it is hard to believe that they, as youngsters, captured insect prey in great scythe-like jaws and then sucked out the victim's blood. But the nerve-wing insects include in their ranks those terrors of ants, the ant-lions or doodle-bugs; also those aphis destroyers, the young of the lacewing-flies; that great scourge of water life, the dobson larva, or hellgrammite; the rapacious young of the serpent-flies and fish-flies.

Investigate the leaves of oleander or rosebush in the spring. You will find plant-lice, or aphids, and perhaps also the tiny larva of a lacewing-fly, the great curved jaws of which speak destruction for the aphids there. If a lacewing-fly larva is not found, then perhaps you may see a leaf that has, along its undersurface, a row of threads with insect eggs dangling from their ends. So rapacious are her offspring that the female lacewing-fly must place her eggs at the ends of threads, else the first to hatch would pitch upon and devour the unhatched brothers and sisters.

Beneath any tree that has an undisturbed layer of dust at its base, look for the pits of the famous ant-lion, the doodle-bug of child verse and legend. In the evening, if there is a light above the doodle-bug pits, you may see the delicate grown-up ant-lion fluttering on gauzy wings about the glow. Hard, then, to believe that this delicate creature could have been the great-jawed "dragon" that waited for ants in the dust at the bottom of the pit; hard to believe that it has just come from the pupa in a stiff-walled silken ball that the doodle-bug spun in its dusty world beneath the surface of the ground.

Ephemerida, the May-flies (Fig. 68). The May-flies are the "insects that last but a day," if we take literally the meaning of the scientific name. And literally, or almost literally, it may be taken if we consider only the adults of this interesting order. But the young are naiads and hence water-dwellers, and they may require one, two, or three years for their growth before they can come forth from the water and transform to the delicate, winged adult. The young have chewing jaws and live on minute plant life in the water, but the mouth parts of the adults are reduced and useless. So it comes about that the long life in the water culminates in but a day or two, rarely longer, upon the land. In that day or two they crawl from the water, leave their naiad covering at the water's edge, and assume the adult form.

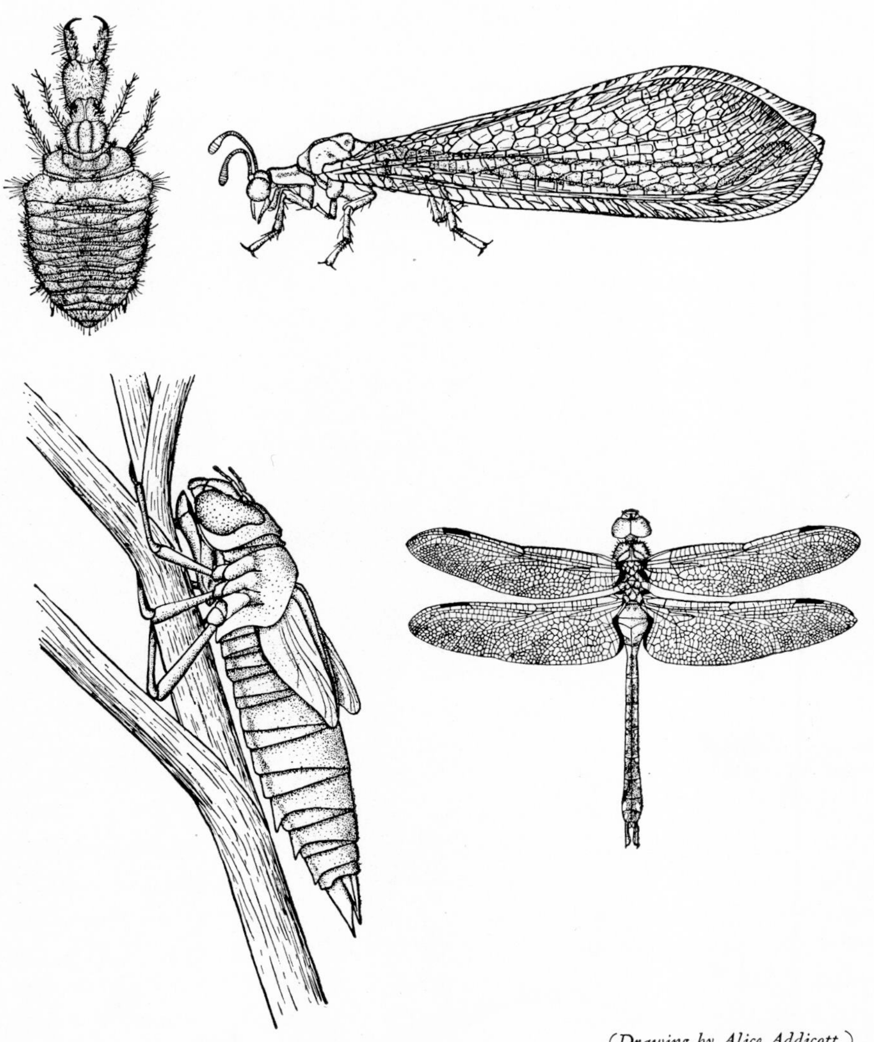

(*Drawing by Alice Addicott.*)

Fig. 117.—Stages in the Life History of a Member of the Order Neuroptera, and Stages in the Life History of a Member of the Order Odonata.

Above, the larva and the adult ant-lion, or doodle-bug. Since a pupa stage should come between these, see Fig. 116. Below, a dragon-fly naiad and adult. The dragon-fly naiad lives in water, as do the young of all the Odonata.

Then they do an astonishing thing, something no other insect does: they molt again and leave one more cast "skin" clinging to stones, to trees, or the walls of the buildings in the vicinity of their watery home. The final discarded skin has the form of the adult, not of the naiad, all parts of the new adult's body being represented, a skeletal layer having been peeled even from the wings. The winged May-fly then performs a famous dance above the water and finds there a mate; the female lays her eggs, and both then die.

May-flies are most famous in the region of the Great Lakes, in Central United States. There, as regularly as July comes, Lake Michi-

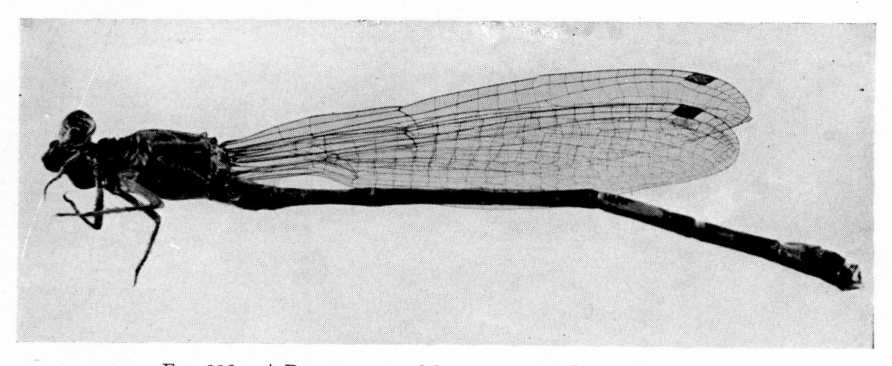

FIG. 118.—A DAMSEL-FLY, A MEMBER OF THE ORDER ODONATA.
Damsel-flies and dragon-flies are the two great groups of the order Odonata. Damsel-flies differ from dragon-flies in that their eyes are widely spaced and they close their wings parallel to the body when at rest, whereas dragon-flies' eyes are closely set and they hold their wings at right angles when at rest.

gan, for instance, gives up its May-flies in countless millions within a short week or two. The adults flock to the city's lights, die in their futile fluttering about these deadly attractions, and cover the ground beneath until their bodies have stacked up inches deep. In the Far West lights near mountain lakes attract great numbers of them; and the large rivers of the great central valley of California rear May-flies in quantity.

May-flies form a basic food supply for much of the life that lives in streams and lakes, and so they have an important place in the scheme of nature. Upon them, directly or indirectly, many of the fishes of the great fresh-water bodies depend.

Odonata, the dragon-flies and damsel-flies (Figs. 1, 22, 52, 53, 69, 80, 81, 117, and 118). One need not describe a dragon-fly, for this is one insect, with its four gauzy, airplane wings, its great head, and long slender body, that everyone knows. Still, one should add that it is no "snake doctor," that it never "sews up a body's ears," that it is not a "snake feeder," and only in folklore is it the "devil's darning needle." As it skims here and there through the air, in a flight as skillful and dexterous as ever any insect knew, it is intent upon catching mosquitoes and midges for its food. These insects are caught in its legs that are held forward like a basket.

When a dragon-fly alights, its basket legs extend forward and the body anchors almost at right angles to its upright support. The related damsel-fly, however, attaches itself nearly parallel to its support; and while it is there its wings are folded along the sides of the body and not held stiffly at right angles as are the wings of the dragon-fly. Its eyes, too, are on stalks on either side of its head, and its weak, jerky flight, with its rustle of silken wings, dooms it forever to a region not far from its early home.

Dragon-flies roam far and wide, but both dragon-flies and damsel-flies are always more numerous where there are quiet streams or ponds or lakes, for it is in the waters of ponds or streams or lakes that both grow up. And if grown-up dragon-flies and damsel-flies are interesting, their young are even more so. The young of dragon-flies are water gnomes that catch their food with a long lower lip (Fig. 53) and breathe by taking water into the hinder end of the intestine. The young of damsel-flies, slender and somewhat awkward water sprites with the widely spaced eyes of the adults, have three long plates appended to the end of their abdomen with which they get oxygen from the water. They, too, catch food with a prehensile lower lip. These young are called *naiads*, and when they have eaten enough mosquito wrigglers and other small water fry to become full grown they crawl out of the water, climb onto some shore-side stem, split their old suit down the back, so that the mature dragon-flies or damsel-flies may crawl forth to dry new wings, and go skimming or flitting over sedges or meadows.

Plecoptera, the stone-flies (Figs. 16 and 119–121). Well named are the stone-flies. Many a rock in the water of a mountain brook or wave-washed shore of lake will prove why stone-flies are stone-flies. For, as you turn the rock, curious little naiads, with odd hieroglyphic markings on their backs, go slithering away. These are the young of stone-flies, and one of the most certain finds in every gurgling stream. Irrigation ditches have also become homes for stone-flies. If you want to be sure of them, look for two long "tails," and at the base of every leg notice the little tuft of "gills."

On stones or shrubs beside the stream, the winged adults may be found. Their four membranous wings lie flat upon their abdomen, and the under pair is folded up in plaits.

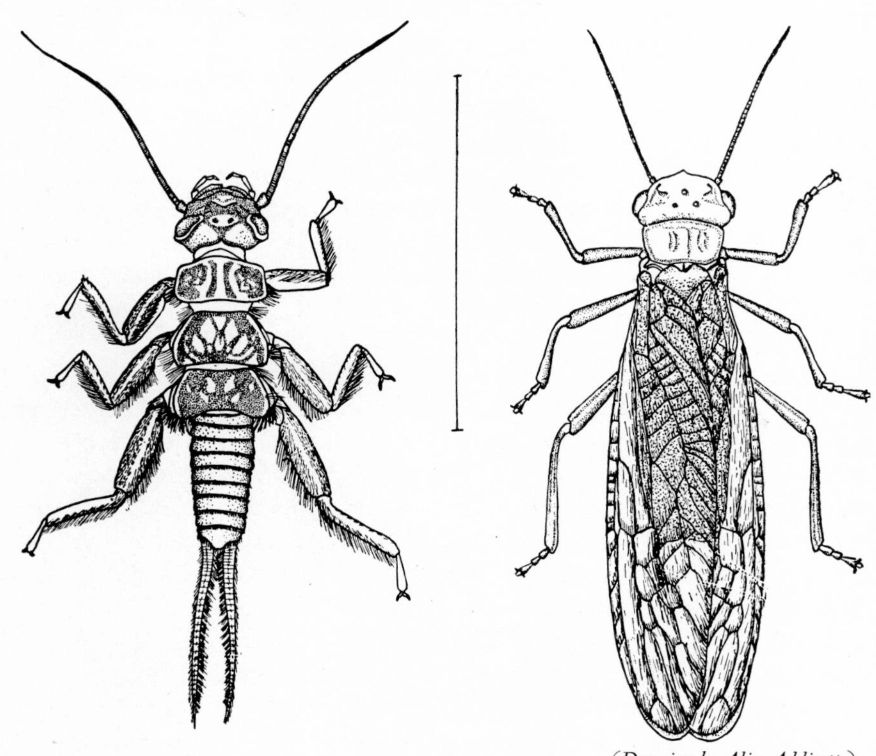

(*Drawing by Alice Addicott.*)

FIG. 119.—STAGES IN THE LIFE HISTORY OF A STONE-FLY, A MEMBER OF THE ORDER PLECOPTERA.
Stone-fly naiads live under stones in flowing streams. When they are grown, they come out of the water, and the winged adults emerge.

Corrodentia, the psocids and book-lice. Of all insignificant insects, the psocids and book-lice head the list. Yet there are those who believe that these tiny creatures may be the most abundant of all living things. Every bit of soil, every pile of leaves, every strip of loose bark, every stack of old books or papers may harbor some of them. But so tiny are they that almost always they are overlooked. Only the adults have wings, of course, and not all of these. The young, or nymphs, are gray or mottled of body and big of head, and often occur in colonies

Fig. 120.—A Living Adult Stone-fly, a Member of the Order Plecoptera.
This insect lived as a naiad beneath the stones in a rapidly flowing stream. When the adult emerged from the naiad, it rested on stems above the stream.

Fig. 121.—The Gauzy-winged Adult Stone-fly, a Member of the Order Plecoptera.
For a photograph of a stone-fly naiad see Fig. 16.

under a thin silken roof. Only one or two species of them ever do damage to things that interest man (such as cereals and book-bindings), so most of these insects are as unknown as they are tiny.

Mallophaga, the bird-lice (Fig. 122). The word *mallophaga* means "wool-eaters," though it ought to mean "feather-eaters," for that is what most of these insects do. Almost all of them are parasites upon the bodies of birds (only a few upon mammals), and there they eat feathers and scales from the skin. Why they cause birds so much discomfort, since they do not eat blood as do true lice, is a bit hard to say, yet they are one of the serious problems for every bird and poultry

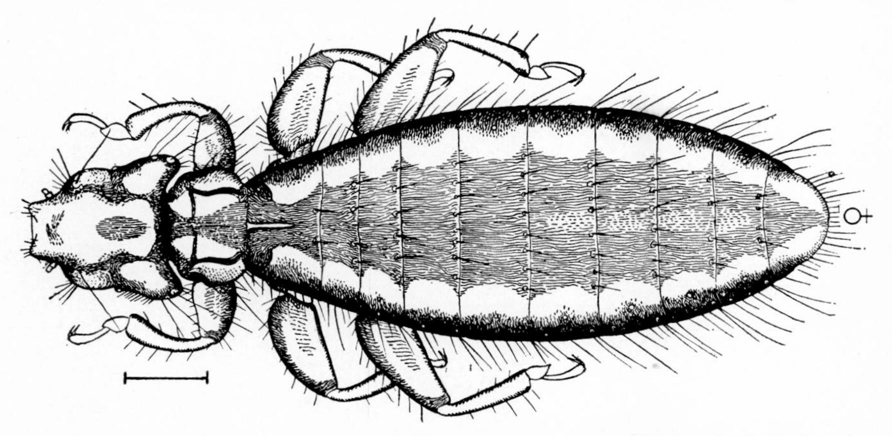

(*Drawing by G. F. Ferris.*)

Fig. 122.—A Biting Louse, a Member of the Order Mallophaga.

Biting lice live on birds and mammals, feeding on hair, feathers, and skin scales. The better-known lice that annoy mammals, including human beings, are sucking lice. Biting lice are sometimes called bird-lice.

breeder. It is probable that almost every group of birds has its own group of distinct bird-lice, and those birds with the heaviest feathers have the greatest number. Thus wild ducks are always well supplied, and even owls and hawks have a goodly number.

Did you ever wonder why the chickens take dust baths? Did you ever speculate upon the apparent absurdity of a Song Sparrow getting itself bedraggled in a pool of water? Did you ever wonder why birds take baths at all? It is almost certain that bird-lice are the answer. Dust or water may be the means that nature directs birds to employ in ridding themselves of their uninvited guests. Perhaps that further explains why ducks and owls have an unusual number of bird-lice—they do not take dust baths, and ducks really cannot get wet.

Embioptera, the lively ones (Fig. 123). If it weren't that California and Texas are among the few places in the world where the lively ones occur, they would not be mentioned at all. But in these states a search beneath the stones on a rocky hill will often disclose a mat of webbing in which there may be a lively one. Try to catch it. It runs forward on stumpy but agile legs. When you almost have it, it may run backward more rapidly than it went forward.

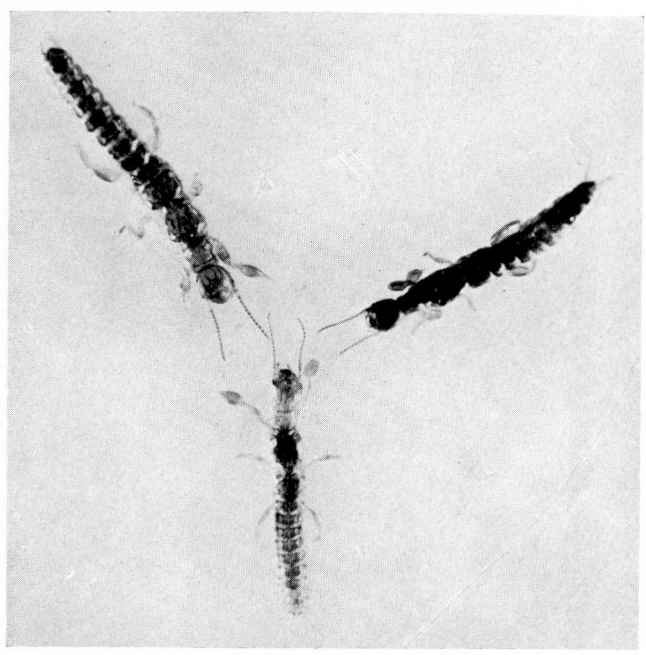

FIG. 123.—CALIFORNIA EMBIIDS, MEMBERS OF THE ORDER EMBIOPTERA. There are few representatives of this order; the one shown here lives in California.

These Embiids of California and Texas are the only lively ones common in this country, the only representatives of an order. In February or March, webbing among grass roots, clods, and cow chips, or under rocks will always show their whereabouts.

Thysanoptera, the thrips. Thrips are not likely to come into your ken unless you really look for them. That is not because they are so rare, but because they are so small. Yet a careful inspection of a daisy blossom, or the blossom of almost any member of the sunflower family, or the blossom of any fruit tree, will show these tiny fringe-winged insects. Many of them, when young, feed upon aphids or insect eggs, and the adults live on blossoms; but certain species attack fruits and vegetables and thus do considerable damage.

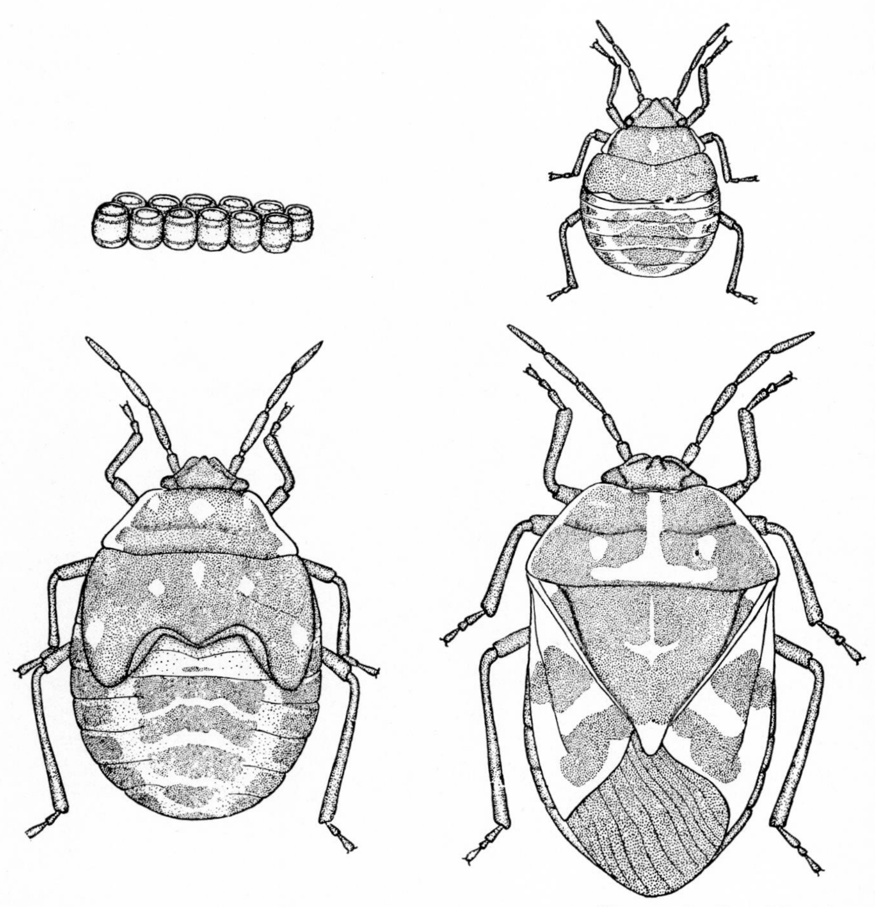

(*Drawing by Alice Addicott.*)

FIG. 124.—FOUR STAGES IN THE LIFE OF A HARLEQUIN CABBAGE-BUG, A MEMBER OF THE ORDER HEMIPTERA.

Upper left, a group of barrel-like eggs; upper right, a very young nymph; lower left, a nymph showing wing pads; and lower right, the adult, the upper wings of which show the leathery upper portions and the membranous and overlapping lower portions that provide the name Hemiptera, or "half wings," for this order.

Anoplura, the true lice. Ask any man who served in front lines during the World War about "cooties." His answer will be full of expletives. This is by way of proving that true lice like the human body. Of course, man is just a mammal after all, and mammals have their lice, as birds have theirs. Bird-lice have chewing mouth parts and live on feathers, hairs, and scales, but the true lice go in for better things, with a piercing and sucking beak that gets blood.

Schoolma'ams of the old-fashioned schools were often troubled by children from uncleanly families that had "nits," the eggs of the Head Louse, in their hair. Even today the school nurse looks over the youngsters of a modern generation with this in mind.

Just as every bird has its own particular type of bird-louse, so almost every mammal has its own type of true louse. In fact, some mammals go the others one better; the human being, for instance, is

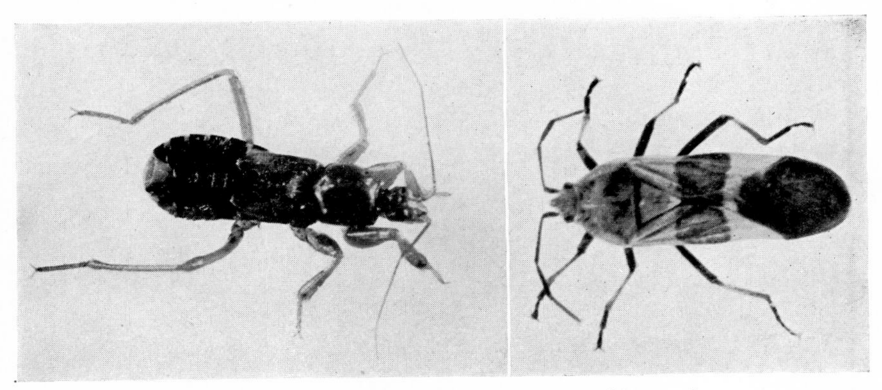

FIG. 125.—MEMBERS OF THE ORDER HEMIPTERA (*Continued*).
The bug on the left is a nymph of the Western Corsair, one of the assassin-bugs; the bug on the right is the Common Milkweed Bug.

afflicted by three different varieties that attack three regions of his body.

Hemiptera, the true bugs (Figs. 7, 15, 21, 43, 61, 66, 75, 105, 124, 125, and 181). *Bugs* is such a convenient term to apply to everything that creeps and crawls, wriggles and squirms, leaps and flies, that it is too bad it cannot be used correctly that way. However, there is only one group of true bugs and that is the Hemiptera. Hemiptera means "half wings," and adult true bugs have upper wings that are about half leathery and half membranous. This half-and-half appearance, plus the fact that the membranous parts of the two wings overlap, provides one of the certain means of knowing a true bug from all other "bugs."

True bugs change but little as they grow, except by the gradual addition of wings. Thus, if once you get the configuration of a true bug in mind you need have no hesitancy in turning at once to Hemiptera when a specimen comes to hand.

The piercing and sucking beak of true bugs is also a characteristic that is nearly always obvious. It is this beak that makes some of them —the back-swimmers, the Giant Water-bugs, and the assassin-bugs, for instance—rather dangerous to handle. The beak is sharp, may

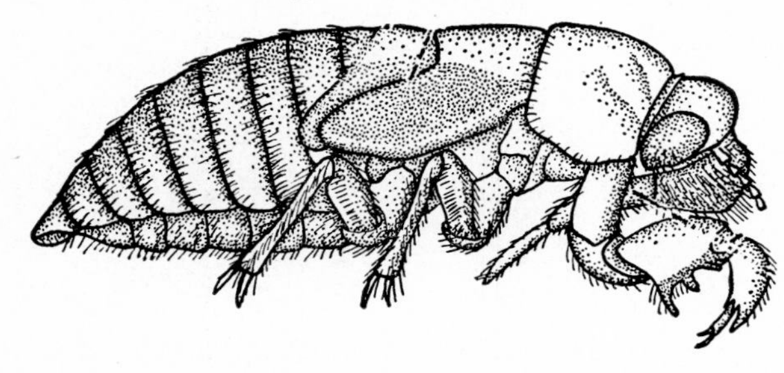

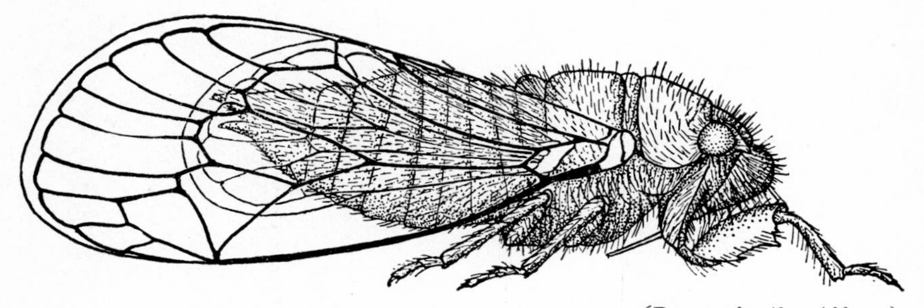

(*Drawing by Alice Addicott.*)

FIG. 126.—TWO STAGES IN THE LIFE OF A CICADA, A MEMBER OF THE ORDER HOMOPTERA. The upper drawing is that of the nymph; the digging legs proclaim its underground life, and the piercing and sucking mouth parts show an important characteristics of the order. The lower drawing is the adult. Note that its wings, like those of all the members of the order, are entirely membranous and are held roof-like over the body. (See also Fig. 98.)

pierce deeply, and has a slightly poisonous effect. Remember the beak in handling all bugs and give them no chance to use it.

True bugs are numerous and form an insect group that will be frequently represented in net collecting, whether in plant sweeping or in water seining. Such collecting will secure the Squash-bug, the Box Elder Bug, the Tarnished Plant Bug, assassin-bugs, stink-bugs, the Harlequin Cabbage-bug, water-striders, back-swimmers, water-boatmen, water-bugs (you may get a male with eggs on his back), and many others. Among the true bugs are many of the agriculturist's pet grievances. Many of the illustrations of this book are of true bugs.

Homoptera, the cicadas, leaf-hoppers, aphids, scale-bugs, and relatives (Figs. 19, 39, 49, 63, 84, 98, 126, 127, 172, and 173). Homoptera means "same wings" or "uniform wings." Except for this condition of their wings, these insects might be true bugs and are so considered by many entomologists. But their upper wings are alike throughout and not half-and-half, and are held arched above the abdomen and not flat, as Hemiptera hold them. Furthermore, their heads are so turned under that their piercing and sucking beak rests between their forelegs when it is not in use.

Here is an order comprising a great collection of strange, unusual, bizarre, and weird insects. Here belong the brownie-bugs, the pixie-

FIG. 127.—A WILLOW STEM WITH OYSTER SHELL SCALE-INSECTS, MEMBERS OF THE ORDER HOMOPTERA.

Scale-insects are among the freaks of the insect world. With many highly specialized scale-insects, only the young and the males have legs. The females, after the short time necessary for them to move and find new feeding grounds, settle down, lose their legs, secrete a scale-like covering of wax, insert their piercing mouth parts into the plant's juices, and spend the remainder of their lives without moving from the spot.

bugs, the musical cicadas, the insects that spend their lives beneath scales of their own making, and that immense tribe, the plant-lice or aphids. A few, like cicadas, are large and fully winged as adults, but many are small and so distorted by scale covers, cottony masses, or lack of wings that they would be hard to place in any insect order if their life histories were not known.

This order contains some of the agriculturist's greatest enemies. They are serious for several reasons: their piercing and sucking mouth parts make them immune to many insect poisons; the scales of the scale-bugs are almost impervious to other poisons; the complicated life histories of the aphids often bring them back to a crop after they have once been removed.

At the same time some of the most interesting of all insects are in this order. Remember that here is the cicada that spends, as a nymph, from three to seventeen years underground before it comes forth and changes to a winged adult for a brief climax of a few weeks. The famous Lac insect from which shellac is obtained is one of these. And here are the aphids with their complicated life histories that may go through generation after generation without a male appearing, since the females can reproduce without the other sex. Then, too, one who

FIG. 128.—THE EUROPEAN EARWIG, A MEMBER OF THE ORDER DERMAPTERA.
The European Earwig is abundant in certain districts in Eastern United States and in the Northwest and is now found in central California.

first sees a brownie-bug will clap his hands in glee and be thankful for the Homoptera.

Dermaptera, the earwigs (Fig. 128). It is unlikely that earwigs ever crawled into human ears, but folklore so states, and from this ancient belief the insects receive their name. The insects are mostly quite small, rarely abundant, and during the day they hide beneath boards and stones and bark of trees. They have one structure that will always identify them: a pair of curved forceps at the tip of the abdomen.

Coleoptera, the beetles (Figs. 25, 42, 44, 56, 73, 74, 76, 77, 85, 103, 106, 129, and 178). In the world of insects there are four orders, the "Big Four," that have become more successful than any of the others: the order of beetles, the order of flies, the order of bees and ants, and the order of moths and butterflies. Their success seems to have been brought about by two great factors: they have developed in the young a condition which makes that stage a most successful eating machine; and they have developed an adult, a stage grown up, that is, preeminently a machine for reproduction. To get from sluggish, worm-like, eating machine to active, flying, reproducing machine, an important stage has been interposed. This is the pupa. In

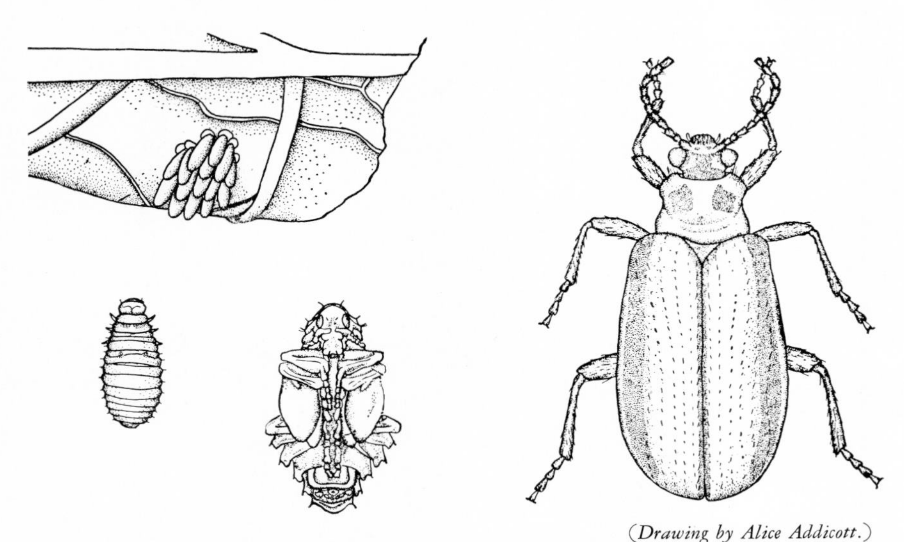

(*Drawing by Alice Addicott.*)

FIG. 129.—FOUR STAGES IN THE LIFE OF A BEETLE, A MEMBER OF THE ORDER COLEOPTERA.
Upper left, a mass of eggs; lower left, the larva; lower middle, the pupa; and right, the adult. All beetles have these stages in their life histories. Drawings are not to scale; pupa is redrawn from F. H. Chittenden, *U.S.D.A. Bull.* 892.

this order, then, as in the other members of the "Big Four," there is a worm-like or grub-like larva, a quiet pupa, an active adult.

Coleoptera means "sheath wings," and this condition of the wings, together with the fact that they meet in a straight line down the back, constitutes the surest means of identifying the adult beetle. The sheath wings are the upper, hard, shield-like wings that have for their only function the protection of the lower membranous flying wings. When a beetle flies, the upper wings are lifted and the lower wings are uncovered; the tips of the lower wings unfold, and the beetle goes blundering off. Watch a big beetle after it alights.

Slowly and carefully it will hitch up the underwings as it tucks them under the shields.

All beetles have chewing mouths; even the snout-beetles, which have a snout or proboscis that looks as if made for piercing and sucking. The snout-beetles have their jaws at the end of the snout instead

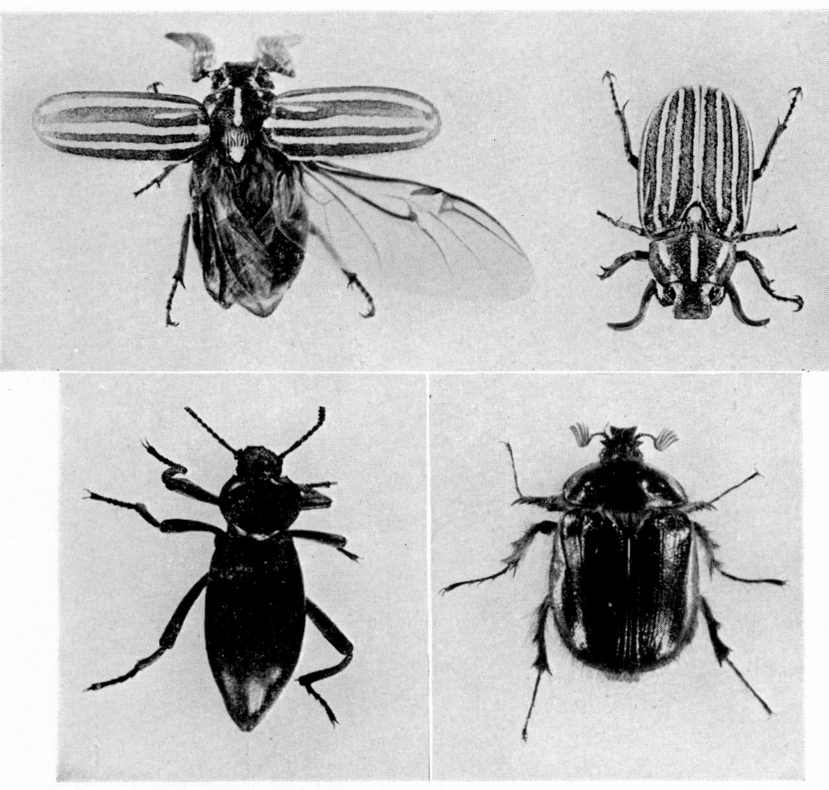

FIG. 130.—MEMBERS OF THE ORDER COLEOPTERA (*Continued*).
The upper two are males of the West Coast Ten-lined June-beetle. The lower left is the Dentate Eleodes, one of the darkling-beetles. The lower right is the Fimbriate June-beetle. These beetles show hard shield-like upper wings (*elytra*); the upper left beetle shows membranous lower wings and the manner in which these are folded when at rest—all characteristics of the order Coleoptera.

of in the usual position. Besides the egg, all beetles have three stages in their life histories: a grub-like larva, a pupa, and finally the adult. Larval beetles can usually be recognized because of their grub-like form. They may have six legs (or none at all if they are living in wood) and always they will have a big head.

Mecoptera, the scorpion-flies (Fig. 131). Like the embiids, or lively ones, the scorpion-flies would not be mentioned were it not for some

FIG. 131.—THE WINGLESS HANGING-FLY, A MEMBER OF THE ORDER MECOPTERA.
This is an appropriate name, for the fly spends much of its adult life hanging by its first pair of legs. It is quite necessary that it hang thus, for it cannot walk on any broad surface. Moreover, it uses the other four legs to catch its small insect food.

unusual members with unusual habits. In the Far West, for instance, is one of the oddest of all insects, the Wingless Hanging-fly. First of all, it has no wings, though most of its relatives have four. Then, too, it has its mouth on the end of a downward projection, in which respect it is like all its relatives. Like some of its relatives, too, it spends its life hanging by its two forelegs (in other words, it "hasn't a leg to stand on"), and it catches its food with the other four. On

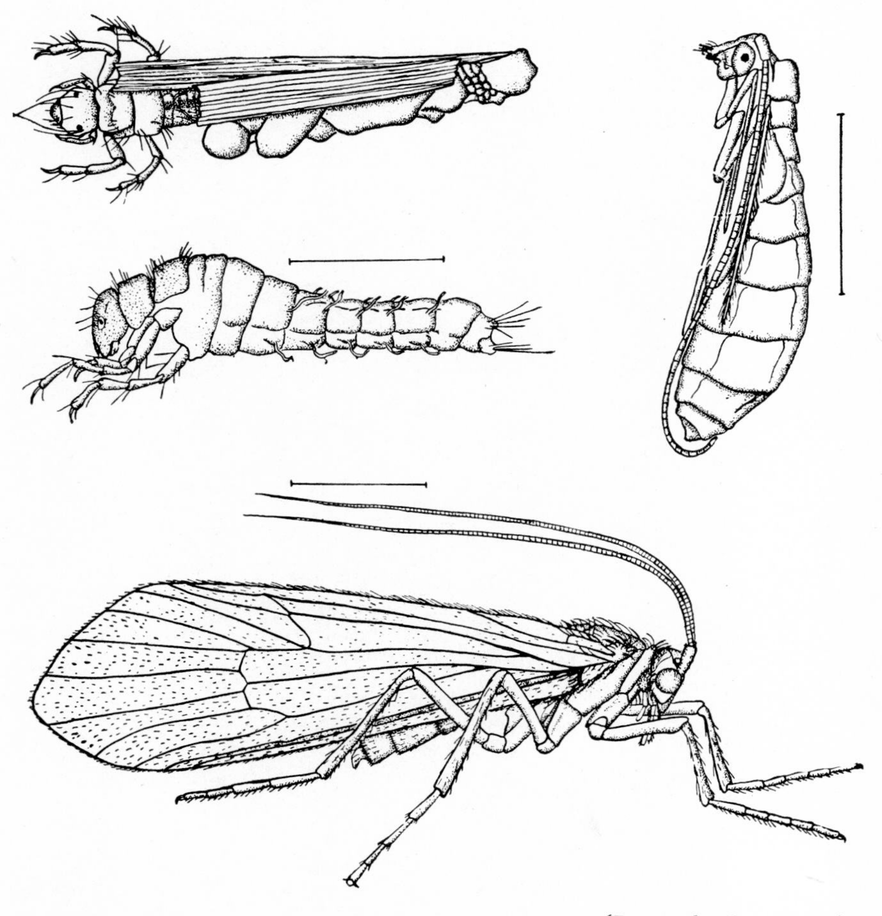

(*Drawing by Alice Addicott.*)

FIG. 132.—STAGES IN THE LIFE OF A CADDIS-FLY, A MEMBER OF THE ORDER TRICHOPTERA. Upper left, a caddis-fly larva in the case it builds and drags about on the bottom of streams; middle left, a larva removed from its case; upper right, a pupa; below, the adult that comes out of the water to live a winged life on land.

wet or cloudy days it may sometimes be seen swinging through the grasses.

Trichoptera, the caddis-flies (Figs. 132–134). If adult caddis-flies had scales on their wings instead of tiny hairs, they would pass for small moths. But larval caddis-flies, which live in water and build nets or cases for themselves, would never be mistaken for caterpillars. This business of building cases, or houses, of sticks or pebbles and then dragging the dwelling about wherever the inmate goes is one of the most fascinating activities of water insects. The cases, too, are built in just as many fashions as there are different kinds of caddis-flies. Some have the sticks laid log-cabin fashion; others lay them like scantlings on a roof; others stick pebbles together like the mosaic

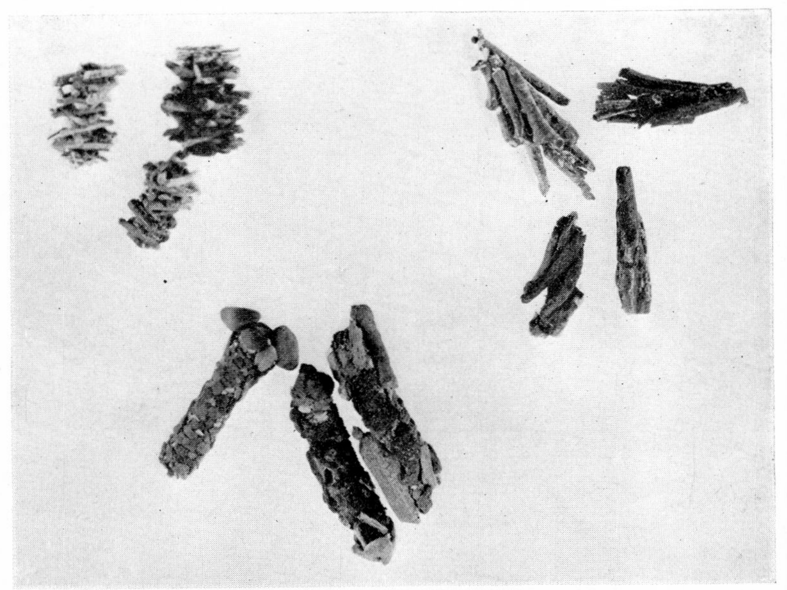

Fig. 133.—Most Larval Caddis-flies Live in Cases Which They Drag About in Their Water Homes.
Some of the cases may be permanently attached to stones.

of a cobblestone chimney. Not all caddis-fly larvae build houses that can be moved. Some stick permanent shelters of pebbles to the sides of large stones, and from the opening in front they build a silken net that seines small foodstuff from the water of the brook. When the net is full, it and all its load are eaten, and then a new net is made.

When these casemakers of the mountain brooks change to pupae they remain below the water; but just before transforming to adults they come to the surface where the emerging adults spread their wings for flight in air. As adults, they pass for insignificant woolly moths, and one is likely to overlook the fact that theirs was a novel early life beneath the water.

Lepidoptera, the moths, skippers, and butterflies (Figs. 6, 18, 23, 24, 26–38, 50, 51, 57, 58, 82, 83, 87, 89, 91, 92, 135–138, 162, 163, 165–168, 174, 176, 177, 179, and 186). Here at last is an order that everyone knows. If there is any question at all, it isn't whether this is one of the Lepidoptera, but whether it is a moth, a skipper, or a butterfly. One knows the Lepidoptera because they have four wings that are usually broad and are covered with flat scales that rub off onto the fingers like powder when the wings are touched (Fig. 6).

FIG. 134.—AN ADULT CADDIS-FLY, A MEMBER OF THE ORDER TRICHOPTERA.
It has undergone complete metamorphosis and, though the moth-like adult lives on the land, the larval and pupal stages are passed under water.

The proboscis of adult moths and butterflies fascinates too. For one thing, it rolls up when not in use; for another, it is a siphon that may reach out a greater distance than the moth or butterfly is long. And, speaking of mouth parts, one must mention that there are some adult moths, such as the big Polyphemus, that have no functional mouth parts at all and never take food.

The larvae of moths, butterflies, and skippers are also known to all. They are the caterpillars with the six true legs on the thorax, a pair of props at the very tail end, and a variable number of props, but usually four, between. And the pupae of moths are familiar objects whether they be in cocoons or not; the pupae of butterflies, too, weirdly shaped though they often are, are frequently seen. These are

FIG. 135.—MEMBERS OF THE ORDER LEPIDOPTERA.

The upper is the Achemon Sphinx Moth. The two at the lower left are Western Skippers. At the lower right is the Alfalfa Butterfly. Skippers, moths, and butterflies may be distinguished as follows: butterflies always have antennae ending in blunt or rounded knobs; skippers have antennae ending in knobs, but the knobs are drawn out at their tips into points or hooks; moths have many types of antennae, but never have knobs.

called *chrysalids*. See the chapter on "The Growing Up of a Swallowtail Butterfly."

Diptera, the true flies (Figs. 13, 14, 46, 47, 64, 65, 67, 71, 72, 79, 139, and 177). This is the order of insects wherein the adults have

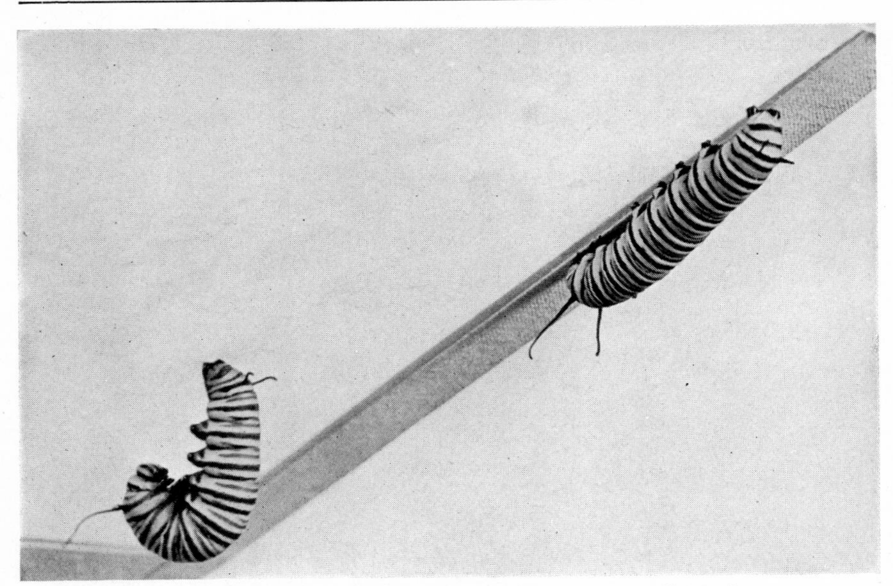

Fig. 136.—Larvae of the Monarch Butterfly, a Member of the Order Lepidoptera.

These larvae have fed on the Narrow-leaf Milkweed (milkweeds of various species together with Dogbane furnish the only foods for Monarch larvae) and are searching for a place to pupate. One has already suspended itself for this process.

Fig. 137.—Pupae, or Chrysalids, of the Monarch Butterfly, a Member of the Order Lepidoptera.

The skins of the suspended caterpillars shrank, blackened, and finally peeled away to leave these gold-studded green pupae where the caterpillars had been. Through the walls of these pupae can be seen the promise of legs, antennae, and wings of the butterflies to come.

but two wings, though two little stubs of the other pair, the *halteres*, still show just behind. The presence of only two wings will always identify the true fly, even though the members of the order are multitudinous in number, size, shape, and form. Most of the larvae, too, are quite distinctive with their maggot shape, their body form that

FIG. 138.—THE ADULT MONARCH BUTTERFLY, A MEMBER OF THE ORDER LEPIDOPTERA.
When the chrysalids of Fig. 137 gave up their contents, gaily marked winged adults like the one shown here came forth.

tapers to the front end, and the complete absence of legs (Figs. 71 and 177). Maggots present the perfect picture of creatures that squirm. They have to squirm; that is the way a legless creature moves. When time for pupation comes, the fly maggot presents a method that is superior to all others: its last larval skin merely hardens and turns brown, and within it the maggot becomes a pupa as effectively as if a cocoon had been spun. This hard brown case is called a *puparium*.

When one thinks of flies one must not forget the mosquitoes that belong here, or the midges, or the gnats. These insects spend their larval and pupal lives in water and differ in several respects from other flies. For one thing, the larvae swim, as only a wriggler can, and though they have no legs they do not closely resemble a maggot. The

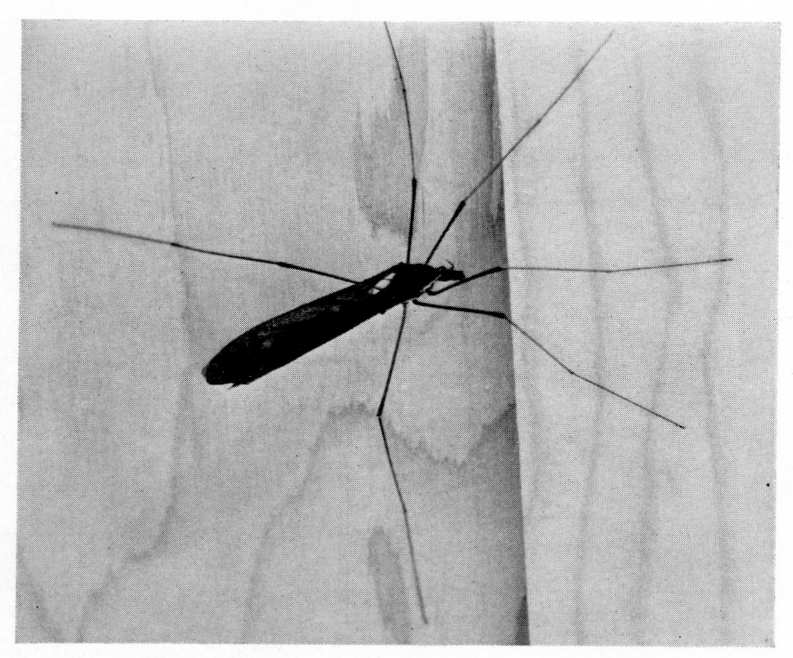

FIG. 139.—THE GIANT CRANE-FLY, A MEMBER OF THE ORDER DIPTERA.
The true flies, with their two wings, are typified by the Giant Crane-fly. Like all flies, it has, in its life history, a larva stage and a pupa stage, in addition to the adult shown here. See Fig. 14 for the other stages in the life history of the crane-fly.

pupae, too, do not form puparia of the last larval skins, but change form and continue as active swimming creatures, and in this way differ from other insects. The tumblers, that one sees among any collection of mosquito wrigglers, are the pupae (Fig. 65). To balance these pestiferous groups one should also note that here belong the tachina flies that parasitize caterpillars and aid in their control (Fig. 177); the syrphid flies that, as larvae, eat aphids; the robber flies that, as big, grown-up pirates, eat lesser flies and other insects.

There are no insects that seem to be so cosmopolitan as flies. There is no place where man can live that insects cannot follow, and one of the most persistent of these will be a fly. The young live in almost every conceivable condition, including pools of oil! Once high on a mountain in vast fields of snow and ice one of the authors came upon some bluebottle-flies that were buzzing about in the sun as if in the midst of tropic warmth and splendor.

Siphonaptera, the fleas (Figs. 140 and 169). The word *Siphonaptera* describes fleas neatly. It means "with a tube and without wings." Fleas can make prodigious leaps, but they have no wings; and anyone who has been punctured by a flea can vouch for the tube they must have for mouth parts. If you add to these characteristics the facts that fleas are exceedingly thin from side to side (the better to slip through the hair of their victims) and have four distinct stages in their life history, then you can see why fleas are distinct from all other insects.

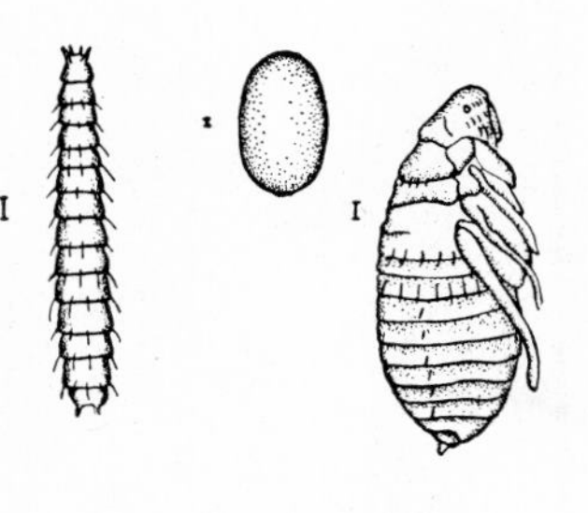

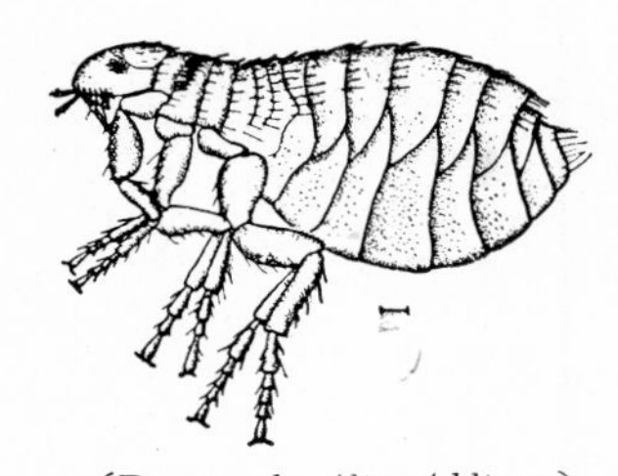

(*Drawing by Alice Addicott.*)

FIG. 140.—STAGES IN THE LIFE OF A FLEA, A MEMBER OF THE ORDER SIPHONAPTERA.

Upper middle, the egg of the flea; upper left, the larva; upper right, the pupa; below, the adult. Not drawn to scale. The hair lines beside each drawing denote the actual sizes. (See also Fig. 169.)

The four distinct stages—egg, larva, pupa, and adult—in the life of a flea are important to consider. In the first place, no other orders of wingless insects have complete metamorphosis. Because of this, scientists believe that fleas once had wings and lost them in their parasitic history. Fleas, then, have gone a long way and merit their position near the top of all insects. Second, it is that life history that makes of fleas such serious pests, especially in the mild climate of the Far West.

Consider your pet cat or dog in connection with fleas, for example. It seems that no matter how frequently you de-flea Gyp, he is scratching himself again within a few days. Did you remember to sterilize his kennel? Did you scrub the basement floor with boiling water or a strong lysol solution or kerosene? Unless you did, there will always be another crop of fleas. Only the adult fleas live upon Gyp. These lay eggs that are scratched out, fall upon the dust of kennel or basement, and there hatch to live a larval life, like a small maggot, content to feed with chewing jaws on organic matter in that dust. These larvae pupate, and when they emerge from the pupa they perch upon vantage points ready to leap upon any object that passes by.

Hymenoptera, the bees, wasps, and ants (Figs. 40, 47, 59, 86, 141, 142, 144–158, 161, 174–176, and 190). Bees, wasps, ants, and their relatives are placed last because many entomologists believe they have gone further than any other insect group. To concede this, one need

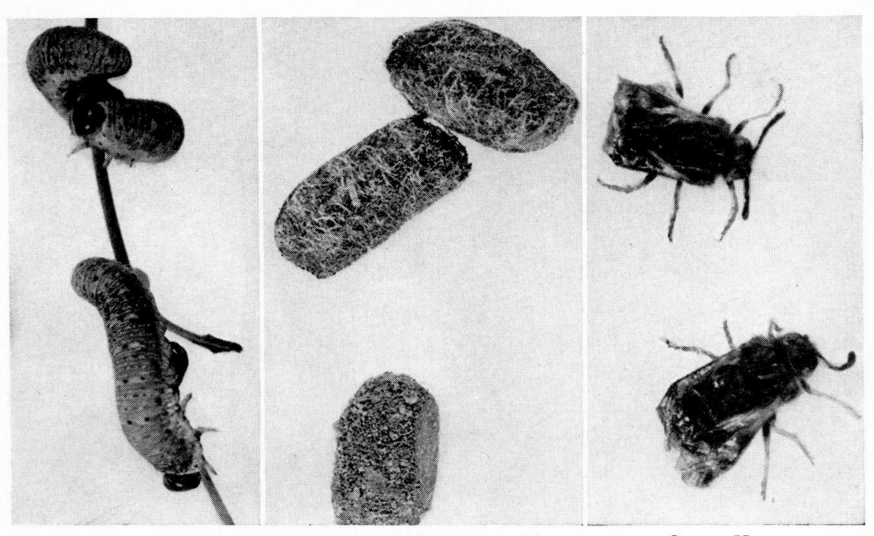

FIG. 141.—LARVAE, PUPAE, AND ADULTS OF A SAW-FLY, A MEMBER OF THE ORDER HYMENOPTERA. These most primitive members of this great order have large-headed larvae which are plant eaters and which spin cocoons for their pupae, but the adults show characteristics typical of the order.

but remember that in this order are those parasites so remarkable that they pass their entire larval life in the egg of another insect! Here are most of those extraordinary insects that have a chemical so potent that it will cause plants to form a "house," a gall, about them as they grow! Here are the wasps with their manifold methods of rearing young! Here is the Honeybee! Here are the ants! And here are those most primitive of Hymenoptera, the saw-flies! There is no more remarkable collection of insects than these.

A characteristic that is strikingly developed in the order, the factor that makes of Hymenoptera the most highly developed of all insects, is the attention and care that is given to the young. This may range

Fig. 142.—Members of the Order Hymenoptera (*Continued*).
The upper is the Thread-waisted Sand Wasp, which builds a nest in the ground and provisions it with paralyzed caterpillars for its young. The center is a Tarantula Hawk, which paralyzes tarantulas to provision its nest. The lower is one of the ichneumonid parasitic wasps (*Megarhyssa sp.*), which uses the long ovipositors at the end of the body to bore into wood and to lay its eggs in the burrows of wood-boring insects inside.

INSECT ORDERS—

	Thysanura	Orthoptera
Meaning of scientific name	Tassel-tails	Straight wings
Common name of members of the order	Bristle-tails, Silverfish, fish-moths	Short-horn and long-horn grass-hoppers, crickets, cockroaches, katydids, walking-sticks, praying mantis
How the insects grow up (metamorphosis)	No change except in size as insect grows (no metamorphosis)	Slight change as insect grows from nymph to adult, wings usually developing gradually (gradual metamorphosis)
Condition of wings	No wings	Four wings in most: the upper two are straight and leathery; the lower two are plaited and closed like a fan when at rest
Condition of mouth parts	Mouth parts are formed for chewing	Mouth parts are formed for chewing
Condition of young	Like adults	Like adults, but without wings or with wing pads only
Types of food	Many types of foods are eaten, such as starches, sugars, leaf mold, humus	Most eat plants; some eat other animals; a few eat both plant and animal food
Where usually found	In pantries, about fireplaces, under wallpaper, under stones, in leaf mold, under bark, and among ground litter	Widely distributed: in vegetation everywhere; under rocks, dead leaves; in the ground and in houses
Miscellaneous characteristics and general information	The name "bristle-tail" describes the appearance of the appendages at the end of the abdomen. Many of these insects have fine silver scales that rub off on the fingers	Many of our best known insects are in this order, some of them very troublesome; many singing insects
Some common examples	The Silverfish of the home; the Firebrat of the fireplace; various campodeids and japygids in leaf mold and under stones, and the machilids	Many species of grasshoppers, katydids, crickets, cockroaches, and phasmids, and many others

A TABULATION

Isoptera	Neuroptera	Ephemerida
Equal wings	Nerve wings	Those that last but a day
Termites	Lacewing-flies, ant-lions, dobson-flies	May-flies
Very slight change as the insect grows; most change in development of wings or wing buds (gradual metamorphosis)	Three distinct growth periods: larve, pupa, and adult (complete metamorphosis)	Two growth periods: the aquatic naiad that does not resemble the adult; the winged adult (incomplete metamorphosis)
Four wings in those forms that develop wings; wings long, narrow, membranous, laid flat on back when not in use	Wings four, membranous, with many wing veins, folded rooflike when at rest	Four triangular, delicate, membranous wings; the forewings much larger than the hind; all held vertical to body when at rest
Mouth parts are formed for chewing	The mouth parts are formed for chewing; in many of the larvae the mandibles are tubular and are used for sucking	Mouth parts of naiads are formed for chewing; mouth parts of adults are reduced and useless
Like adults, but without wings	Unlike adults; usually with long, curved mandibles; six legs	Somewhat like adults, with the same long cerci ("tails") but without wings; with gill plates on sides of abdomen
Practically all eat wood, usually dead wood	Practically all, both as larvae and as adults, eat other insects	Naiads feed upon microscopic plant stuff in the water; adults take no food
In stumps, posts, fallen logs; in the ground near decaying wood; at times in foundations of houses; rarely in the roots of living trees	Many diverse locations, such as in water, under loose bark, on plants infested with aphids, in pits of dust at bases of trees	Naiads occur in ponds, lakes, rivers, and brooks; at certain seasons and places the adults occur in huge swarms about lights
Termites can be distinguished from ants by the absence of a narrow stem (waist) joining abdomen to thorax	These insects are one of nature's means of keeping other insects in control. The lacewing-flies lay eggs on stalks; doodle-bugs live at the bottom of tiny pits; and snake-flies have necks like camels	May-flies are always supplied with two or three long, hair-like "tails." Two or three years may be required for the growth of the naiads in the water; but the adults will live for only a few days
The Common Damp-wood Termite (a large form in rotton logs and stumps); the Common Dry-wood Termite, a medium-sized type that works in fairly dry wood; the Western Subterranean Termite (commonest and most destructive), dark, winged forms of which frequently appear after rains	Fish-flies, snake-flies, mantispids, lacewing-flies, and antlions or doodle-bugs	There are several May-flies, but none has a distinctive common name

INSECT ORDERS—A

	Odonata	Plecoptera
Meaning of scientific name	Those with a tooth	Plaited wings
Common name of members of the order	Dragon-flies and damsel-flies	Stone-flies
How the insects grow up (metamorphosis)	Two growth periods: the young aquatic naiad, that does not resemble the adult; the winged adult (incomplete metamorphosis)	Two growth periods: the young aquatic naiad, that does not resemble the adult; the winged adult (incomplete metamorphosis)
Condition of wings	Four membranous, more or less transparent wings held at right angles to body in dragon-flies, folded parallel to body in damsel-flies, when at rest	Four membranous, heavily veined wings; the hind wings larger and folded in plaits when at rest
Condition of mouth parts	Mouth parts are formed for chewing; in the naiads the lower lip, or labium, is used as a grasping organ in catching animal food	Mouth parts are formed for chewing in young; frequently reduced and useless in adults
Condition of young	Unlike adults; live in water; dragon-fly naiads with rectal respiration; damsel-fly naiads with anal respiratory plates; both with prehensile lower lip	Somewhat like the adult, except with longer cerci (tails); with gill tufts at the bases of legs
Types of food	Both naiads and adults catch animals, chiefly other insects, as food	Most adults take no food at all; naiads in the water live on small plant stuff or are carnivores
Where usually found	Naiads live in water, usually quiet water; adults fly widely here and there, but usually in the vicinity of streams or ponds	Naiads are restricted to the lower surfaces of stones in rapidly flowing streams or on wave-washed shores of lakes; adults will be on plants or stones near by
Miscellaneous characteristics and general information	Another order of insects that serves to control the numbers of mosquitoes and similar small forms	Adult stone-flies are mostly drab insects, but their young are often strikingly marked. Young stone-flies are one of the certain finds beneath the stones of every rapidly flowing brook or even irrigation ditches
Some common examples	The Ten-spot, White-tail, Green Darner, and many other dragon-flies; the Black-wing, Ruby-spot, and several other damsel-flies	The Black-winged Stone-fly (one of the few which have biting mouth parts in the adult stage) that causes damage to fruit blossoms in Oregon and Washington; several other species

TABULATION.—(*Continued*)

Corrodentia	Mallophaga	Embioptera
Those that gnaw	Wool-eaters	Lively ones
Psocids and book-lice	Bird-lice	Embiids
Two growth periods: the young wingless nymph, that resembles the adult, and the winged adult (gradual metamorphosis)	No change except in size (no metamorphosis)	Metamorphosis peculiar: almost none in females, and nearly complete in males
Four membranous wings or none	No wings	Four membranous, long, narrow wings, restricted to males
The mouth parts are formed for chewing	Mouth parts are formed for chewing	Mouth parts are formed for chewing
Like adult, but without wings	Like adults	Like adults, but without wings
Feed upon the paste in book bindings (hence "book-lice"), paste in wallpaper, fungi, lichens, and other dry vegetable matter	Feed upon feathers and dermal scales of birds chiefly; a few feed on hair of mammals (ectoparasites)	Probably decayed organic matter
In books; in dark attics or rooms but little frequented; frequently under the bark of trees and shrubs and in ground litter	All are found at the bases of hairs of mammals or feathers of birds	Comparatively common in Florida, Texas, and California in little silken tunnels under rocks
These insects, so small and insignificant in appearance, are almost always overlooked, yet they are comparatively abundant	Birds take dust baths to free themselves of lice	These curious insects merit mention here for two reasons: Florida, Texas, and California are among the few places in the world where they are found; and they can run backward more rapidly than forward
The Cereal Psocid, the Orange Psocid, the Spotted Psocid	It is probably that nearly every species of bird has its own particular species of bird-louse; to a less extent this is true of mammals; the Common Hen Louse is perhaps best known	Only one or two representatives in this country

INSECT ORDERS—A

	Thysanoptera	Anoplura
Meaning of scientific name	Fringe wings	Unarmed tails
Common name of members of the order	Thrips	True lice
How the insects grow up (metamorphosis)	Very slight change, the young resembling the adults except that adults are winged (gradual metamorphosis)	No change except in size as insect grows (no metamorphosis)
Condition of wings	Four narrow wings that are heavily fringed with long hairs	No wings
Condition of mouth parts	Mouth parts are formed for rasping and sucking	Mouth parts are formed for piercing and sucking
Condition of young	Like adults, but without wings	Like adults
Types of food	Most feed on plants, especially the flowers; others feed on aphids and insect eggs	All are ectoparasites and feed on blood of their hosts, which are human beings and other mammals
Where usually found	These very tiny insects may be found in daisies, clover, and other flowers; frequently found damaging fruit, onions, and other garden crops	Behind the ears of hogs; in the hair of many domestic and other mammals; in the hair or clothing of human beings who are not cleanly
Miscellaneous characteristics and general information	These insects are so small that all but the keenest eyes will overlook them; they are frequently so abundant, however, that they do great damage to fruits and garden crops	It is an unusual schoolteacher who will not someday find "nits" in the hair of some of her neglected pupils; soldiers in trenches during the World War were constantly plagued with "cooties," the Body Louse
Some common examples	There are Cotton, Sunflower, Pear, Citrus, Bean, and Onion Thrips as well as many other species	Human beings are afflicted by Head Louse, Body Louse, and Crab Louse; and, of course, there are many other species that occur on other animals

TABULATION.—(*Continued*)

Hemiptera	Homoptera	Dermaptera
Half wings	Same or uniform wings	Skin wings
True bugs	Cicadas, leaf-hoppers, tree-hoppers, spittle-bugs, aphids, scale-bugs	Earwigs
A slight change as insect grows from nymph to winged adult (gradual metamorphosis)	A slight change only in most as insect grows from nymph to adult, brought about chiefly by the appearance of wings (gradual metamorphosis)	A slight change only as insect grows from nymph to winged adult (gradual metamorphosis)
Four wings: the upper are thickened at the base and have overlapping, thinner tips; the lower are membranous and lie flat upon the abdomen; occasionally none	Wings four, of the same thickness throughout; usually membranous and held rooflike over the body when at rest, or none	Wings four: upper small and leathery; lower larger, membranous, and folded lengthwise and crosswise when at rest
Mouth parts are formed for piercing and sucking	Mouth parts are formed for piercing and sucking; the long beak arises from hind part of lower side of head between forelegs	Mouth parts are formed for chewing
Like adults, but without wings, or with wing pads only	Like adults, but without wings, or with wing pads only	Like adults, but without wings
Most live on plant juices, others on animal juices; these foods they suck up with their beaks	Practically all feed on plant juices	Most feed on flowers and other vegetable materials; some feed on other insects; some are scavengers
Widely distributed on plants, in water, and a few, such as Bedbugs, in houses	Almost every type of plant will harbor on leaf, stem, or fruit some species of aphid, leaf-hopper, or scale-bug	Found chiefly on the ground during the day, under stones, leaves, bark, and in the grass; active at night; all are small and rarely numerous
These, the true bugs, are always, with their characteristic overlapping upper wings, easily identified as members of Hemiptera	Some of the most serious pests of agriculture occur in this large order of insects. Of these, the most destructive are the many species of aphids and scale-bugs	The name *earwig* is derived from an old superstitition that these insects crawl into ears; all have a pair of forceps-like appendages at the tip of their abdomen; they are not abundant
There are many, many true bugs: Harlequin Cabbage-bug, Squash-bug, Box Elder Bug, water-striders, back-swimmers, and water-bugs are only a few of them	Several harvest-flies or cicadas, spittle-bugs, tree-hoppers, leaf-hoppers, aphids or plant-lice, and scale-bugs	The European Earwig which is occasionally a pest, and several other small species

INSECT ORDERS—A

	Coleoptera	Mecoptera
Meaning of scientific name	Sheath wings	Long wings
Common name of members of the order	Beetles	Scorpion-flies and hanging-flies
How the insects grow up (metamorphosis)	Three distinct growth periods; larva, pupa, and adult (complete metamorphosis)	Larva, pupa, and adult periods occur in the life history (complete metamorphosis)
Condition of wings	Wings four: the upper hard and shieldlike; the lower long, broad, membranous, and folded beneath the upper when at rest	Four wings in most; long, narrow, and membranous; no wings in some species
Condition of mouth parts	Mouth parts are formed for chewing	Mouth parts are formed for chewing and are mounted on a long beak projecting downward from the lower side of the head
Condition of young	Unlike adults; grub-like in form; usually with six true legs, but no prolegs; no legs in some wood-boring forms; always a large head	Unlike adults; caterpillar-like, with six true legs and eight prolegs
Types of food	Feed on all possible types of food	Most eat other insects; some adults catch their food with legs
Where usually found	Occur in such a diversity of habitats that anyone looking for insects will probably find more beetles than any other kind	Found crawling through tall grass on cloudy days
Miscellaneous characteristics and general information	Beetles constitute one of the dominant orders of insects; their upper shield-like wings are protective merely, and in flight are held up while the under wings beat the air	Very few species in this order of most remarkable insects; some spend their lives hanging by their forelegs
Some common examples	Ground-beetles, diving-beetles, whirligig-beetles, carrion-beetles, rove-beetles, soldier-beetles, blister-beetles, dermestids, ladybird beetles, darkling-beetles, stag-beetles, long-horned beetles, and weevils	The Wingless Scorpion-fly of the Far West is one of the few fairly common forms

TABULATION.—(*Continued*)

Trichoptera	Lepidoptera	Diptera
Hair wings	Scale wings	Two wings
Caddis-flies	Moths, skippers, and butterflies	True flies
Larva and pupa periods occur in water; the adult is terrestrial (complete metamorphosis)	Larva, pupa, and adult periods (complete metamorphosis)	Larva, pupa, and adult periods (complete metamorphosis)
Four wings, membranous and clothed with long silky hairs, which give caddisflies the appearance of small moths	Four wings that are covered with microscopic overlapping scales	Two wings; a pair of threadlike organs, the "halteres," in place of hind wings
Mouth parts of larvae are formed for chewing; in adults the mouth parts are reduced and useless	Mouth parts of larvae are formed for chewing; those of most adults consist of a long tube for sucking, some adults without functional mouth parts	Mouth parts of larvae are formed for chewing or lacerating; those of adults for rasping and sucking, or for piercing and sucking
Unlike adults; somewhat caterpillar-like but with only one pair of prolegs; living in cases in water	Unlike adults; caterpillars, with six true legs, anal props, and a variable number of prolegs	Unlike adults; most are maggots without legs and with body tapering to a pointed head-end
Many eat the decayed or minute vegetation of stream bottoms; a few catch minute animals in nets spun in the water	Most larvae eat plant stuff, but a very few eat animal matter; most adults sip liquids and nectar; some adults take no food	Every conceivable type of organic food is eaten; plant stuff of all kinds and animal material, dead and alive; many are parasites
The larvae and pupae occur on the bottoms of ponds, lakes, creeks, and rivers; the adults may be found along the margins of such water or about lights near by at night	Occur wherever plants grow, every leaf being a possible home; adults fly freely both day and night in search of liquids or nectar; moths are freely attracted to lights	Widely distributed; no environment where any animal can exist will be entirely free of flies of some species
These are the insects that, as larvae, build the interesting cases of sticks or pebbles and drag them about as they crawl from place to place on the bottom of a stream	These are the best known of all insects; every boy or girl has had the scale dust of the wings rub off on the fingers; many a boy has a prized collection of them	The flies, like their close competitors, the beetles, bees, moths, and butterflies, have those characteristics that have made them successful and dominant over the earth
Several species which build distinctive cases; a few species that build nets but no cases	There are many common forms: the Mourning Cloak Butterfly and Monarch Butterfly, the Polyphemus Moth and White-lined Sphinx Moth, and the Long-tailed and Western Skippers, to mention only a few	Of course the House-fly, crane-flies, gnats, mosquitoes, gall-flies, midges, snipe-flies, horse-flies, bee-flies, dance-flies, syrphid flies, bot-flies, tachina flies, flesh-flies, fruit-flies, bat-flies, and many others

INSECT ORDERS—A TABULATION.—(*Concluded*)

	SIPHONAPTERA	HYMENOPTERA
Meaning of scientific name	With a tube and without wings	Membrane wings
Common name of members of the order	Fleas	Bees, wasps, ants, and their relatives
How the insects grow up (metamorphosis)	Larva, pupa, and adult periods (complete metamorphosis)	Larva, pupa, and adult periods (complete metamorphosis)
Condition of wings	No wings	Four membranous wings
Condition of mouth parts	Mouth parts of larvae are formed for chewing; those of adults for piercing and sucking	Mouth parts are formed for chewing, or for chewing and sucking, or lapping
Condition of young	Unlike adults; maggot-like, without legs; with numerous bristles; very small	Unlike adults: caterpillar-like, but with big eyes, in case of saw-flies; maggot-like in others, but body does not taper; well-defined head
Types of food	All adults are ectoparasites and feed chiefly upon mammals (a few upon birds); the larvae are not parasitic but live upon waste animal matter	Many types of foods are eaten: fruit juices, nectar, green vegetation, wood, seeds, other insects, the flesh of dead vertebrates; many in larval state are endoparasites and live in other insects
Where usually found	Occur on many mammals, including the house cat and dog, mice, rats, gophers, squirrels; the larvae occur in the dust wherever such hosts live	Occur widely wherever plants grow or bloom, or wherever other insects may be
Miscellaneous characteristics and general information	In mild climates the flea is a serious pest, for the mild winters permit the larvae to continue development in the dust of basements, kennels, and burrows. Hence the fleas become more numerous than they do elsewhere	Many females of this order are supplied with a sting, a piercer, or a saw at the end of their abdomen
Some common examples	The Human-flea, the Rat-flea, the Dog-flea, the Cat-flea, and the Ground Squirrel-flea are a few of the common species	Saw-flies, horn-tails, ichneumon wasps, and many gall-making species; ants, wasps, yellowjackets, and bees

from the simple method of saw-flies, which consists merely of a puncture in stem or leaf for the egg, to the method of parasitic forms, which consists of depositing the egg inside the victim; to the method employed by many wasps and solitary bees, whereby a provision of food is stored with an egg; to the elaborate system used by bees, yellowjackets, and ants, whereby the young are fed by mother or sisters until they are fully grown.

The adult Hymenoptera are usually not difficult to recognize, for they have four membranous wings, and the mouth parts are formed for chewing and lapping. A large proportion of them are extremely thin-waisted, and this will always identify, for instance, those castes of ants that have no wings. The larvae may not be so readily identified. Excepting only the young of saw-flies, which look very much like caterpillars of moths or butterflies except that they have large eyes placed well up on the sides of the head, most young Hymenoptera are legless maggots (Fig. 154). Yet they are not headless, as many maggots of true flies seem to be, and often the attending adults will be near to protect, and they will provide forceful identity.

CHAPTER XIV

SOCIAL LIFE AMONG THE INSECTS

THE ORIGIN AND BENEFITS OF SOCIAL LIFE

Most insects, like most other animals of all sorts, live solitary lives. By this we mean that each individual lives for itself and, except when thrown by accident into association with some other animal, lives by itself. It cares not for any other; it does not even concern itself with the welfare of its own young. In fact, it rarely sees its own young; when it does, it fails to recognize them. It does not cooperate with any other organism in the achievement of any common good.

There are, however, many kinds of animals—insects as well as others—which are not solitary in habit. These kinds are found in groups, flocks, herds, and societies. Some of them cooperate with others of their own species, while others do not; and accordingly they are classed as being social or merely gregarious. Many of our common wild birds are gregarious. Swallows, wild ducks, and geese travel in flocks and some birds such as Cliff Swallows, Barn Swallows, and many marine birds nest in colonies of many individuals. Except that they live thus in flocks, these birds do not interest themselves in one another's affairs. Each is an individual, or each pair acts individually without regard to the others. They are merely gregarious. Many insects, also, are gregarious in this sense. The caterpillars of the Mourning Cloak Butterfly are commonly found feeding gregariously on the foliage of elm or willow. The Convergent Ladybird Beetle is gregarious at times, great numbers of the adults assembling in some particular spot (Fig. 143) for reasons not fully understood, but mainly having to do with hibernation.

Then there are the truly social animals, such as man among the mammals, and Honeybees, bumblebees (Fig. 146), many kinds of wasps (Fig. 147), ants (Figs. 144 and 145), termites (Figs. 159 and 160), and certain kinds of beetles among the insects. These creatures are not merely gregarious. They not only live together but they cooperate in more or less diverse ways in the achievement of common benefits. Hence they are social animals. Only among man and the

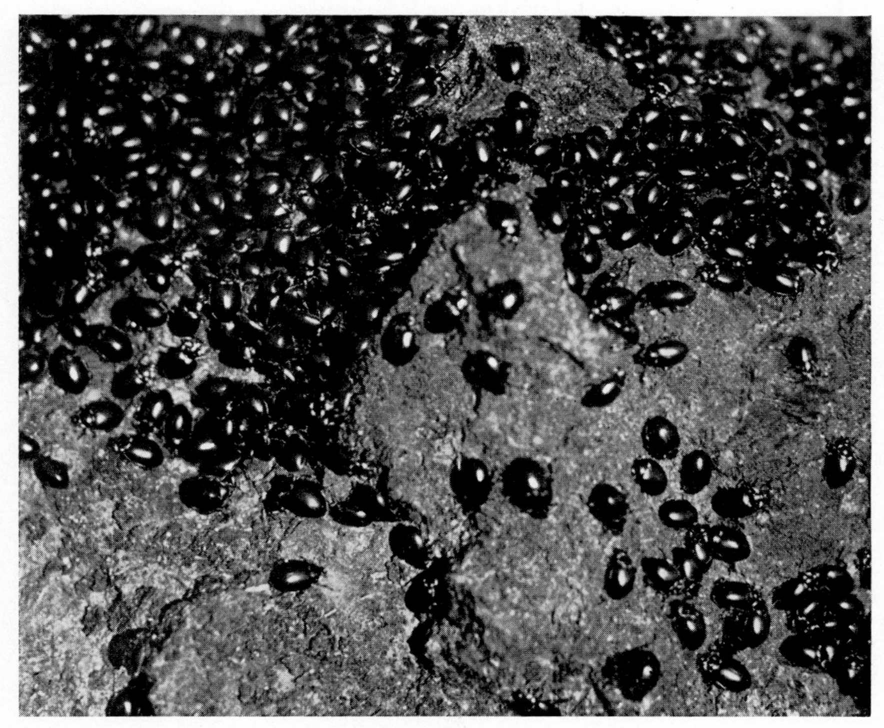

FIG. 143.—LADYBIRD BEETLES ASSEMBLE IN LARGE NUMBERS TO HIBERNATE, BUT THEY ARE NOT SOCIAL INSECTS.

This habit of congregating to hibernate, in the case of this unspotted Convergent Ladybird Beetle (*Hippodamia convergens* var. *ambigua*), is gregariousness, as is the association of many other animals. There may be some intangible benefit that comes from this association, but there is no obvious mutual cooperation as in a hive of bees or in a city of human beings. This ladybird beetle is common throughout North America.

insects has social life been developed to any marked degree. Let us examine briefly the societies of men and insects and see what they have in common, and ponder the problem of how social organization came to be, for primitive organisms were not social in any case.

All known animal societies past the rudimentary stage possess four characteristics in common: first, the component members of a society exhibit more or less active cooperation, which results in mutual benefit or group benefit; second, the group life continues over a period of time greater than the time required for a single individual to attain maturity; third, the society is founded on that type of association between parent and offspring which is termed *the family;* fourth, the existence of the society is dependent on a more extensive and more continuously available food supply than is usually available to non-social animals.

FIG. 144.—ANTS ARE AMONG THE MOST HIGHLY EVOLVED OF ALL INSECTS.
These workers of the Black Carpenter Ant are caring for larvae and for cocoons containing pupae, which they have stacked up like bags of grain. This elaborate care of the young, an essential part of the amazing development of social life, has done much to place ants above all other insects. The social life of the Honeybee is highly perfected but less complex than that of certain ants; that of the termites is similar in complexity but the termites themselves are of a lowly organization and their life cycle is simple by comparison.

Gregariousness and the development of social life are not necessarily closely related. The one does not appear to lead directly to the other. There are many cases of gregariousness without the least suggestion of true social behavior, and there are many cases of social behavior which appear to have developed quite independently of ordinary gregariousness. Animals may be gregarious without being closely related as individuals. Animal societies, however, whether or not characterized by marked gregariousness, nearly always consist of more or less closely related individuals. Except in man, the members of a given society are limited to the descendants of a common parent, or at most, common parentage is removed by no more than two or three generations.

Social life undoubtedly had its beginnings in the association of individuals of opposite sex for the purpose of mating. So long as the association endured only for the period of the mating act, there was no social life. Then came a time in the case of birds, mammals, and certain insects, when the association endured longer than the single mating, and social life was begun. Birds and other vertebrate animals living in pairs for one or more seasons exhibit a rudimentary social life. Not until the association became more permanent, however, and the progeny as well as the parents remained in association did true societies come into being.

John Fiske[1] and other writers have contended that human society owes its origin to a lengthening of infancy and childhood, since this necessitates more elaborate care of the young by the parents and at the same time affords the young greatly increased opportunities for learning. These consequences of a lengthened infancy and childhood are certainly marked characteristics of human society; but Dr. William Morton Wheeler[2] points out that another necessary condition for social life is that the life of the parent shall be long enough to cover the period of retarded juvenile development. He further states that "the insects show us that the lengthening of the adult stage comes first and makes social life possible," for it must be obvious that a lengthened juvenile life could not lead to a society founded on the association of parent and offspring if the parent died while the offspring was still in infancy. The Periodical Cicada has a juvenile life as long as seventeen years, yet it could not become a social insect, for the adults die before their eggs hatch or shortly thereafter.

A requisitely long parental life and a prolonged juvenile life of the offspring do not of necessity, however, produce a society. Houseflies and certain other insects often live for a considerable time after their offspring have attained maturity and in turn have produced young, yet they do not form societies. Something else is necessary. This second prerequisite for the development of a society is that the young shall possess a "meaning" for the parents, such as that manifested by ants (Fig. 144). Some benefit, even if only a psychological one, must accrue to the parent from association with its offspring. Certainly this is true of human societies, and it seems to be equally

[1] John Fiske, *The Destiny of Man, Viewed in the Light of His Origin*, Houghton Mifflin Company, Boston, 1886.

[2] William Morton Wheeler, *Social Life Among the Insects*, Harcourt, Brace & Company, New York, 1923.

true of insect societies. The soft skin of a human baby, its cooing prattle, and its manifold activities in play are the source of much

(*Photograph by Lester Brubaker.*)

Fig. 145.—Worker Argentine Ants Tend Their Aphid "Cattle" on the Undersurface of a Leaf.

Social insects exploit many creatures to secure food. These soft-bodied aphids suck enormous quantities of sweetish juice from plants but digest only a portion of it. The balance, concentrated by extraction of considerable water, is passed through the bodies of the aphids and exuded as a sirupy excrement known as *honeydew*. This is eagerly sought by many insects, social and otherwise. Only the ants and certain wasps, however, express any proprietary interest in the aphids or give them any protection in return for the honeydew received.

interest and amusement for the parents. But few people rear children from a sense of social duty alone. On the side of the insect, Wheeler says, in speaking of the interest of the parent wasp in its young: "Probably this interest is aroused and sustained in the mother by simple, pleasurable, chemical (odor), and tactile (touch) stimuli emanating from the egg or larva."

In the case of specialized or highly evolved insects of social habits the larvae may even contribute to the food supply of the parents.

FIG. 146.—BUMBLEBEES ARE SOCIAL INSECTS, BUT THEY FALL FAR SHORT OF THE ANTS, HONEYBEES, TERMITES, AND MANY OF THE SOCIAL WASPS IN THE DEVELOPMENT OF THEIR SOCIAL ORGANIZATION.

The waxen cells of bumblebee nests lack the symmetry displayed by the waxen cells of the Honeybee and the paper cells of wasps. This bumblebee stands on a group of capped cells containing bumblebee pupae and faces a waxen honeypot which, from the time of its building, has been used only for storing honey. Behind the bumblebee are cells which have cradled young. At least one of these also, now that the young have matured and left the cells, is being used for the storage of honey.

The larvae of ants and social wasps produce a sweetish salivary secretion which is eagerly sought after by the parents. Much of the solicitation lavished on larvae by ants and social wasps undoubtedly owes its origin to the desire on the part of the parents for the secretion which they receive in return from the larvae. Strange behavior? True, yet how does it differ fundamentally from the behavior of human parents who put their children to work to support them, or who look to their children for support and comfort in their old age, whether or not their previous conduct toward their children justly entitles them to such support?

Thus we see that insect societies have much in common with human society. They have arisen out of similar conditions and they have developed many similar characteristics—many more than the above brief analysis suggests. Social insects build elaborate structures in which to live; they carry on agriculture, make war on each other, and enslave their own kind. They even domesticate animals. Wheeler says the ants have domesticated more animals than man. But let us cease generalizing and get acquainted with insect societies at first hand. Let us see how the above statements are borne out by what we may observe for ourselves. A colony of termites or a colony of yellow-jackets, which may be found in almost any community, will supply us with an abundance of material, and the observation of the manifold activities of the colony will enlighten and entertain us for many days to come.

THE LIFE OF THE YELLOWJACKET

Everyone knows something about yellowjackets and hornets. If not known from actual experience, then from hearsay, for many are the tales, mostly highly exaggerated, of the belligerence and stinging power of the yellowjacket and the hornet. It is well known that they nest in the ground or in trees and that they develop populous colonies similar in some respects to those of the Honeybee. Those who have watched a colony at close range (as they may be watched in comparative safety) and have peered into the interior of one of the marvelous paper nests to learn how the wasps really live, and how they rear their young and perform the hundreds of other tasks so necessary in the maintenance of a complex communal life, have had a most stimulating experience, an experience to be long treasured. Those who have not had this experience have something to look forward to. For them this account has been written.

Characteristics of the vespine wasps (Fig. 147). Most of the vespine wasps (the yellowjackets and hornets are so called because they constitute the subfamily Vespinae of the wasp family Vespidae, both of which names are based on *Vespa*, the ancient Latin name of the common wasp of Europe) are cross-banded black and yellow on the abdomen and have the head and thorax black with yellow spots and bars. A few species have the yellow replaced by white and a few have the black partially or completely replaced by reddish or rust color. Only the European or Brown Hornet, which has been introduced into this country and has become naturalized in a number of states along the Atlantic seaboard, departs markedly from this general pattern. It is a very dark brown or black, barred with yellowish brown. With all of them the abdomen is broad and truncated at the base, as if it had been chopped off with a knife, very much as it is in the Honeybee.

FIG. 147.—THE MALE, THE WORKER, AND THE QUEEN FORM THE CASTES IN A YELLOWJACKET COLONY.

These are the castes of the Common Yellowjacket (*Vespula vulgaris*). The male or drone is at the left; note his slender body and long antennae. The worker is in the center, and the queen at the right. Both worker and queen are females. They differ chiefly in size, the worker being smaller. Her reproductive organs are not highly developed. These types or castes exist among most social insects.

Beyond the base the abdomen tapers conically to a sharp point where, if the wasp is a queen or a worker, the sting is concealed. The eyes are large, covering most of the sides of the head. They are kidney-shaped and bear deep, rounded indentations on their front margins. The wings, when the wasp is not in flight, are folded lengthwise down the middle and are held flat along the back. No other common wasps present this same assemblage of characteristics, though wasps belonging to related subfamilies closely approximate it.

Kinds. There are many kinds of vespine wasps in North America, Europe, Asia, and the East Indies. Some fifteen or more kinds occur in the United States. Most of these are superficially similar, but are easily distinguished when the details of their structure and coloring are examined. With one exception the North American species fall into two groups: the wasps of the genus *Vespula*, which nest underground (Fig. 150), and those of the genus *Dolichovespula*, which hang their nests from trees and shrubs or from buildings (Fig. 148). These two groups differ not only in the location of their nests, but also in the details of nest construction, in the duration of life of the colony, in the time of the year when males and queens are produced, and in the physical structure of their own bodies. The one vespine wasp found in this country which does not belong in either of these groups is the European Hornet, which has been described on a preceding page. It is a large wasp as big as the end of one's finger, but is a relatively slow-moving, mild-tempered species. Asia has several species of hornets but this, our only true hornet, is not native. Our so-called White-faced, or Bald, Hornet is not a true hornet, but a *Dolichovespula*.

If a wasp is captured remote from its nest, it is an easy matter to tell whether it is a *Vespula* or a *Dolichovespula*. The species of *Dolichovespula* are distinctly long-faced (*dolicho* means long). They show a distinct space on the side of the head between the lower end of the compound eye and the base of the mandible, whereas the species of *Vespula* are short-faced and lack this space. The species of *Dolichovespula* exhibit also a fine ridge running up and down on the sides of the prothorax, and they have long hairs on the tibial segments of the legs, whereas the species of *Vespula* lack these features.

Caste differentiation. All the vespine wasps, except a few parasitic species, consist of three types of individuals. These three types, or castes as they are called, are the queen, the worker, and the male or drone (Fig. 147). The queen and the worker are both females. They differ principally in size, the queen being much larger than the worker, for she has fully developed reproductive organs whereas those of the worker are more or less rudimentary or stunted. There are slight average differences also in color pattern. Both queens and workers sting, for the sting is a modification of the egg-laying structure. The males are longer bodied and more slender than the females and have longer antennae. They have one more segment in the antennae than the queen and the worker, and one more obvious segment in the abdomen. They also have the tip of the abdomen blunt or rounded instead of pointed; they have no sting, and they differ slightly in color pattern. Males are present in a colony or on the wing only in summer and fall, mostly in the fall, and hence are rarely seen by the average person.

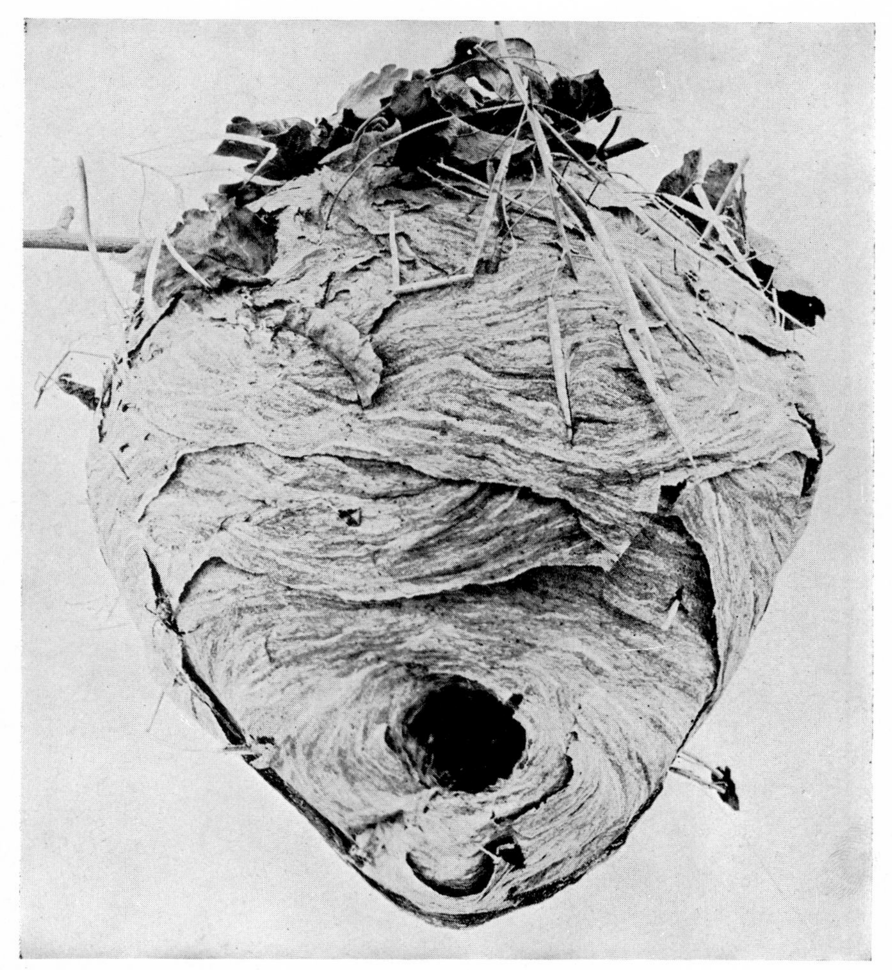

FIG. 148.—THE DIABOLICAL YELLOWJACKET HANGS ITS PAPER NEST FROM SHRUBS OR TREES. This yellowjacket (*Dolichovespula arenaria*), and other members of the same genus, hang their nests in the open from trees or shrubs or buildings. This particular nest was suspended only a few inches from the ground in a Poison Oak shrub, a Pacific Coast relative of the eastern Poison Ivy. An entry hole is seen near the bottom, and the walls are made of sheets of paper, wrapped around like the folds of an Oriental turban. This nest is shown opened in Fig. 149. The Diabolical Yellowjacket occurs over the whole breadth of the North American continent, though it appears to be absent in the arid southwestern portions.

General features of the nest. All vespine wasps, whether aerial or subterranean in nesting habit, build large nests of paper, which they make of wood pulp. These nests are generally globular or oval, though when built among obstacles, as in stony ground, they may

FIG. 149.—A PART OF THE WALL IS REMOVED SO THAT WE MAY LOOK INTO THE NEST OF THE DIABOLICAL YELLOWJACKET.

The wall is formed of many overlapping sheets of paper, and the saucer-like combs are hung one below the other, like floors in a tenement house. The young are reared in cells that hang from the lower side of these combs—a position very different from that of tenement-house children. The nest grows by the tearing out of inner walls and putting on of outer; the combs grow, too, at their edges. Here the combs at the edges show partially constructed cells, but toward the center are the cocoons spun by full-grown larval yellowjackets.

be irregular in shape. Each nest consists of a series of paper combs, usually five to eight in number (Figs. 149 and 151), which resemble the wax combs of the Honeybee in the hexagonal shape of the cells (Fig. 152). They differ from the combs of the Honeybee, however, in several respects. Each comb of the wasp consists of but one layer of cells instead of two as in the comb of the bee, and the combs are placed horizontally with the open ends of the cells facing downward, whereas the combs of the bee are placed vertically with the cells opening outward on each side. Furthermore, the combs of wasp nests are used only for the rearing of brood, whereas the bee uses part of the combs for the storage of food in the form of honey. Vespine wasps do not store food. The combs of the wasp nest are suspended, each from the one above, by one or more paper supports called *suspensoria* (Fig. 151). In *Vespula* nests (the underground ones) each suspensorium is in the form of a slender cord or rod and there are many suspensoria to each comb, the central one, the first one built, being the largest. In *Dolichovespula* nests (the aerial ones) there is usually only a single large suspensorium, the central one, but this is braced by ridge-like buttresses which extend outward from it.

Surrounding the tiers of paper combs in a wasp nest is a paper wall. The aerial wasps (those of the genus *Dolichovespula*) build nest walls of more or less complete and well-separated envelopes (Figs. 148 and 149); the underground wasps (those of the genus *Vespula*) make their walls of numerous overlapping scale-like pieces (Fig. 150). In aerial nests the entrance hole is either at the bottom or on one side below the middle; in underground nests that have attained any size, the entrance hole is well up on the side or even on top. Between the wall and the edges of the combs, as between the individual combs, there is a space big enough to permit the wasps to move about freely. The combs are not attached to the nest wall except in the upper half of the nest. In *Dolichovespula* nests the combs often are attached to the wall only where the suspensorium of the topmost comb penetrates the nest wall to attach itself to the support from which the nest hangs.

Duties and functions of the workers. The chief duty of the workers, as their name implies, is to work. During most of the life of a colony the workers perform all the tasks required for the maintenance of the colony: building nests, foraging for food, caring for the brood and for the queen, and defending the colony. They are not, however, so consistent workers as the poets and other sentimental observers of the past and present would have us believe. Worker wasps often loaf; they

Fig. 150.—The Western Yelllowjacket Makes Its Paper Nest in the Ground.
This yellowjacket (*Vespula pensylvanica*), and other members of the same genus, build their nests in the ground. Such nests are usually begun in abandoned field mouse, gopher, or ground squirrel holes, the holes being enlarged by constant digging as the nest grows. The entrance tunnel (to the upper left) is kept smooth and dust-free by a dried plastering of mud. This tunnel leads to the oblong opening into the left side of the nest. This nest is shown opened in Fig. 151.

often spend time and energy in more or less aimless and useless running hither and yon, accomplishing nothing. They are not always so dutiful and so home-abiding as might be expected, either, for worker wasps occasionally stay out overnight, not returning to the nest until the rising of the sun has announced the beginning of a new day. On the whole, however, they are industrious laborers. Perhaps their strenuous activity most of the time entitles them to occasional nights out.

Papermaking. The making of paper and the incorporation of this into the structure of the nest is one of the principal duties of worker wasps. A worker engaged in papermaking leaves the nest and flies afield, looking for weathered wood of some sort from which she may scrape or cut wood fiber. She may select a fence post or fence rail, the side of a weathered unpainted building, the limb of a dead tree from which the bark has fallen, or the dead stem of a last year's weed. It matters little what the object is so long as it can supply the needed wood pulp. The wasp may even gather pulp from a paper bag discarded by some picnicker!

From the selected source the wasp bites and tears the fiber with her mandibles. The breaking of the fiber makes a clicking sound which is often audible several feet away. The wasp cuts enough fiber to make a small pellet about an eighth of an inch in diameter. This she holds beneath her chin, using her front legs to help her mouth parts. As soon as enough fiber is collected, the wasp carries it back to the nest. The wasp chews each pellet of collected fiber and mixes saliva with it to convert it into a doughy mass. This is the paper pulp.

Then, having arrived at the nest, she alights astride the edge of an unfinished layer of paper in the nest wall or on one of the combs and presses her ball of pulp against the old paper, biting it to fasten it in place. Then, still biting the ball of pulp, she slowly walks backward, causing the ball to lengthen out into a string, and this is fastened throughout its length to the older paper. On reaching the end of the string she runs forward and then once more backs up, biting the string of pulp to flatten it out. Now she has finished, and the ball of pulp has been converted into a narrow strip of new paper. In a few moments the moisture evaporates from the new paper and it becomes an integral part of the nest. Meanwhile the worker flies away for another load of fiber.

The strips of paper made by *Dolichovespula* wasps, though sometimes curved slightly, are more often nearly straight. They are fitted into the nest wall so as to run more or less horizontally (Fig. 148). The strips of paper made by *Vespula* wasps, on the other hand, are strongly curved like little arches. Some of them are even circular. In the *Vespula* nests the strips of paper are placed so that the convexity of the arch is upward (Fig. 153).

As the colony increases in size and population during the spring and summer the nest has to be enlarged. The enlargement is accomplished in a simple manner. The innermost layers of paper in the nest wall are torn down to make room for the enlargement of the combs, and at the same time new layers are added to the outside of the wall. Thus the nest is constantly being expanded to meet the needs of the colony. Part of the paper torn from the inner layers of the nest wall is used to enlarge the combs. In fact, much of the paper in the combs, except in very small nests, is derived from the inner layers of the wall. Some of this torn-down paper is carried outside and added to the newest wall layer. None of it is wasted, but neither is any of it used without being chewed again into paper pulp, just as if it were freshly collected wood fiber.

A little of the torn-down paper is added to the suspensoria to thicken and strengthen them, for as the nests grow the weight of brood in the combs borne by the suspensoria becomes considerable. A little of this torn-down paper is also occasionally used in another way. In large nests the uppermost combs, which are the oldest, are often abandoned for brood rearing and, in some cases, the cells in these old combs are papered over and closed. Whether this is done for sanitary reasons or as part of the general task of strengthening the upper part of the nest remains to be learned.

Digging a nest chamber. With the underground species, the workers not only must make paper and enlarge the nest, but they must also excavate the chamber in the ground in which the nest is built (Figs. 150 and 151). This is no inconsiderable task, as often the nests are built in dry, hard ground. The actual work of excavation has not been observed, for it occurs underground in the dark; but in various ways evidence as to how the digging is accomplished has been secured. The wasps visit some convenient source of water, drink so much of it that frequently they can hardly fly, return to the nest cavity, and disgorge the water on the surface where the excavating is going on.

Fig. 151.—A Part of the Wall Is Removed so That We May Look into the Nest of the Western Yellowjacket.

The wall is much thinner and more fragile than that in the nest of the Diabolical Yellowjacket (Fig. 149). The combs, too, are different in that they are not saucer-shaped, and are hung by many more supports. But the combs are hung in the same tenement-house fashion, and the cells are on the undersurface.

Each drop of water disgorged makes a little spot of mud which can then be scraped up with the wasp's mandibles to form a little pellet and carried away. Most of the excavated mud is carried some distance from the nest and then dropped. Wasps can be seen carrying these pellets as they leave the nest entrance. If, as often happens, the nest chamber consists of an enlargement in an old gopher or squirrel burrow, then the scraped-up mud pellets may be carried into the parts of the burrow leading from the nest chamber and deposited there. As much as a quart of these mud pellets has been found in one part of a gopher hole adjacent to a wasp colony.

Food getting. The workers spend much time collecting food for the colony. Their foraging consists of two distinct types of activity, resulting from the fact that adult wasps and wasp brood, for the most part, eat different kinds of food. Adult wasps eat a great deal of sweets, such as nectar from flowers and the honeydew produced by scale-insects, aphids, and other bugs. They also eat liquid exudations from wounds on trees and shrubs and the juices of ripe fruit, such as grapes, prunes, and apples. The wasp larvae (Figs. 152 and 154) eat chiefly animal matter, such as the fleshy tissues of caterpillars and flies or the flesh of dead vertebrates. The workers, therefore, collect sweets and also hunt living prey and carrion.

When a wasp is collecting sweets it goes from flower to flower drinking nectar, or it eats honeydew or fruit juice, until it is completely engorged. Then it returns to the nest and disgorges a large part of this food to feed other workers in the nest, to feed the queen, or to feed males, if it is the season for males. In the opinion of several observers, some of the sweets thus collected is given to the larvae, but the bulk of the food of the larvae undoubtedly consists of animal matter.

The workers which are collecting food for the brood go a-hunting. A hunting worker flies back and forth a few inches above the herbage of a field or just in front of the foliage of a tree or shrub, looking for some unlucky insect on which it may pounce. Wasps hunt chiefly by sight, but their eyesight is not good; at least, they do not see distinctly. If a wasp sees an object that looks like prey, she pounces upon it; if not deceived and her pounce is successful, she makes a capture and kills it, but not by means of the sting, as might be supposed. The so-called solitary wasps sting their prey, but the yellowjackets and hornets kill theirs by biting. The lack of acuteness of vision in wasps is proved by the fact that hunting wasps will sometimes attempt repeatedly to capture the brown nail heads that show on a white-

FIG. 152.—CELLS OF A YELLOWJACKET COMB WITH MORE THAN ONE EGG IN EACH PROVE THAT THE QUEEN HAS DIED OR HAS BECOME VERY FEEBLE, AND WORKERS HAVE TAKEN OVER THE EGG-LAYING FUNCTION.

This, the lowest and last comb of a nest of the Common Yellowjacket (*Vespula vulgaris*), was collected late in the fall. Before it was taken the queen had died or greatly weakened, for she would never have made the mistake of laying two or three eggs in a cell, as can be seen here. Some worker, or workers, had taken over the egg-laying function and displayed their hitherto dormant reproductive instincts. Around the outer portion of the comb are a few cells with fully grown larvae, and some cocoons containing pupae.

washed wall, obviously mistaking the nail heads for flies or other insects until the moment of actual contact.

When a fly or other small winged insect is captured, the yellow-jacket usually bites off the head, wings, legs, and abdomen, choosing only the thorax to take back to the nest. This selection is due, no doubt, to the fact that the thorax is filled almost entirely with muscle tissue, whereas the other parts of the body are much less nutritious. The captured and dismembered prey is next chewed into a pulp and carried away. Sometimes the dismemberment and chewing of the prey are postponed until it has been carried to the nest, or the

FIG. 153.—THE WESTERN YELLOWJACKET MAKES ITS PAPER BY LAYING DOWN CONCENTRIC STRIPS OF WOOD PULP.

Each small strip, in this sample of yellowjacket nest paper, indicates one load of chewed wood pulp. Count the number of strips in one little block, remembering that this is but a small portion of the entire nest (Fig. 150), and the fabulous number of loads of wood pulp required for the making of a nest can be realized. The patchwork effect is brought about by the use of woods of different colors and different types.

procedure just outlined may be varied in other ways. At any rate, the food is eventually converted into a sort of insect "hamburger" and this is given to the larvae.

Feeding the brood. When feeding the larvae, a worker walks about over the surface of a comb carrying a pellet of the insect "hamburger" from which she bites off little bits, giving a bit to each of several larvae until the pellet is gone. The larvae are fed daily or possibly several times a day until they are fully grown.

The feeding of the larvae is not an unrequited service on the part of the workers, however, for they exact a toll from the larvae in return. The toll consists of salivary secretion. This is copious and sweet. It is given freely by the larvae, though usually not at the exact moment they are being fed. The workers, and also the queen and drones, are fond of this larval saliva, and induce its production by tapping or biting the faces of the larvae. This reciprocal feeding of the adults by the larvae is practiced by ants as well as by wasps. Bees and termites, on the other hand, do not practice it though they exchange food in other ways. Reciprocal feeding appears to be one of the strongest of the bonds holding the members of a colony of social insects together.

Renovating old cells. In addition to nest building and brood care, it is the duty of the workers to keep the nest clean and to renovate vacated cells that they may be used again for brood rearing. Soon after a new adult wasp emerges from the cocoon and leaves the cell in which it has grown up some experienced worker trims the edge of the cell and cleans it out in preparation for the new egg that will shortly be laid in it by the queen. Cells in wasp nests do not long remain idle unless they have been permanently abandoned.

This immediate reusing of vacated cells, together with the manner in which wasp nests are continually enlarged during the life of the colony, results in an interesting zonation of the brood in the combs (Fig. 155). Each comb has new cells added to its margin all the while. As soon as a new cell is large enough to hold an egg the queen lays one in it. Thus it happens that the cells around the margin of a growing comb always contain newly laid eggs. The cells a little way in from the edge are older and there has been time for the eggs in them to hatch; therefore they contain small larvae. Farther inward there are cells with older larvae. Then a point is reached where the young wasps have completed the larval stage and have spun white-topped cocoons, within which they have transformed into pupae. Still farther inward, if the comb be old enough, the pupae have completed their development and have transformed into adults. These have cut the caps from the cocoons and emerged, leaving empty cells in which the queen has again laid eggs. Inward from these, again, are cells with young larvae, cells with old larvae, and cells with cocoons. Thus there are concentric zones of brood of different ages in each comb, and as the days and weeks pass these zones continually expand and new ones start

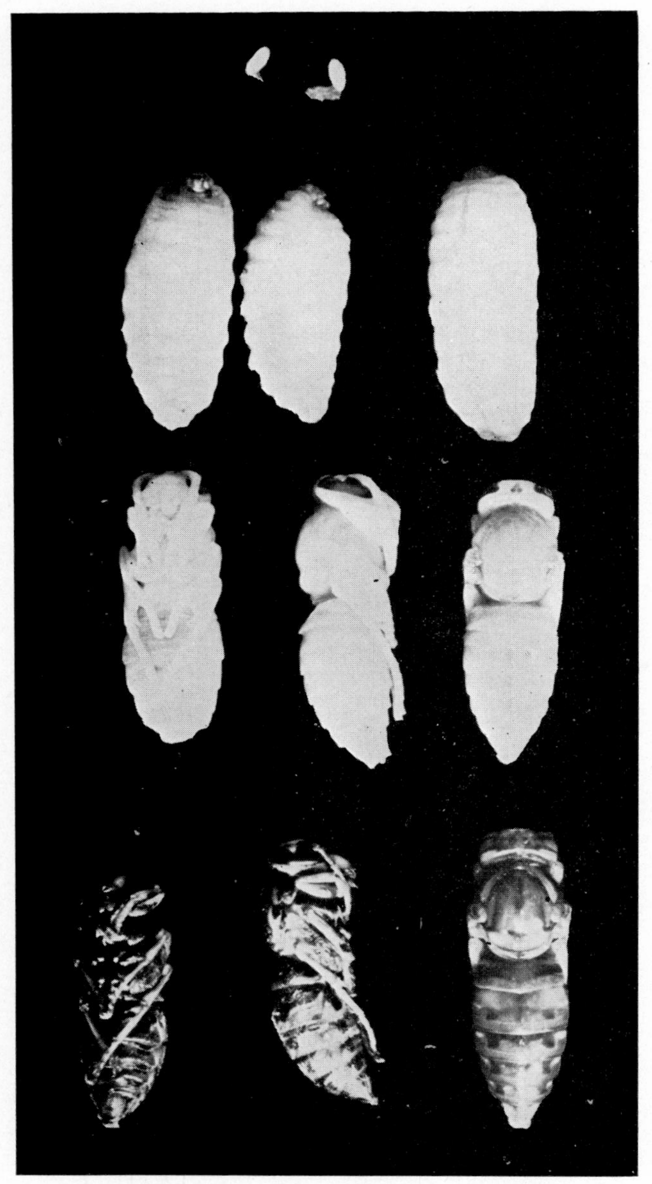

Fig. 154.—Here Are Eggs, Larvae, and Pupae of Two Ages of the Common Yellowjacket.
The eggs are at the top; below them are fully grown larvae; in the center are immature pupae; at the bottom are pupae with the dark color of the stage that just precedes the adult. All these stages occur in the cells of the paper combs.

from the center, like ripples spreading on the surface of a pool into which a stone has been dropped.

Defense of the colony. Worker wasps manifest a strong attachment for the colony and they cooperate promptly and effectively to defend it; yet, contrary to common opinion, they are not actively belligerent or spiteful. They do not look for trouble and will not wantonly attack a passer-by. They sting only on some provocation, though that provocation may be unintentional or even "fancied." A thriving colony of yellowjackets may be watched in comparative safety at close range, provided the watcher is not too conspicuous. To stand in front of an aerial nest or lean over an underground one, however, is to loom large on the horizon and to appear as a threatening object, and such behavior may lead to trouble. To stand in the traffic lanes followed by wasps coming to and from a nest may lead to a collision with a flying wasp, and such a collision is interpreted as provocation. Wasps which get into automobiles occasionally sting an occupant, but they have been excited by the collision with the automobile or they are leaned against or sat on or otherwise disturbed. If a wasp happens into your car, open a window and shoo it out; do not become panicky. The notion that wasps can sense fright in a person and will sting those who show fear is without foundation, though a person in a panic, by virtue of his excited actions, may excite the wasp also, and so lead to stinging.

Repairing damaged nests. Whenever a yellowjacket nest is damaged or partially destroyed the workers promptly set about repairing it. This is certainly true of aerial nests, and probably also of underground nests, though observations are still needed in this connection. A damaged nest is not abandoned, even if it is torn down and broken up. No matter how complete the destruction of the nest itself, any uninjured workers return to the old site and build a new nest. They usually build a faulty nest, one lacking the excellence of proportion of the original, but they do rebuild. Frequently wasp colonies endure but a short time after rebuilding because the queen is killed in the catastrophe which destroyed the original nest.

Egg laying by workers. There is a curious reaction on the part of worker wasps in connection with the rebuilding of a nest that has lost its queen-mother. If the queen is killed when the original nest is wrecked, many of the workers take up the duty of egg laying. The same thing occurs in an undisturbed nest if the queen dies or becomes greatly enfeebled. The reason for this change in function remains to be explained, but it has been observed many times. The workers,

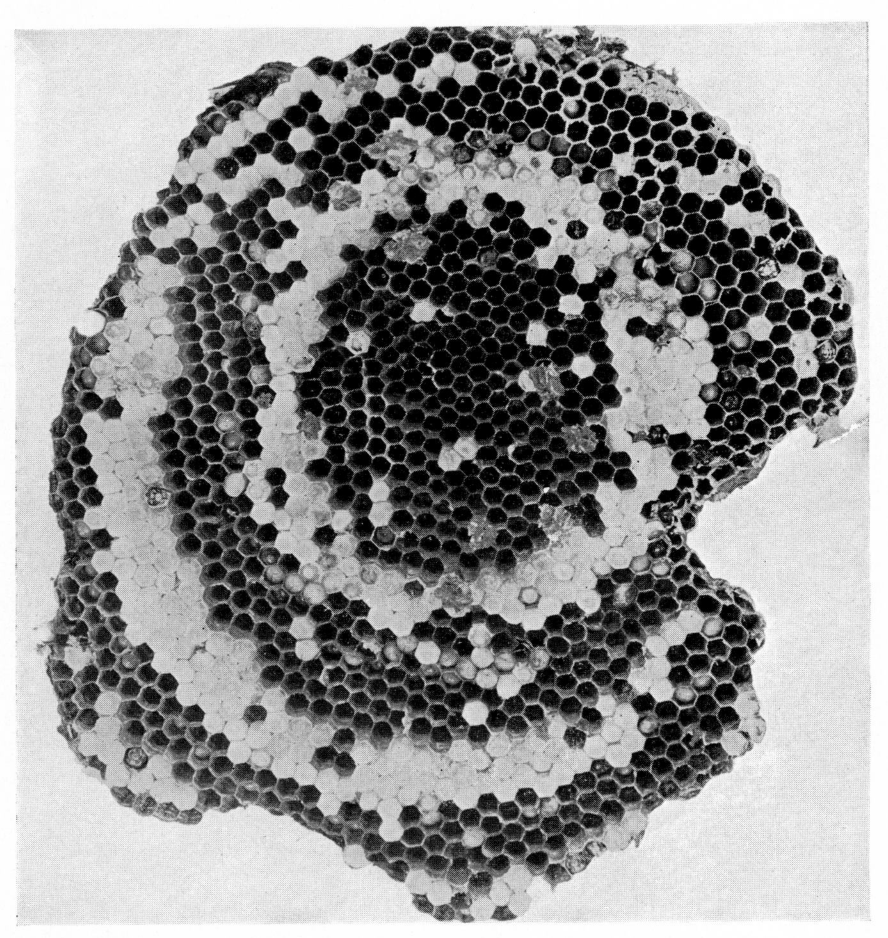

FIG. 155.—THIS OLD COMB OF THE WESTERN YELLOWJACKET SHOWS ZONES OF BROOD OF DIFFERENT AGES.

Combs of the yellowjacket are used only for the rearing of young. Throughout a long season the combs are enlarged, and eggs are laid in new cells as rapidly as they are built. In the meantime, the inner cells are built consecutively to full size, yield up their young—now grown to adulthood—and are made ready for a new brood. So it comes about that an old comb shows, in concentric circles, cells with eggs, cells with larvae, and cells that are white-capped by cocoons containing pupae. In the second zone of cocoons, on the left, the head of an emerging yellowjacket may be seen.

however, not having been mated, lay only unfertilized eggs. Nevertheless, these eggs may hatch as do unfertilized eggs laid by queens, and like those laid by queens they give rise to male wasps only. Egg-laying workers do not show the same adaptation to the problems

FIG. 156.—A YELLOWJACKET QUEEN "LIKED" THE OLD COMB OF A WASP RELATIVE AND HUNG FROM IT HER BELL-SHAPED HOME.

It probably was merely a coincidence that the yellowjacket queen chose this old *Polistes* comb as the proper place to establish her new household, but the coincidence brought together the covered home of a yellowjacket and the uncovered home of a related wasp. This new queen home would have been enlarged, eventually, into a big baggy nest, with thousands of workers, had not an accident befallen the queen.

concerning egg laying that queens do. A queen lays only one egg in a cell, but workers may lay six or eight (Fig. 152), though only one larva can possibly be reared from the lot. The presence of such supernumerary eggs in a wasp nest, therefore, indicates fairly certainly that the colony is queenless.

Activities of the queen wasp. In the early springtime when a wasp colony has its beginning, the queen performs not only the duties concerned with egg laying, but also all those usually performed by workers, for in the beginning of a colony the queen is the only inhabitant of the nest. She begins the nest alone. She gathers the wood fiber, makes the first paper comb and the nest wall, lays eggs in the cells, hunts insects with which to feed the young, and cares for the brood. It is necessary that she do all these things, for there are as yet no workers to help her. Figure 156 shows a small new nest built by a queen wasp of the genus *Dolichovespula.*

After her first brood matures—possibly not immediately but shortly thereafter—the queen gives up all these duties except that of egg laying. She no longer leaves the nest; she remains in its interior, circulating about over the combs and laying eggs in empty cells wherever she can find them, no matter whether they are newly made cells or renovated old cells from which wasps have emerged. Her job of egg laying she does well; so well, in fact, that there are few empty cells to be found in a nest, even though it be a large one.

Thousands and thousands of times, all through the spring and summer and into the autumn, the queen yellowjacket thrusts her abdomen deep into the cells to attach eggs to the walls. She may lay thus as many as twenty thousand eggs. As a result, by the end of a season she becomes literally worn out. When the nest is founded in the spring the queen is robust, her wings are complete, and her body is covered by a layer of soft hair (Fig. 158). By the end of the season, however, her appearance has changed. Her wings are frayed, often being worn down to mere stubs, little more than half their former length. The hair which covered her body has been worn off in all except protected places, and her body has become smooth and shiny (Fig. 158). Finally the old queen dies.

The drones. The male yellowjacket, or drone, has but one function, which is to mate with and fertilize a young queen. Except in orphaned colonies in which there are egg-laying workers, males are produced only toward the close of a season. This is true also of queens. The males mate with young queens from their own or from other nests, no discrimination apparently being made. A male is able to mate several times with as many queens. Whether a queen mates more than once remains to be determined. The males remain in the nest a few days after emerging. During their residence in the nest they are fed by the workers or they subsist on salivary secretion obtained from the remaining larvae. After leaving the nest the males spend their time feeding on nectar from summer and fall flowers. After a few days or weeks of feeding the males die. Not one endures until the following spring.

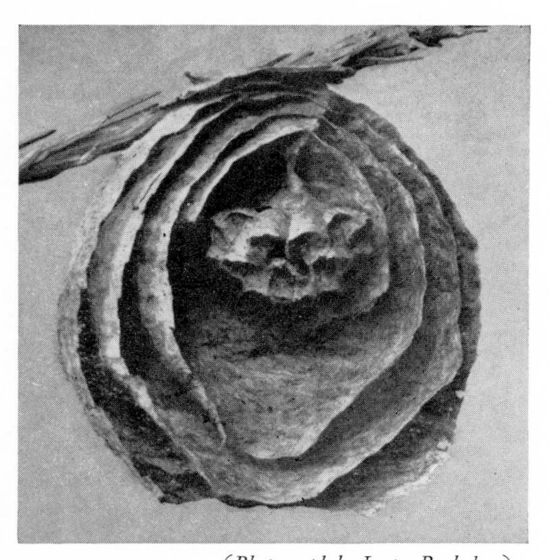

(*Photograph by Lester Brubaker.*)

FIG. 157.—A QUEEN YELLOWJACKET SUSPENDED HER NEST FROM A TWIG OF COAST REDWOOD. This queen nest made by an arboreal yellowjacket has had half of the wall removed. It shows the original comb of but a few cells made by the queen, together with the concentric envelopes of paper with which the queen surrounded the comb.

Seasonal history. Shortly after mating, the young queen yellowjackets go into hibernation. They hibernate singly in a great variety of places. Some crawl beneath loose bark on dead trees, some penetrate old beetle burrows in rotten logs and stumps, some crawl into cracks in rocks or beneath stones in fields, some burrow in the litter of leaves and twigs beneath trees, some crawl into piles of lumber or cordwood, and some crawl into the folds of old clothing hanging in sheds and attics. Whatever the location, the hibernating wasp remains in seclusion until the following spring. She folds her wings and tucks them under the sides of her abdomen, folds her antennae behind the margins of her head, and appears to go to sleep (Fig. 158). Actually she is merely dormant, her physiological processes being greatly slowed down. Oftentimes, just before becoming dormant, she seizes a fiber of wood or a shred of cloth with her mandibles and clings tightly to it. During the hibernation period she becomes quite torpid, for the weather is cold. She then may be mauled badly without making any response whatever; only when warmed does she become aroused.

With the advent of warm days in late winter or early spring the queen arouses herself and sallies forth in the sunshine to feed at the early flowers. As soon as the weather is continuously favorable she selects a site for a nest, aboveground or beneath it according to her species, and begins to build.

The first nest, the so-called *queen nest*, consists of one comb of twelve to fifteen cells surrounded by a wall of but two or three envelopes of paper, but what a beautiful thing it is (Fig. 156)! This nest is always attached firmly to some overhead support, whether the nest is built aboveground or belowground. The one shown in the figure, a nest of *Dolichovespula*, was attached to an old nest of the previous year belonging to a related wasp of the genus *Polistes*. The *Polistes* wasps build single combs and do not surround them with a wall. Underground nests are suspended from roots or from pebbles.

Until the first brood matures the colony grows slowly, but once the nest contains workers it enlarges rapidly. The first brood and the next several broods consist only of workers. Finally, however, broods are produced which consist of new queens and males. The appearance of these broods marks the beginning of the decline of a colony. In *Dolichovespula* nests this decline begins early, often by midsummer and in a few cases on the Pacific Coast as early as late June. *Vespula* nests, however, continue in full vigor until late September or longer. By the time a colony has produced its quota of males and new queens there is only a handful of workers left. The life of a worker endures but a few weeks, and they die off gradually as the young males and queens grow up. A few weeks more and the nest is entirely deserted, to be drenched with winter rains and, if it is an aerial nest, to be battered by winds until it goes to pieces. Once more the wasp population of a region is represented only by hibernating queens, awaiting the coming of another spring.

From the above account it may be seen that normally a wasp colony endures for but one season; normally it is mothered by but a single queen, whether the colony be large or small; and normally no nest is used a second season. Rarely, however, as is proved by two

FIG. 158.—AT THE TOP IS A HIBERNATING YOUNG QUEEN YELLOWJACKET THAT HAS NOT YET LAID AN EGG; BELOW IS A FRAYED AND WORN OLD QUEEN THAT HAS LAID MORE THAN TWENTY THOUSAND EGGS.

The young queen (*Vespula pensylvanica*) hibernates with antennae tucked behind her head and with wings below her abdomen. A down of fine hairs covers much of her body. The old queen (*Vespula vulgaris*) has lost the hairs, her body has been worn until smooth and shining, and her frayed wings have had more than a third of their length worn away because of her endless backing into and out of brood cells in the work of laying eggs.

nests found in California in recent years, the normal course of events is modified, and a colony lives on into a second season. One of these was a colony of the common Western Yellowjacket, *Vespula pensyl-*

vanica. It was found on the campus of Stanford University in the spring of 1923. It had been built beneath the roots of a large pine stump which evidently had protected it and postponed its dissolution. This colony lasted until early summer, a full eight months longer than the normal span of life for this species.

The other nest was more remarkable still. It was found in June, 1931, in the California State Redwood Park, Santa Cruz County. It was a nest of the Common Yellowjacket (*Vespula vulgaris*) and was in a thriving condition. Had it not been destroyed in being dug out, it would undoubtedly have endured until the end of its second season and possibly longer. This nest was enormous, measuring 4 by 3 by nearly 2½ feet. Built beneath some timberwork at the edge of a highway and protected from rain and inclement weather by the asphalt paving above it, this colony had survived its first winter in good condition. The original queen had died, but several of her daughters had taken her place. Twenty-one of these were found in looking through the nest after it was dug out, and there must have been upwards of thirty thousand workers!

Much remains to be learned about yellowjackets and their relatives. It is hoped that this account will stimulate interest in these fascinating insects and lead to new discoveries, for in the world of yellowjackets there is always something new "just around the corner."

THE LIFE OF THE TERMITE

What termites are. Thirty years ago, if a person had mentioned termites at an ordinary gathering of people, the reaction would have been a blank stare on the part of most of his hearers, for few of them would have had any notion as to what he was talking about. If the speaker had said in explanation that termites were the so-called *white ants*, understanding would have replaced the blankness on most countenances, for "white ants" were well known. At any rate, well-read persons knew of them. They were one of the scourges of the tropics which ate the floors out of houses and burrowed into furniture from below in an insidious manner and in a few days so riddled the wood inside, though never disturbing the exterior, that tables broke under the weight of food and dishes placed upon them, and chairs crashed to the floor when one sat upon them. Nearly everyone knew something about "white ants," for they were mentioned in innumerable books and articles written by travelers who returned from the tropics. Thank God there were none of them in this happy and civilized land!

Time, however, brings many changes. During the past thirty years termites have been much in the public eye, increasingly so in very recent years, until the word *termite* has become almost commonplace. It is quite possible that more persons now are familiar with "termites" than are acquainted with "white ants." This is true at least in the southern two-thirds of the United States, for it has become apparent that we *do* have termites in this land of ours, and lots of them. Their work is frequently seen in damaged building foundations, though relatively few persons, aside from entomologists and the pest control men who undertake to repair termite damage, have seen the insects themselves.

Termites (Figs. 112, 159, 160, and 189) are not ants, white or otherwise. The only reason they ever were confused with ants is that individually they are small and live a social life in large and populous colonies. Termites stand close to the bottom of the scale of insect life, judged by their anatomical features, whereas ants stand close to the top. Termites and ants, then, could hardly be farther apart. Termites are more closely related to cockroaches than to any other existing insects, but they are not in the cockroach order. Instead, they constitute, as was indicated in Chapter XIII, an order by themselves, the order Isoptera. Isoptera means "equal wings" and signifies that whenever a termite has wings (Fig. 112) the four wings are almost identical in structure. In ants the hind wings are much smaller than the forewings. Termites have broad thick waists like those of cockroaches and grasshoppers, whereas ants have slender waists like those of wasps. Furthermore, termites undergo only the gradual type of metamorphosis, whereas ants undergo complete metamorphosis. It is well, then, that the term *white ant*, obviously a misnomer, be abandoned.

The origin of termites. The termites of the United States, contrary to common belief, are not foreign insects which have accidentally been imported. They are native species which evolved right where they now occur. Many kinds are native to this country, several dozen at least. The fact that they did not attract general attention earlier is explained partly by the behavior of the termites, but even more by the behavior of man. Termites feed on wood or on materials containing woody substance. Before this country was settled, the food supply of termites was limited largely to dead stumps, logs, fallen branches (Fig. 41), and twigs in natural woodland and along watercourses. They ate buried leaves, the dead roots of weeds, and weed stems, but their available food supplies were far less extensive and in consequence the termites became much more localized than they are today. There were doubtless large areas of treeless country which had no termites at all, but the great quantities of lumber made from trees and stacked in lumberyards to cure, the innumerable dead stumps and root systems resulting from lumbering operations and from the clearing of land for agriculture, the millions of boxes and other wooden articles that find a resting place on the ground, the conveniently spaced telegraph and telephone poles, railroad ties and fence posts, the bridge timbers, and the hundreds of thousands of wooden buildings put up by man, have tremendously increased the food supplies and the nesting sites of termites. The termites have responded "enthusiastically" to man's unwitting beneficence, and have multiplied greatly.

Types and kinds of termites. The termites native to the United States fall into three rather easily defined classes on the basis of their moisture requirements and the relation of their colonies to the soil. These types are the *damp-wood termites*, the *dry-wood termites*, and the *subterranean termites*. There are several species of each class. The illustrations accompanying this chapter however, show only the Common Damp-wood Termite, *Zootermopsis angusticollis*. They are more abundant in the more southerly and western states, however, than elsewhere, and two states, North Dakota and South Dakota, as yet are not known to possess any at all. Damp-wood termites constitute the most primitive type. As their name implies, they require wood with a relatively high percentage of moisture for the development of their colonies. They are absent from the drier and more desert parts of the country. They construct their galleries wholly or almost wholly in wood, not digging in the soil to any considerable extent. Dry-wood termites are of medium size but otherwise are similar to the damp-wood termites. The moisture requirement of dry-wood termites is relatively low. In consequence, they are able to develop colonies in wood that has no contact with the soil or is remote from the soil and becomes quite dry in summer, such as timbers in the roofs and walls of buildings, or dead branches high in trees. Dry-wood termites are more abundant and troublesome in Southern California and other parts of the Southwest than elsewhere. Subterranean termites average the smallest of the three groups. Their moisture requirements vary, but usually are intermediate between those of damp-wood termites and dry-wood termites. Subterranean termites are the most widespread and destructive of all that occur in the United States. They develop the most populous colonies, constructing more or less extensive galleries in the soil. These they extend into wood that is wholly or partially buried or wood that is in contact with the soil or in close proximity to it.

The castes of termites. Like the ants, the social wasps, and the social bees, termite individuals are differentiated into several physical types or castes, each of which is specialized for the performance of certain functions in the colony. The following principal castes occur among the termites native to the United States (Figs. 112 and 160): *reproductives* ("kings" and "queens"), *workers*, and *soldiers*. Each caste consists of two or more subcastes. There are *primary* and *supplementary*, or *substitute*, *reproductives*. Workers exist in the form of *large*, or *major*, *workers*, and *small*, or *minor*, *workers*. Soldiers exist in three forms: *major soldiers*, *intermediate soldiers*, and *minor soldiers*. Not all the subcastes develop in any one colony, though as many as six may be present in a single colony of subterranean termites. An even larger number is stated to occur in a single colony of certain tropical termites.

Both sexes are represented equally in all the castes and subcastes, and both sexes are equally long-lived. There are thus no drones among the reproductives as there are among the bees, wasps, and ants. King termites live as long as queen termites, engaging with the latter in all the activities falling to the lot of reproductives. There are, also, both male and female workers, and male and female soldiers.

The reproductives, except for a short time while new colonies are being established, take little part in the work of the colony. They devote themselves to the business of reproduction. In large colonies, at least in the more highly evolved species, the reproductives live deep within the colony nest in specially constructed "royal chambers."

Primary (also called first-form) reproductives are the only individuals in a termite colony which become at all dark colored, or acquire wings or fully developed compound eyes. The wings are retained until the end of the brief dispersal flight which closes the stay of the newly matured primary reproductives in the parent colony. The winged state may last for several weeks, but the wings are used only once and then generally for just a few minutes. As long as they possess wings, primary reproductives are known as *alates*, from the Latin word *ala*, a wing. At the close of the dispersal flight, the alates as a rule spread their wings at a peculiar angle and rub them against some object, or against the ground, and break them

Fig. 159.—This Royal Pair of Termites Had Long Gauzy Wings Shortly before This Picture Was Taken (Figs. 112 and 113) but Now, Having Made Their Only Flight from Their Respective Homes (Termites Use Their Wings but Once), They Have Broken Off Their Wings, Chosen Each Other as Mates, and Are Ready Together to Found a New Colony.

Unlike the short-lived males of other social insects, termite males are as long-lived and as active as the females. Also, they are almost identical in appearance with the females. Those males which attain sexual maturity, like the male of this royal pair, become "kings" and with their queenly consorts share in the founding of new colonies. Thereafter the kings and queens live in constant association in the royal chambers of the colonies. Males which do not become sexually mature, and females as well, develop into workers and soldiers.

off. The break occurs at a special joint close to the body. The termites are now said to be *dealated*. The dealated individuals (Figs. 112, 113, and 159) pair, and each pair seeks a favorable location for the establishment of a new colony. With the founding of a new colony each pair of dealated primary reproductives becomes the "king" and "queen" of the new colony. A complete list of the functions of the primary reproductives includes reproduction (their major function), dispersal of the species (by means of the dispersal flight), the finding of new colony sites, the founding of new colonies, and the feeding of the first brood of worker young until they become large enough to assume the work of the colony. Most of these functions will be discussed later in the chapter.

Sometimes a termite colony is "ruled" by supplementary, or substitute, reproductives. The members of this caste never possess functional wings or fully developed compound eyes, though they often have wing pads and partially developed compound eyes. They consist of two types, *secondary* and *tertiary;* and they develop from nearly mature individuals which originally were destined to become workers but were stimulated by conditions in the colony to mature their reproductive organs and instincts. Secondary (also called *second-form*) reproductives (Fig. 112) develop wing pads and often incomplete compound eyes as well. They also darken in color to a tan or a pale brown. They can be recognized easily. Tertiary (also called *third-form*) reproductives develop no eyes and no wing pads, except perhaps the merest stubs, but they darken in color. Otherwise they look exactly like workers.

Supplementary reproductives appear in termite colonies under any one of three conditions. When a colony is so enormous that the outlying portions are remote from the royal chamber and the influence of the primary king and queen is feeble in these portions, supplementaries are developed. Whenever one or both members of the primary royal pair die, supplementary reproductives develop to take their places. If a colony becomes accidentally divided, the separated parts which become isolated from one another develop supplementary reproductives and continue their existence as separate colonies. The new colonies arising in this manner are said to be founded by *fragmentation.*

Supplementary reproductives do not engage in dispersal flights; they do not found new colonies in the manner of primary reproductives; and they do not feed or give any care to the young of a colony. Otherwise their functions are the same as those of primary reproductives.

Worker termites are, without exception among our species, pale, whitish or cream-colored, soft-bodied creatures with a very immature appearance. They never develop wings or even wing pads and never have eyes. Except for size, then, fully grown workers have the same general characteristics that they had when they left the eggs. Heads and legs are the only hard parts which the workers possess. The mandibles are especially hard, for it is with these that the work of the colony is done.

Once they have passed their brief period of immaturity, it is the duty of the workers to perform all the work of the colony except its defense. The work includes the following activities: (1) the excavation of galleries and runways in the soil and in the wood which serves as food supply for the colony, including a royal chamber for the king and queen and brood chambers for the eggs whenever such are necessary; (2) the sealing of all crevices and holes in surrounding soil and wood which might permit the access of enemies or the loss of needed moisture from the nest; (3) the building of exploratory tubes of earth, sand, or wood dust above the soil surface to permit the colony to reach new supplies of wood for food, or new sources of moisture; (4) the establishment of new colonies when these are founded by fragmentation; (5) the feeding of very young termites of all castes and of adult soldiers and reproductives; (6) the making of openings from the nest to the outside whenever these are needed to permit a dispersal flight of alates, or whenever it becomes necessary to eject from the colony any quantity of excretal wood pellets; and (7) the grooming of one another and of the reproductives and soldiers. Workers are developed as a distinct caste in most species of termites. Our damp-wood termites, however, have no distinct worker caste. The work in their colonies is done by the nymphs of the other castes. These working nymphs are sometimes called *toilers* to distinguish them from the true workers.

Soldier termites have bodies much like those of workers, but their legs and heads, especially the mandibles (except in certain species the soldiers of which have small mandibles), are much larger and harder (Fig. 160). The sole duty of soldier termites is to defend the colony.

The only enemies of any consequence that termites have in this country are the ants which nest in the same soil or wood masses in which the termites live. The ants do not actively search for termites, but in extending their own colonies they occasionally cut or dig their way into termite galleries. Then an alarm is sounded and the soldier termites move into the gallery where the breach has been made and oppose the ants. Sounding an alarm is accomplished in the following manner: The first termites to be encountered by the ants (or for that matter to be disturbed in any other way) rapidly shake their heads and bodies up and down, rattling them against the walls of their galleries. Other termites "take up the cry," so to speak, and rattle also, and the excitement quickly spreads through the colony. Whether termites hear the rattling sounds they produce or merely feel the vibrations, no one knows, nor does anyone understand how the soldiers "know" just where the ants are entering the colony.

Any invasion by ants is likely to be stopped rather quickly, with the loss of only a few termite victims, for the openings made by ants are generally small and one, or at most only a few, termite soldiers are capable of blocking one of them completely. An ant can do little to harm the hard, horny head of a soldier termite. Besides, the reckless ant which blunders too close to the great gaping and snapping jaws of a soldier termite may get its head crushed or its body cut in two.

In addition to powerful jaws, the soldiers of many species of termites have peculiar glands which secrete a sticky fluid that acts like "tanglefoot" and is used to disable ants. This termite tanglefoot is discharged through a pore on the "forehead" of the termite soldier. In certain tropical species which have specialized in this mode of warfare, mandibles have been abandoned, and the discharge pores of the glands are found at the tips of long tubular outgrowths from the head. These, veritable "tanglefoot guns," shoot the gummy secretion at the invading ants. Among the termites of the United States, only certain species of subterranean termites make use of this type of warfare.

How new termite colonies are established. As has been stated briefly already, there are two methods by which new colonies of termites are founded. The more spectacular, and probably the more usual, method is that which follows the dispersal flight of alates from the parent nest. It may be called the *normal* method. The second method is that of fragmentation, or the accidental breaking up of existing colonies.

Termite dispersal flights occur at various times depending on the species and on weather conditions. Flights of subterranean termites usually occur in the forenoon of an autumn or spring day, just following a rain or even between showers, while the surface soil is wet and the air humid. Damp-wood termites often fly at dusk, or earlier if the day be cloudy or the sky overcast. High atmospheric humidity is essential. When conditions are just right, worker termites open "doorways" to the outside air and the termites come forth. A few workers and soldiers come out and wander about near by, but the

(Photograph by Lester Brubaker.)

Fig. 160.—Here Are Termites of Different Ages and Castes at Home, in Burrows Which They Have Excavated in Solid Wood.

This picture, taken through the glass wall of the artificial termite nest illustrated in Fig. 189, and believed to be the most remarkable photograph of termites yet taken, shows in one view a majority of the types of behavior distinctive of termite social life. The large individual with huge dark head and dark legs, in the upper right, is a mature soldier; resting near the center is a pale-bodied individual which has recently molted and is in the transition from worker to soldier; below the latter and somewhat to the left are two toilers (see text, page 284) with down-bent heads, eating wood; close to the bottom edge of the figure a larger individual is eating the abdomen of a termite which has died; immediately to the right, and also near the upper left-hand corner, are large nymphs with wing pads; a medium-sized toiler is licking the middle leg of the large soldier to the evident satisfaction of the latter; a small toiler is similarly grooming a large one to the right of center; and another small toiler is soliciting food by mouth from the same large toiler. Over much of left fifth of the figure, and outlining the galleries at various places, may be seen the smooth gray plastering of excrement, originally semiliquid, which is used by the termites for closing chinks in the wood and thus sealing the galleries against outside air. The granular material visible in the same areas, some of which is in the form of definite pellets, consists in part of less liquid excrementitious matter and in part of earthy matter carried up from the soil beneath the nest.

alates, the "princes" and "princesses" of the termite world, crowd or even literally jam the doorways in their eagerness to leave the parental home. By twos and threes, by tens and dozens, they take to the air. Their actual mating instincts are unaroused as yet, but a few minutes later, stimulated in some magical way by the exercise of flight, these instincts begin to function. The flying termites drop to the ground and break off their wings. Each male then seeks the nearest female, evidently attracted by an odor she produces, and together the pair set out on a search for a homesite. In this the female leads, the male following immediately behind.

During the dispersal flights enormous numbers of primary reproductives are eaten by other animals. Termite flight is feeble and the termites are quite incapable of any resistance. Birds of many species, lizards, toads, frogs, and various predatory insects and spiders gorge themselves on termites while the flight and pairing last. Fortunate is the pair of termites that escapes this onslaught of hungry animals.

The termite pair that does escape finds a soft spot in the soil, a niche beneath a stone, a chip or a fallen leaf, a crevice behind a loose slab of bark on a dead tree, a loose shingle on a house roof, a space between a window casing and the stucco or rustic that covers a house, or a place where a door threshold or porch floor overhangs a wooden step. Whatever the place selected, the termite pair, now the prospective "king" and "queen" of a new kingdom, dig themselves a small chamber which is the beginning of a new termite nest. This they seal off against outside air, which may be too dry, and against enemies.

Within the chamber mating occurs. The queen lays a number of eggs, each of which hatches into a tiny nymph that is quite unable at first to feed itself. Its jaws are too weak to chew wood. Besides, it does not yet possess any of the tiny, one-celled animals (Protozoa) and the one-celled plants (Bacteria) which throng the intestine of an older termite and without which the termite cannot digest the wood it eats. For the first few days or weeks, therefore, the young nymphs are fed by the king and queen. Their food consists of regurgitated and partially digested wood from the parents' stomachs. Such food is called *stomodeal* food (from a Greek work referring to the mouth). As the young termites grow they begin to eat wood themselves. They also eat a liquid substance given off from the anal opening of the parents, together with pellets of incompletely digested wood emitted as excreta by the parent termites. Such food, coming as it does from the anal opening, is termed *proctodeal* food (from a Greek word referring to the anus). With the proctodeal food, the termite nymphs acquire the protozoans and the bacteria which they need in their intestines to make them independent of their parents in the matter of food.

As soon as the young termites are able completely to feed and care for themselves, they take over the work of the colony. During the remainder of their growing period, and thereafter as long as they live, they perform all the various and sundry tasks which fall to the lot of workers. The queen lays more and yet more eggs, gradually increasing the rate of egg laying as more and more workers are available to care for the young and to enlarge the colony habitation. Not until many workers have been produced does any termite nymph grow up to be a soldier. Then gradually soldiers appear, one by one. They never become numerous, however, in comparison with the workers, for one soldier represents adequate defense for many workers.

Colony founding by fragmentation, as has been suggested, results from accidental causes. A gopher or other burrowing animal may dig through a subterranean termite nest, completely isolating one part of the colony from the rest. Other causes of fragmentation are the moving of trees with boxes of soil around their roots, the moving of termite-infested lumber or of houses by man, and the breaking and transporting of tree limbs, logs, or other infested driftwood by streams in times of high water.

Whatever the cause of fragmentation, the termites in each division seal off the damaged galleries, and life goes on much as before. The only change is that, in the absence of a king and queen in the severed fragments of the colony, supplementary kings and queens are developed from certain of the larger nymphs.

The ease with which new termite colonies may be established by fragmentation simplifies the problem of the student of termite biology. Artificial termite nests, such as that shown in Fig. 189, wherein nearly every aspect of termite behavior may be observed under practically normal conditions, may be set up with the greatest ease. The making of such a nest and the establishment of a termite colony in it are described in Chapter XVIII. No device for the keeping and rearing of insects known to the authors will provide more hours of fascinating and worth-while experiences at so little cost than one of these artificial termite nests.

Termite foods and feeding activity. The principal food of termites, as already stated, is wood. Termites make use not only of the wood of trees and shrubs, obviously the most abundant supply, but of woody substance in whatever form it occurs, whether it be "wood" in the usual sense or not. Every fibrous or hard grass or weed stem, every stringy or woody root or other vegetable growth, every stiff or leathery leaf contains some woody tissues, and such tissues, after the succulent parts have died and dried or decayed away, is good food for termites. So, depending on abundance, availability, and circumstance, any plant growth that contains woody tissues or any manufactured product made from plant growth may be utilized by termites. In the ability to feed on wood, thus broadly conceived, lies one of the important reasons for the success of termites as social animals, for few organic materials are as abundant as wood and none is more continuously available.

There are, however, certain limitations on the nature of the woody materials that may be eaten by termites. Some woods, such as the heartwood of the Redwood trees of California, are inedible to termites, apparently because they contain oils or other chemical principles poisonous to them. Such woods are strictly avoided by termites, though the lighter colored and immature sapwood of Redwoods is eaten freely.

Termites also possess food requirements that are not satisfied with wood alone. Wood supplies an abundance of energy-yielding substances, but it is deficient in proteins, the principal source of nitrogen for animals. The termites obtain these from fungi; it is also necessary, therefore, that the wood be infected by fungi of some sort. The infection need not be extensive, not even enough to be recognizable to the unaided eye, but fungi in some amount must be present. Termites will not thrive on wood that is absolutely free of them.

The potentialities of termites in bringing about the breakdown or decay of vegetable materials and the return of their substance to the soil and the air is obviously great in view of the wide range of plant materials which they consume. When engaged in effecting this decay process in woodlands, along streamsides and roadsides, and in fields and meadows generally, termites, along with other organisms causing decay, render a beneficial service of great value to life on the earth, including man. Termite potentialities in the destruction of materials of vegetable origin which man desires to preserve, obviously, are equally great, and from a human point of view such destruction is anything but a service. How man can retain the valuable services of termites and at the same time prevent destruction of his properties is explained in Chapter XVI.

The consumption of woody substance by termites, particularly of "wood" in the usual sense, cannot be appreciated or understood by a simple recital of the fact that termites eat wood. Most animals cannot digest wood, so there must be something peculiar about termites that confers upon them this extraordinary digestive ability denied to so many other creatures. Just what this peculiarity amounts to is not yet completely understood. But we do know that the intestines of most termite species literally swarm with hosts of protozoans—squirming, wriggling, one-celled animals of several species—and with equally or even more numerous bacteria. In fact, the intestine of a termite is a combination botanical garden and zoological park, and in some way this makes possible the digestion of wood. At any rate, if a termite be deprived of its intestinal inhabitants it suffers from malnutrition and dies. If a nymphal termite be prevented from securing a stock of protozoans and bacteria it fails to grow and develop.

It would appear that the protozoans and bacteria bring about the digestion of the wood, or its partial digestion, and thus make available food for themselves and for the termites. At the same time the termites, in possessing ample intestines of an acceptable type, and in eating wood in the first place, make life possible for these particular protozoans and bacteria, for they exist nowhere except in termites.

The strange dependence of termites on their numerous intestinal inhabitants raises the interesting question as to how individual termites secure their stock of protozoans and bacteria, and where, as a group of insects, they got them originally. The answer to the former question is known, that to the latter can only be blindly guessed at. It so happens that wood is only incompletely digested in one passage through the alimentary canal of a termite. The ejected excretal pellets, therefore, are eaten again. With them, the needed protozoans are secured.

Termites of all castes and of all ages, except the very young, eat numbers of the excretal pellets. They also consume more or less of the liquid proctodeal food produced from the anal opening, as was described in the case of young termite nymphs. The protozoans and bacteria are obtained in both these kinds of food.

But the story is not yet complete. Whenever a termite dies the other termites eat all the consumable parts of its body (Fig. 160). Thus, in still another way do termites secure their protozoan and bacterial inhabitants. The inedible parts of dead termites, the mandibles and skulls, are then plastered over with liquid excrement and debris of various sorts and so, in a sense, are buried.

All termites also, after the manner of the very young, and regardless of caste or age, solicit and eat stomodeal food produced by others. One final kind of food requires mention. This consists of fatty exudations given off from the skin of every termite. These exudations are much sought after by other termites. Hence termites spend much time apparently "grooming" one another. In all probability the grooming is done more to secure the exudates than as an altruistic service.

Constructional activities of termites. The excavation of galleries in soil and wood has been described briefly or alluded to earlier in this chapter, but certain facts and relationships omitted thus far remain to be presented.

Termite galleries serve their inhabitants in several ways. They provide shelter from the inhospitable factors in the nonliving environment and protection from living enemies. Termites shun light and avoid exposure to the air outside their galleries. Experiment has proved, however, that they are actually injured by neither light nor air. What they must avoid is heat and dryness; and where light is, and moving air, there moisture is likely to be too scarce and variable, and temperatures often too high, for termite survival. So termites, which are blind, are able by a sensitiveness, residing perhaps in the general body surface, to distinguish between light and darkness. They are equipped, moreover, with an instinct which leads them to seek darkness, and thus to find habitats in which the air is more humid than elsewhere and more uniform in its humidity. At the same time protection from other animals which would eat them is assured. A hidden habitation of excavated galleries is not enough. Termites seal their galleries against outside air. With wood particles chewed off the nearest source, with the powdery frass left in the galleries previously made by other wood-boring insects, with soil particles carried up from below, with secretions from their own mouths, and with liquid excrement the worker termites close up cracks and crannies of every sort, sharply outlining their own galleries and sealing out other living things as well as outside air.

The result of the nest-sealing behavior is an "air-conditioned" system of galleries wherein the relative humidity is always high and often close to the saturation point. Termites, in fact, "invented" air conditioning ages before it was dreamed of by man. The supply of moisture is obtained from the wood through which the galleries extend or from the soil beneath. Only a low moisture content in the wood itself is needed to provide almost complete saturation for enclosed air. Termite galleries, therefore, serve also as conduits through which needed moisture is diffused to all parts of the colony home.

Enlarged portions of the termite galleries serve as the royal chambers in which live the kings and queens attended by many workers to feed and groom them and to remove the numerous eggs as these are laid. Smaller chambers serve as depositories for the eggs until they hatch and later as nurseries for the young nymphs.

Termite galleries serve as exploratory channels or mines, protecting the termites during their searches for new sources of wood or moisture. For purposes of exploration, subterranean termites excavate galleries for long distances through the soil. In addition to excavating galleries, termites (the subterranean species at least) build enclosed passageways aboveground. These take the form of tubes or towers made of soil particles, frass, or wood dust, cemented together with a glue-like salivary secretion. The tubes or towers may be branched or unbranched. They are built upward from the soil over the brick or stone or concrete foundations of buildings, or over or around ventilating pipes and plumbing until wood is reached. The towers often are erected straight into the air beneath buildings until contact is made with flooring or with timbers supporting the floor. Occasionally, for no apparent reason unless it be that the wood is excessively dry or hard, tubes are built across the surface of timbers and only shallow grooves eaten out of the wood beneath. At times, too, tubes like stalactites are built downward from flooring or joists in an apparent attempt to reach the soil.

The various tubes, towers, and "stalactites" also appear to be exploratory devices made in a search for additional food supplies or moisture whenever a shortage develops. Certain subterranean termites of arid and semiarid regions, on the other hand, build tubes for a different though related purpose. These species feed to a considerable extent on weeds, grass, and other low-growing herbage, either before or after it is dead. When a particular plant has been selected to be eaten, these termites cover it during the night with a shell of agglutinated soil particles. Within the protection afforded by this shell the termites later eat out the plant completely.

CONCLUSION

In closing this account of social life among the insects, certain contrasts may be pointed out between the two types—yellowjackets and termites—chosen to illustrate the subject. Owing to differences in the nature of their food supplies, their building methods, and the longevity of the reproductive individuals, yellowjacket colonies are seasonal in character, each colony passing through a definite and particular sequence of changes from its founding to its dissolution, whereas, termite colonies exhibit relatively little seasonal change. What change they do undergo consists mainly in retiring deeper into wood or soil (or the reverse movement) in adjustment to changes in temperature or moisture, together with increase or decrease in the general rate of all activities. A second contrast is noteworthy. As a result of the capacity of termites for developing supplementary reproductives, termite colonies are perennial and, potentially at least, immortal. Barring accident or the exhaustion of food supplies or moisture, there seems to be no reason why a termite colony should ever decline.

This survey of social life among the insects may appear to have been accorded more than its share of space in comparison with other topics. Actually, in the light of its possibilities, the treatment has been brief. The authors commend the study of insect social life to anyone who would banish boredom and find variety and freshness in living; it is a subject as fascinating as it is complex, a subject so filled with surprises and so fraught with unsolved problems as to seem inexhaustible!

CHAPTER XV

THE VALUE OF INSECTS

HUMAN society as now constituted could not exist without insects! If the world were suddenly deprived of insects, there soon would be no more fruit of most kinds; melons, beans, peas, and many other vegetables would disappear from the market; when the present surplus had been exhausted, there would be no more silk or cotton; clovers and alfalfas would gradually cease to exist, for there would be no more seeds to replace the present plantings. Nearly every land bird would disappear; most fresh-water fishes would go from the streams. The soil would suffer through lack of tilling by burrowing insects; there would be no honey, no beeswax, and several pretty dyes would be missing in the woolen apparel of that insectless day. And in a new world with many dying animals there would be no insect scavengers to help clean them up!

And, presuming that the human could adjust himself to a situation wherein grasses supplied the chief vegetable foods and many trees were gradually disappearing, there would be, in that world, no butterflies to delight us with their color, and no humming bees to fascinate us with their industry.

All this is by way of saying that an assemblage of animals so vast and so diversified as insects has developed interrelations with nearly everything that exists on the earth. In fact, the evolution of insects and the evolution of most of the higher plants and many of the terrestrial animals have gone forward hand in hand. Practically all plants with conspicuous flowers—and this includes most flowers as we normally think of them— have developed those features which attract the insects that pollinate them, with fertilization resulting. Several whole families of birds have become adapted to eat insects exclusively, and many others must have insects to feed their young.

Even seed-eating birds would be deprived of many forms of seeds if insects failed to pollinate the flowers that produce them; and the best control of "harmful" insects does not consist of birds or even human agencies, but of the parasites and the predators among the insects themselves. In the complexity of the "web of nature" the insects have

FIG. 161.—THE POLLEN-LADEN HIND LEGS OF THIS BEE GUARANTEE THAT MANY FLOWERS WILL BEAR FRUITS.

In the work of gathering pollen it was necessary for this bee to visit many flowers. Thereby some of the pollen was brushed onto the stigmas of flowers and they were thus pollinated. Since flowers must be pollinated to produce fruits and to perpetuate many of the plants upon which man depends, and since many flowers depend upon bees and other insects for pollination, man is heavily indebted to insects.

evolved into a position that makes them of vast importance to the human race. We bewail the "harm" that insects do, but we could not do without them!

Insects and plants. The most important role played by insects in the scheme of things involves their relationships to plants. It is true that plants serve as the basic food supply for insects, as they do for human beings; but the insects reciprocate by making many of the plants possible. It is somewhat surprising to consider that except for insects there never would have been a poppy! Except for insects

FIG. 162.—EXCEPT FOR INSECTS THERE WOULD BE NO FAIRY MOTH TO "STAND" IN THE AIR BEFORE A THISTLE BLOSSOM AND SIP NECTAR THROUGH A TUBE.

For every child—and for grownups too—no fairy could be lovelier than this White-lined Sphinx at a thistle-blossom meal.

there never would have been an orange! Except for insects there never would have been an apple! The dependence on insects for pollination—the carrying of pollen from anthers to stigmas of flowers—has developed in many plant families. Grasses and conifers are pollinated by the action of the wind; but lilies, roses, mustards, peas, mints, and sunflowers, to mention but a few flower families, require insects. Incidentally, many of the things we eat are members of these families. And so to insects we owe most of our fruits and many vegetables.

A flower is beautiful because of insects. It possesses showy petals in addition to stamens and pistils because there are insects. In the development to attract insects, flowers have produced those things which make them, incidentally, attractive also to man. The colors of their sepals and petals, the odors they produce, are devices which attract insects. Flower shapes are further developments adapting them to special kinds of insects. A petunia has odors which attract insects, and a deep tube so that only the ong-tongued butterflies and hawk moths can pollinate them (Fig. 162). There is nectar at the base of the Red Clover blossom, but the tube is narrow and deep so that only bumblebees can get it. Thank insects for beauty and for variety in flowers.

The cotton blossom requires an insect to pollinate it before it will produce its boll of cotton. To insects, therefore, we are indebted for cotton fiber and the multitudinous things made of cotton.

Insect products. As has been noted, insects indirectly make possible many of the foods we eat. Insects also produce directly some of the foods that we utilize, and several other products that have a commercial value. In this connection one thinks at once of honey, a typical insect product. Honey is concentrated and preserved nectar from flowers. In its gathering, the Honeybee performs a double service. The nectar is produced by plants to attract bees in the first place. By attracting bees the plant secures the cross-pollination that is necessary for the production of its fruits. In return for this service the plant gives up its nectar. The bees make honey of the nectar and we human beings rob the bees of a portion of the result of their labors. Thus, we are indebted to the bees not only for honey but for the bigger service they do the flowers, and us, in its collection.

A product of insects, that for centuries has been a matter of great import to milady, is silk. In fact, its production has become so important to the Japanese, for instance, that the loss of its revenue would cause that nation almost irreparable damage. And to modern human beings a lack of silk would necessitate a radical revision of habits of dress. Now, all this activity is due to the product of a caterpillar, the larva of the silk-moth (Fig. 38). When full grown, the larva exudes from the salivary glands of its mouth a long delicate thread of glutinous fluid that hardens immediately into silk. With this the silk-worm spins a cocoon in which to pupate. If the silk is to be used by human beings, the caterpillar that pupates in this silken cocoon is never allowed to emerge as a moth, for in doing so it would break the threads it has spun about itself. For its silk, therefore, man sacrifices the insect. And so the pupae in the cocoons are killed in hot water or by steam—some twenty-five thousand of them to make a single pound of silk. What we owe to silk-worms becomes apparent when it is noted that to produce the several hundred million dollars' worth of silk marketed each year some fifty to one hundred million pounds[1] of the threads are unwound from cocoons.

In addition to honey and silk, the best known of insect products utilized by man, there are several others of importance. Shellac is made from a product secreted by certain scale-insects of India. Beeswax is the secretion from the underside of the Honeybee's abdomen. Cochineal and crimson lake are pigments made by drying the bodies of certain cactus scale-insects of the American tropics; though these pigments have been supplanted largely by aniline dyes, they are still used for food decorations and cosmetics. Galls caused by insects have been used for making tannic acid to tan leather, and also for inks and dyes.

Insects as food for other animals. We are constantly reminded that birds are the gardeners' and the farmers' friends because most of them eat insects. Here for a moment reverse your idea and thank the insects for the birds! Bird lovers, and that includes all of us, need to be reminded that, though birds are said to assist in holding insects in check, there would be, on the other hand, few birds if there were no insects! Insects are absolutely necessary for many birds. Even weed seeds, as has been noted, would be greatly reduced in amount for seed-eating birds if insect pollinators were removed. Much, much of the great evolution that birds have shown has been built upon the widespread occurrence of insects as food. As a matter of fact, birds eat

[1] C. L. Metcalf and W. P. Flint, *Fundamentals of Insect Life*, McGraw-Hill Book Company, Inc., New York, 1932.

insects without discriminating between those insects which might be of benefit to man and those which might be harmful to his products; so the "good" that birds do is about balanced by their "mistakes" in insect catching. The debt we owe to insects for our birds becomes the more impressive when this is considered.

The fresh-water angler is indebted to insects for his sport, for most fresh-water fish depend directly or indirectly upon insect food.

Fig. 163.—Only Insects Are Capable of the Magic That Will Change a Woolly Bear Caterpillar into a Snow-white Princess.

This lovely Acraea Moth was once a Woolly Bear caterpillar. It spun a cocoon, pulling out all its hairs to make part of the covering; and then, without any Aladdin's lamp to help, it emerged again—this time an insect jewel!

Other fishermen than the sportsmen are in debt to insects. Many fish in Middle West markets come there because there is a large group of aquatic insects.

Insects and insects. In the vast stretches of time in which they have evolved, insects have built up interrelationships with many other living things. And this is more true of the relationships among the insects themselves than among any other group. The fundamental food habit of insects, it is true, is that of the plant-eater, the vegetarian. Though this vegetarian habit among insects may send them out to seek nectar and so cause them to pollinate flowering plants, the habit also causes insects to do the things that are harmful to man. But the best control of the plant-eater among the insects is not a bird, not a spray, not a fumigant, but other insects. For every insect except the most minute will have, if not an insect predator that will eat it wholly, most probably an insect parasite that will cause its eventual destruction.

While you are deploring the damage done by insects, while you are glooming over the "insect menace," stop a moment to give thanks for ladybird beetles, for ground-beetles, for dragon-flies, for lacewing-flies, and for syrphid flies, because these eat the aphids and other plant-eaters that beset your garden plants and vegetables. Thank, then, tachina flies, ichnuemon wasps, braconid wasps, chalcid wasps, and scelionid wasps, for all these are parasites upon other insects. Now, of course, Mother Nature did not have man in mind when parasites were developed, and so she goes one step further and produces insects that parasitize the parasites, and those that parasitize the parasites of the parasites (see chapter on "Insect Foods and Feeding Habits"). We egotistic human beings will say that the parasite of the tussock-moth that damages our shade trees is "beneficial," but the parasite that parasitizes the parasite of the tussock is "harmful," for it reduces the number of original, or primary, parasites; but if there is a parasite of the parasite of the parasite that first attacked the tussock-moth, we say again that this last parasite is "beneficial." However, one should not lose sight of the fact that there was a parasite in the first place and it caused the death of the tussock-moth.

Insects themselves. No single chapter can do full justice to the value of insects. There is the matter of insect scavengers that help the bacteria and fungi keep the surface of the earth free of spoiling things; there are insects that till and fertilize the soil; there are insects that primitive tribes use for foods; there are insects that are important for certain types of scientific research; there are insects that control weeds; and lastly one must mention the satisfaction that can be derived just because there are insects. Would you like a world without the color of a butterfly? Would you like a world without a katydid? Would you like a world without an insect song at night? Would you like a world without a single busy bee? Would you like a world without an insect?

CHAPTER XVI

INJURIOUS INSECTS AND THEIR CONTROL

A PRELIMINARY SURVEY

SINCE long before the dawn of history, mankind has been indebted to certain useful insects and has been troubled by certain harmful or objectionable ones. He has treasured and domesticated the bee for the honey and wax it produces and the silk-worm (Fig. 38) for the silk it yields, but at the same time he has dreaded the mosquitoes (Fig. 65) which torment him and the locusts (grasshoppers, Fig. 2) and crickets (Fig. 164) which occasionally appear in countless millions, as they have done in recent times in the West, Middle West, and Southwest, to destroy his crops and bring famine to his lands. In times past, however, the good and the harm done by insects have in the long run remained relatively constant; but with the development of our modern type of civilization the situation has changed. The number of kinds of insects to which we are directly indebted seems to have decreased. This is due to the development of rayon as a competitor to silk, to the growth of the sugar industry which has made us largely independent of honey as a source of sweets, and to the invention of dyes to replace cochineal. At the same time, the number of insect species that are harmful or objectionable seems to have increased greatly.

To combat insect pests successfully it is necessary to learn everything possible about insects of all kinds. It is necessary to become acquainted with numerous insect species, with the way they live and grow and reproduce, to know how they are affected by conditions in their environment and how they respond to various natural laws, to understand their numerous contacts with other living things, both plant and animal, and the intricate interrelationships which have grown out of these contacts. Finally, it is necessary to know what bearing all the manifold activities of insects have, directly, indirectly, or even remotely, on human welfare. There is not a fact or principle presented in this book or in any other book on insects but contributes

Fig. 164.—Mormon Crickets Occasionally Develop in Tremendous Hordes in Some of Our Western States and Denude Large Areas of Almost Every Shred of Low-growing Vegetation.

The crickets shown here (*Anabrus simplex*) are feeding on Russian Thistle, a troublesome weed, but they eat cultivated crops with equal readiness. Fortunately they are wingless and can easily be kept out of trees or these would be destroyed also. Low fences of sheet metal prevent their spreading into new territory, and they are trapped easily with ditches into which they fall. They are then killed by pouring oil on them or simply by burying them.

something to the solution of man's insect-pest problems. The first step, then, is to learn the general facts and principles on which the control of injurious insects is based.

GENERAL FACTS AND PRINCIPLES

A point of view. To refer to a particular insect as a pest, for example, the Codling Moth (Fig. 168), is to speak from a purely human point of view. Actually, in a broad biological sense, man is as much of a pest as the Codling Moth, for he does everything in his power to kill Codling Moths, whereas all they do is to eat, in the caterpillar stage, the apples, pears, quinces, haws, and walnuts which nature has created and placed in their world to be eaten. They are pests to man because they compete seriously with him for certain food materials.

Another thing to bear in mind is that few insects are wholly good or wholly bad, even from a purely human point of view. The Imported Cabbage-worm (*Pieris rapae*), that is cursed by the producers of truck crops, grows up to be a lovely white butterfly which, along with other butterflies, carries the pollen of plants having slender, tubular throats too deep for the mouth parts of the bee, such flowers as Sweet William, Verbena, marigolds, and certain daisies. Thus it helps to make seed production possible for these flowers.

To deal intelligently with the problem of insect pests it is necessary to weigh the evidence in each case rather than to condemn any insect utterly, and to decide in which cases and under what conditions the harm done by an insect outweighs the good. Only then is a rational program of insect control possible.

The balance of nature. In a state of primeval nature a sort of balance, or major equilibrium, exists between the activities of all living things. It is a fluctuating equilibrium, but it is never seriously disturbed for long. Also, it is made up of innumerable minor equilibria, each of which fluctuates also.

For example, if vegetation that is due to especially favorable seasonal conditions becomes excessively luxuriant, then plant-eating insects thrive and tend to check the unusual plant growth. Should this lead to an excessive number of vegetarian insects, the predatory and parasitic insects which feed on the vegetarians increase and reduce the vegetarians once more. Or a bacterial or fungus disease breaks out and takes a terrific toll of the vegetarians. Occasionally parasites and predators almost exterminate a vegetarian species. This reacts on the parasites and predators, for, owing to the scarcity of hosts or prey which their own activities have brought about, large numbers of the parasites and predators starve or fail to reproduce. Their numbers are thus brought down to a level proportionate to that of the greatly reduced vegetarians.

Role of nonliving environmental factors. In determining abundance and distribution, the elements of the nonliving environment play a significant role. The heat and cold, rain and snow, sunshine and cloudiness, atmospheric humidity, and the winds that make up our changing seasonal weather, profoundly influence insect life. Dry air makes of a desert an impassable barrier to many species of insects. The heat of open sunny areas to a large extent restricts the delicate stone-flies (Figs. 16 and 119–121) and caddis-flies (Figs. 132 and 134) to the shelter of the wooded strips along watercourses and around lakes.

Topographical and geographical features of a country likewise affect both the abundance and the distribution of plants and animals. Mountains, lakes, rivers, oceans, and deserts obviously are physical barriers. A north-facing slope, because the sun's rays strike it more obliquely than they do a south-facing slope, is cooler and more humid. It, therefore, supports a richer vegetation, and a more abundant insect population. Sandy soils differ chemically from clay or adobe soils and warm up more quickly. The life which they support differs accordingly.

The interrelations of plants and animals. The relationships which plants and animals bear to each other determine in no small measure the character of the equilibrium which constitutes the all-important balance of nature. These relationships and their effects are often obscure, especially in the case of insects; and painstaking study may be required to bring them to light, but their importance can hardly be overestimated.

Severe competition for the necessities of life—space, light and the energy it brings, air, and food—often determines how many and which insects shall live in a given habitat (Fig. 173). On the other hand, cooperation as developed among the social insects (Figs. 144 and 146–160) gives to these creatures advantages not possessed by others and permits their populations to rise to relatively high levels.

On the whole, however, we may arrange the various plants and animals in a series of antagonistic groups, each pitted against the other, and each so reacting on the other that, in the long run, all get their share of the necessities of life and none achieves extreme domination at the expense of the others. Truly the balance of nature constitutes an intricate and extremely complex web of life; but it is one that must be understood if man is to know why certain insects become pests while others do not.

HOW INSECTS COME TO BE PESTS

What an insect pest is. To call any insect a pest, as some persons do, simply because it eats plant life or sucks the blood of a backboned animal, is to be guilty of careless thinking. Such insects are not always even potential pests, although many of them are. Properly speaking, an insect is a pest only when it is so abundant that its activities obviously interfere with the welfare of man. Whenever the feeding of an insect species noticeably reduces the volume of a crop, as in the case of the Cotton-boll Weevil (*Anthonomus grandis*), or lessens its quality, as in the case of the Pear Thrips (*Taeniothrips inconsequens*), or frequently transmits a destructive plant disease, as in the case of the Beet Leaf-hopper (*Eutettix tenellus*), then clearly that insect is a pest. In like manner, whenever an insect species contaminates man's food with disagreeable odors, as the cockroaches do, or torments him or his animals, as bedbugs and horse-flies do, or when it regularly transmits dreaded diseases to man or to his livestock, as the House-fly, the Yellow Fever Mosquito, and the Cat- and Dog-flea do, then equally clearly that insect is a pest.

In the majority of cases insects become pests only when the balance of nature is seriously disturbed or destroyed. Such disturbances can be grouped into two classes: purely natural disturbances, such as those due to fluctuations in weather, and artificial disturbances, those due to the activities of civilized man. Purely natural disturbances are temporary in character. Sooner or later a drought always ends, rainy seasons pass, and floods subside. Insects which owe their pest status to temporary natural disturbances, therefore, are only temporarily troublesome. The changes brought about by civilized man are often permanent. Pests which become such as a result of changes wrought by man, in consequence, are likely to be permanently pestiferous. In the control of insect pests it is necessary to vary the methods according to the manner in which the pest originated.

Temporary pests and the factors which cause them. The general abundance of certain insects is sharply limited by weather conditions. For example, many species of aphids (Figs. 39 and 145) and leaf-hoppers thrive only during the season of bountiful moisture while plants are actively growing and succulent foliage is available. An unusually long rainy season, therefore, may be accompanied by an excessive abundance of aphids and leaf-hoppers. A drought will tend to check the multiplication of these insects and terminate their destructive activities. On the other hand, continuous rainfall (and the associated high relative humidity) may act as a check to these insects because it favors bacterial and fungous diseases.

The Shothole Borer (*Scolytus rugulosus*), a beetle that breeds in dead branches of oaks and other trees, including fruit trees, is present usually in only moderate numbers. It thrives only in wood of a certain degree of dryness. Perfectly healthy trees are able to resist these beetles. By pouring out gummy and resinous secretions at points attacked by the beetles, the trees simply prevent them from boring

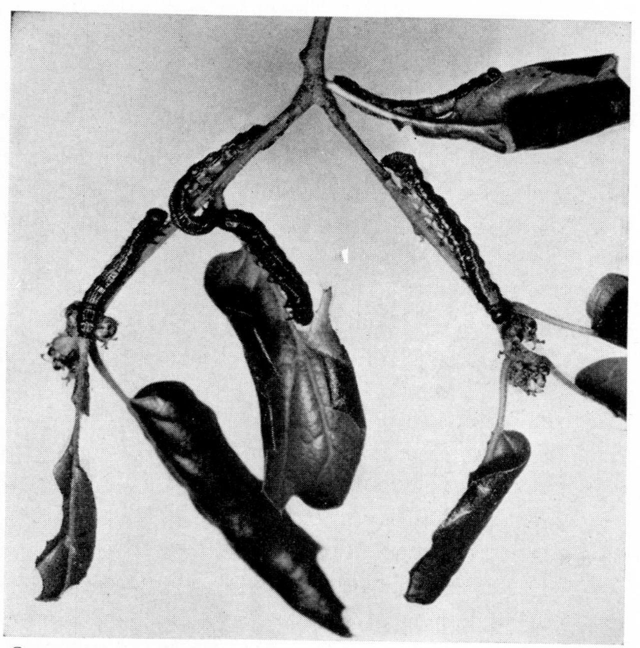

Fig. 165.—Caterpillars of the California Oak Moth Occasionally Completely Defoliate Oak Trees on the Pacific Coast so That They Are as Bare in Summer as Deciduous Trees Are in Winter.

The California Oak Moth (*Phryganidea californica*) is a native insect that generally is kept down to small numbers by several species of parasitic insects. Occasionally, however, as a result perhaps of weather conditions unfavorable to the parasites, the oak-moth population increases tremendously and the insect becomes a severe pest. Three or four years are required for the parasites to regain the upper hand but when this is done the moth once more becomes scarce and inconsequential. The caterpillars feed only on oaks, which is a boon, and they are easily controlled by poisonous sprays.

into their trunks and branches. Whenever rainfall drops to below normal, the trees lose vigor. More branches or whole trees die. The amount of suitably dry wood increases and the Shothole Borers become more abundant. They become so abundant, in fact, that by sheer force of numbers they succeed in infesting many still-living trees. This was strikingly shown on the Pacific Coast recently. Following some seven successive dry years, the Shothole Borer developed into a major agricultural pest. Many fruit trees were killed outright and thousands of others so badly damaged that they were pulled up and burned. A return of normal rainfall checked the outbreak.

In frequent instances the explanation of an outbreak of pests is not so simple. The weather of one or more seasons may favor a vegetarian insect just a little more than it does the parasites and predators which prey on the vegetarian. For a while the vegetarian, may show only a gradual increase in abundance. Then it quickly

FIG. 166.—EGGS, PUPAE, AND AN ADULT OF THE CALIFORNIA OAK MOTH ON DAMAGED LEAVES AND TWIGS.

The eggs, shown at the left, are nearing hatching time. When freshly laid they are cream-white pearls without a trace of dark pigment. The naked pupae, uniformly light colored at first, soon change to objects of great beauty, strikingly patterned in black and white, with here and there a touch of violet and of light yellow. The moths possess a beauty that is more somber though none the less real.

gains reproductive momentum and multiplies to enormous numbers. The result is disastrous (temporarily) for the plants on which the creatures feed. Eventually, favored by some change in weather or perhaps by an entirely different set of factors, the parasites and predators regain control and the troublesome vegetarian ceases to be a pest. Occasionally the return to normalcy is brought about so swiftly as to be positively dramatic, literally millions of pest individuals being wiped out overnight.

The California Oak Moth (Figs. 165 and 166) is an example of a pest, the abundance of which appears to be determined in the manner just described. For years it is relatively rare. Then, increasing rapidly, a time comes when its caterpillars strip the oak trees of every vestige of foliage over large sections of country. For two years, three, or perhaps more, the caterpillars continue to be destructive. Then almost as if by magic they cease to reappear, except in small numbers.

Some other well-known and more or less temporary pests which owe their rises and falls to natural causes are the Mormon Cricket (Fig. 164), which has been so destructive in Utah, Idaho, and Nevada in recent years, and various grasshoppers (Fig. 2). The year 1938 saw outbreaks of grasshoppers in the Rocky Mountain states from the Canadian to the Mexican border, such as hardly have occurred since the eighties of the past century.

Many of the destructive forest and range insects which, in severe epidemics, levy toll on our forests and range lands, are likewise pests of temporary character. The forests and the range plants are so adapted to their respective pests that, under perfectly primeval conditions, they readily survive any damage done by the insects. It is only since civilized man has put an additional (and far greater) tax on forests and range lands that the situation has become really serious.

The role of weather in this connection was well illustrated by the forests on the dry eastern slope of the Sierra Nevadas during the same dry years that brought about the epidemic of Shothole Borers described on pages 306 and 307. In that period, according to forest entomologists in the service of the United States government, although there was no marked epidemic anywhere, damage done by insects, as well as fungi and other natural causes, increased until the amount of timber destroyed each year was actually a little greater than the amount of new timber grown.

Other factors, besides weather, influence insect abundance and occasionally lead to outbreaks. Forest fires, especially those of the ground-fire type, sometimes scorch tree trunks without killing the trees, but lower their vitality to the point where they succumb easily to the attacks of bark-beetles.

Exceptionally high tides are responsible at times for outbreaks of pestiferous mosquitoes. The mosquitoes in question are species which breed in brackish water. The eggs are laid in the mud of coastal marshes in places only occasionally covered by water. When, as happens every few years, an unusually high tide floods the land containing the mosquito eggs, billions of mosquitoes are produced in a few weeks. The same sort of thing occasionally takes place in the bottom lands of large rivers. In these cases the offending insects are flood-plain mosquitoes.

Pests, temporary or permanent, consequent upon the activities of man. Civilized man is without doubt the most disturbing creature the world has ever known. In his attempts to remake the earth's surface to suit his own wishes, man has done more to disturb the balance of nature and bring trouble on himself than have any dozen other causes combined. To be sure, man has accomplished many things of great worth and in the main has greatly improved his status, but there have been times when he has come perilously near to upsetting the biological applecart altogether. In the following paragraphs the various actions of man which have added and are adding to the number of insect pests from which man suffers will be enumerated and examples given.

1. Man introduces into new regions crop plants or ornamentals that are closely related to wild species native to these regions, but which are more attractive to the native insects than the wild plants are. The insects in question, therefore, move onto the cultivated plants and thrive. Sometimes the wild plants are tough, and much of the energies of the insects feeding on them must be used in merely extracting a living, whereas the new imports are tender and juicy. A larger percentage of the insects thus live to the adult stage on the new plants and reproduce. The insect population, therefore, rises to a much higher level.

An example is that of the prettily striped Colorado Potato Beetle (*Leptinotarsa decemlineata*), which originally fed on the foliage of the Buffalo Bur (*Solanum rostratum*) growing along the eastern slope of the Rocky Mountains. When the Rocky Mountain region was settled and the common Irish, or White, Potato (*Solanum tuberosum*) was introduced as a crop, the beetles adopted the potato as their food plant. Man has been fighting potato beetles ever since.

2. Man destroys native vegetation and supplants it with alien crops. The native insects, deprived of their natural food, attack the crops. Sometimes the crops are better food for the insects than the native plants were and sometimes not. Sometimes the insects are favored by man's agricultural practices and sometimes not. According to circumstances, then, the insects concerned become temporary pests which die out after a few years or they become permanent pests.

The so-called *wire-worms*, which are rather hard-surfaced, long, slender grubs shaped like brownish-yellow pieces of jointed wire, illustrate this method of pest origin. Wire-worms live in the soil, feeding on the roots of plants, especially in prairie regions. Often two or three years are needed for them to grow to the adult stage, but eventually they transform into the familiar click-beetles (also called jack-snappers, snap-beetles, and skipjacks). When a piece of virgin prairie, or land that has lain fallow (untilled) for several years, is plowed and a crop planted on it, the wire-worms naturally eat the roots of the crop plants, often doing considerable damage. They do not survive cultivation well, however, and in two or three years cease to be troublesome.

3. Man establishes habitats or food supplies for particular insects where none existed before, or he supplies them in greater number or quantity. Several examples may be given here. The afore-mentioned Colorado Potato Beetle originally did not occur farther east than the base of the Rocky Mountains, its distribution being limited by the range of the Buffalo Bur, but when supplied with potatoes on which to feed it spread eastward to the Atlantic Ocean. It spread westward also, but to date it has been kept out of many important agricultural areas. It does not occur in the valleys of California.

The Cotton-boll Weevil (*Anthonomus grandis*), native to Mexico or Central America where it fed on wild relatives of the domestic cottons, late in the past century adopted cultivated cotton as a favored food plant. From 1892 to 1922 the weevil spread through more than ninety per cent of the Cotton Belt of the Southern states. There it destroys annually[1] from twenty to forty per cent of all the cotton grown.

The settling of the South and the West, with the construction of thousands of buildings and the irrigation of thousands of acres of land, has undoubtedly led to a great increase in the population of termites (Figs. 41, 112, 113, 159, and 160), and of the Black Widow Spider, which is not an insect. The wood used in buildings, in the conveniently spaced posts in miles of fencing, and in telegraph and telephone poles has supplied the termites with an abundance of food and nesting sites in regions which had few or no termites before. The dark corners in basements, attics, and outhouses have given the

[1] C. L. Metcalf and W. P. Flint, *Destructive and Useful Insects*, McGraw-Hill Book Company, Inc., New York, 1928.

Black Widows a great number of new and ideal dwelling places, while the increased general population of insects resulting from the irrigation of arid lands has provided the food supply for the additional spiders.

In a comparable manner, great areas in the Sacramento Valley of California were without significant population of malarial mosquitoes until rice was grown there as a crop. Now the extensive rice fields, flooded for many weeks at a time, provide breeding grounds for great

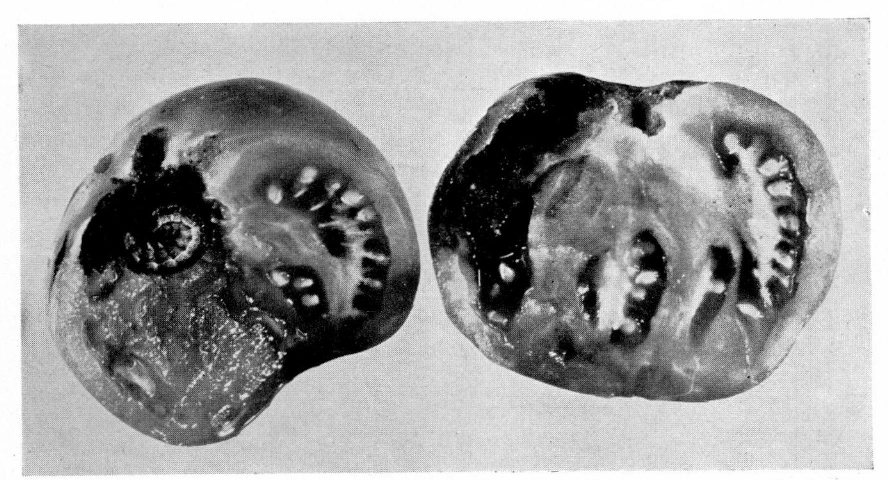

Fig. 167.—A Versatile Insect of Many Names and Catholic Tastes Is the Insect Responsible for the Damage to These Tomatoes.

Known as the Corn Ear-worm, the Cotton-boll Worm, and also, though mistakenly, the Tobacco Bud-worm, the caterpillars of the moth, *Heliothis obsoleta*, damage corn, cotton, tobacco, lettuce, string beans, and other crops. The tomato at the left in the figure shows one of the caterpillars. The insect is a perennial pest and effective control is difficult owing to the concealed habits of the caterpillars and the nature of the plants or plant parts attacked.

numbers of these mosquitoes. Malaria, in consequence, has become a common disease in the Sacramento Valley whereas originally it had been rare.

4. Man plants his crops in close-set rows and in dense masses covering large areas with almost pure stands of single species or varieties of plants. In nature, except in forests and certain prairies, comparable conditions rarely exist. Many plant species are intermixed and the individuals of any one species often are spaced relatively far apart. The difficulties experienced by insects in finding another plant, after devouring or exhausting the juices of one, have prevented many an insect from becoming overly abundant under natural conditions.

In cultivated fields, on the other hand, the insect population builds up until checked by some other factor. Years of growing the same crop in the same fields leads at times to the development of enormous populations of pest insects.

Insect pests especially favored by close planting are those insects which attack field crops. This list is a large one and includes such species as the Corn Ear-worm (*Heliothis obsoleta*) (Fig. 167), the Tomato Hornworm (*Protoparce sexta*) (Fig. 87), the Carrot Beetle (*Ligyrus gibbosus*), the Larger Corn-stalk Borer (*Diatraea zeacolella*), the Harlequin Cabbage-bug (*Murgantia histrionica*) (Fig. 124), the Snowy Tree Cricket (*Oecanthus niveus*) (Fig. 95), the Alfalfa Butterfly (*Eurymus eurytheme*) (Fig. 135), aphids of several species, mealy-bugs (Fig. 172), the Wheat-stem Maggot (*Meromyza americana*), the Potato Flea Beetle (*Epitrix cucumeris*), the Striped Cucumber Beetles (*Diabrotica vittata* and *trivittata*), the Squash-bug (*Anasa tristis*), and the Potato Tuber Moth (*Phthorimaea operculella*).

5. Man accumulates vast quantities of dried vegetable and animal products which he keeps in storage. Never before have such quantities of these materials existed. They include fruits, seeds, cereals made from seeds, fibers, crude drugs, tobacco, spices, furs, hides, dried meats and fish, biological specimens in museums, wood, and wood products of every sort. All these materials are eaten by insects. When, therefore, conditions favor infestation by insects, the latter develop to incomprehensible numbers.

Well-known insect pests which often owe their abundance locally to the existence of stored materials accumulated by man are termites (Figs. 41, 112, 113, 159 and 160), the Silverfish (*Lepisma saccharina*) (Figs. 108 and 170), the Tobacco Beetle (*Lasioderma serricorne*), the Drug-store Beetle (*Sitodrepa panicea*), the Carpet Beetles (*Anthrenus scrophulariae*) and (*Anthrenus piceus*), the Case-making Clothes-moth (*Tinea pellionella*), the Larder Beetle (*Dermestes lardarius*), the Cheese Skipper (*Piophila casei*), the Granary Weevil (*Sitophilus granariae*), the Confused Flour Beetle (*Tribolium confusum*), the Saw-toothed Grain Beetle (*Oryzaephilus surinamensis*), the Angoumois Grain Moth (*Sitotroga cerealella*), the Mediterranean Flour Moth (*Ephestia kuehniella*), the Common Bean Weevil (*Mylabris obtectus*), the powder-post beetles (Family Lyctidae) (Fig. 42), and many others.

6. Man introduces insects into countries new to them and fails at the same time to introduce the parasites, predators, and diseases

which kept them in check in their native lands. Probably the majority of our very destructive agricultural pests owe their origin as pests to this fact.

The Hessian-fly (*Phytophaga destructor*), introduced from Europe into the colonies during the American Revolution, has spread to

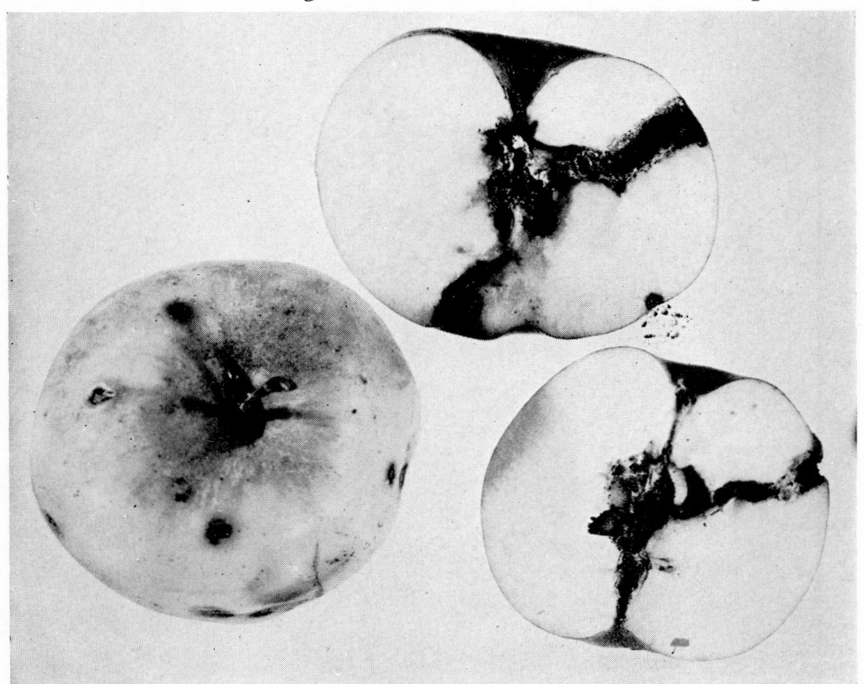

FIG. 168.—THESE APPLES SHOW THE WORK OF THE CODLING-MOTH, A PERMANENT PEST OF THIS FRUIT.
The Codling-moth, or Apple-worm, is the best known and most widely distributed pest of the apple. It also regularly attacks pears and, in some sections, English walnuts. It is, of course, not the adult moth, but the larva that does the damage. The apple on the left shows the spots and holes made by the "worms." Above is an apple showing the burrow, and below both the burrow and the "worm."

nearly all the wheat-growing sections of the country. It sometimes destroys over fifty per cent of the wheat crop. The Gypsy Moth (*Porthetria dispar*), introduced into New England from Europe in 1869, has done tremendous damage to forest and shade trees. Several millions of dollars have been spent in combating it. The Japanese Beetle (*Popillia japonica*), introduced into New Jersey about 1916, has severely damaged all kinds of fruit and vegetables. It has spread to many other sections of the country, and no end to its destructiveness is in sight. The Cottony-cushion Scale (*Icerya purchasi*) (Fig. 173), to be discussed more fully in the latter part of this chapter, also became a pest through having been introduced without its parasitic and predatory controls. It came from Australia.

7. Civilized man explores and colonizes wilderness lands wherein abound blood-sucking insects capable of carrying human diseases or those of livestock. In some cases native peoples and their domestic animals are relatively immune to the diseases in question, whereas the peoples and livestock of European origin are not. Consequently, the latter suffer greatly. In other cases the natives are no more immune than the explorers and colonists, but the diseases in question have a very limited distribution until they are disseminated along trade routes established by the newcomers.

For years the completion of a canal across the Isthmus of Panama proved impossible of accomplishment because the mosquito-borne malarias and yellow fever killed nearly every European assigned to work on the project. Not until the mosquito-carriage of these diseases was demonstrated, and methods of control worked out, was the building of the canal possible. The Canal Zone is now among the most healthful regions in the world.

Exploration and trade development in Africa during the past century spread the dreaded Tsetse-fly-borne sleeping sickness from its origin in West Africa over much of the humid tropical parts of the continent. Millions of natives perished within a few years. In east Central Africa a similar fate befell imported cattle and horses because of a related disease, Nagana, also borne by a Tsetse-fly.

8. Man cultivates so-called "marginal land," land so poor that only under the very best conditions will it give a fair return in crops for the money and energy required to farm it. On such lands an attack by pest insects which could be borne readily by the crops in a rich productive region may be serious enough to wipe out all profits and reduce the farmers to a state of near poverty. Marginal lands in the arid portions of some of the Western states where alfalfa and sugar beets are grown suffer at times from grasshoppers, the Beet Leafhopper (*Eutettix tenellus*), and alfalfa insects, and thus impoverish their owners.

9. Finally, many of man's habits of building, farming, growing livestock, disposing of wastes, carrying on of commerce, and of waging war create situations favorable to the development of insect pests.

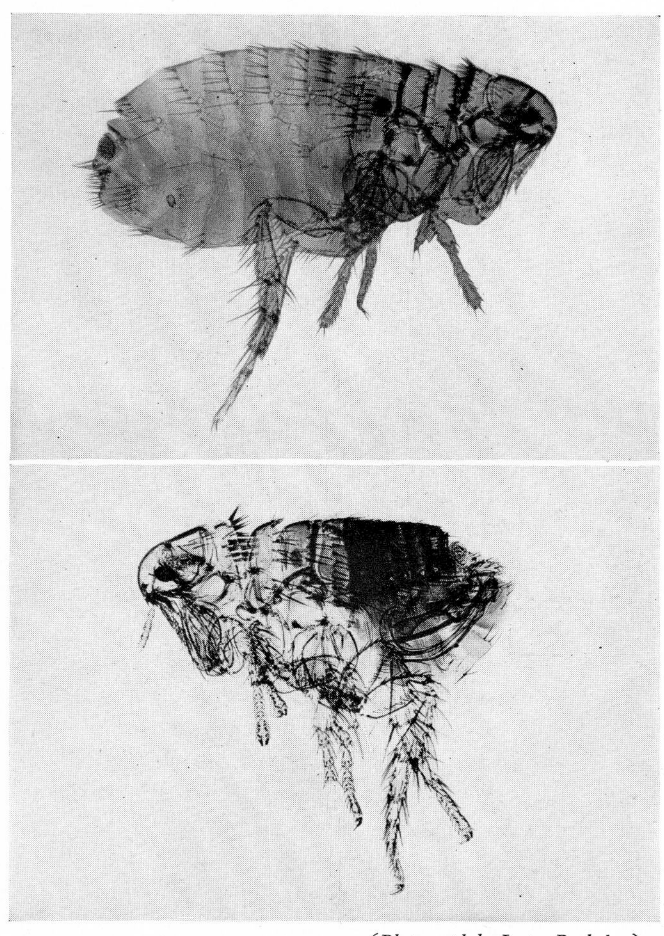

(*Photograph by Lester Brubaker.*)

FIG. 169.—MALE AND FEMALE FLEAS COOKED IN A LYE SOLUTION TO REMOVE ALL THEIR SOFT TISSUES, AND MOUNTED ON MICROSCOPE SLIDES, REVEAL THE FLATTENED BODIES AND NUMEROUS SPINES WHICH ENABLE THEM TO GLIDE BETWEEN HAIRS AND ELUDE PURSUIT SO READILY.

Only adult fleas remain on the host animals. The females (the larger one in the picture is a female) lay their eggs loosely among the hairs or clothing of the host, whence they are shaken off onto furniture, the ground, or the floors of buildings. In cracks between flooring boards, in upholstering, and in ground litter, especially in the sleeping places of dogs and cats, the thread-like flea larvae grow, feeding on fallen hairs, skin scales, and other animal debris. The lesson is obvious: keep pets clean and out of houses as much as is practicable, and periodically disinfect upholstered furniture and floors to which dogs and cats have access, as well as the animals' quarters.

Garbage, sewage, cannery and slaughterhouse refuse when improperly disposed of, as when dumped into slowly moving streams, often produce enormous numbers of blow-flies (*Lucilia caesar*, *Phormia regina*, *Calliphora erythrocephala*, and *Calliphora vomitoria*), Screw-worm Flies (*Cochliomyia macellaria*), Drone-flies (*Eristalis tenax*), Latrine-flies (*Fannia scalaris*) and Lesser House-flies (*Fannia canicularis*). From uncared-for manure in stables and barnyards come House-flies (*Musca domestica*) and Stable-flies (*Stomoxys calcitrans*). From open privies come more Latrine-flies and Lesser House-flies. All of these species, in varying proportions, swarm to our houses, food stores, dairies, nurseries, and hospitals. The use of modern screens excludes the majority, but when they are sufficiently numerous a few slip by the safeguards in spite of all our vigilance. As long as these flies are uninfected they are not actually injurious, but a large population of filth-frequenting flies completely free of disease germs rarely, if ever, exists. Almost always numerous flies are infected with the germs of some fly-borne disease such as typhoid fever, diarrhea or summer complaint, tuberculosis, or pinkeye. Hence their presence in any numbers in a community is a constant menace to human health.

The crowding of people in poorly built tenements, accompanied as it is with squalor and filth, creates ideal conditions for the multiplication of lice, fleas (Figs. 140 and 169), cockroaches, and bedbugs. Even worse conditions develop in countries ravaged by war or in regions suffering from disastrous fires or floods, with the disruption of normal communication, transportation, hospital, and waste-disposal facilities. In fact, whenever the mechanical and hygienic foundations of modern social organization break down, crowding and human suffering result.

Under the conditions which then develop, epidemics of fly-, louse-, and flea-borne diseases arise and take their toll of human health and human life. Two of the more recent such outbreaks were the flea-borne bubonic plague in San Francisco following the earthquake and fire of 1906, and the outbreaks of the louse-borne typhus fever in the war zones of Europe from 1914 to the end of the initial reconstruction period following the war.

Most of our insect problems are due to such causes as those just outlined. Some of the problems are the unavoidable accompaniments of human progress and social change; others are preventable. Regardless of their inevitability or preventability, however, to deal with them requires knowledge of many sorts.

INSECT CONTROL

Theoretical bases of insect control. The applied control of insects, as distinguished from the natural control already discussed, is based on several well-established principles. These involve a knowledge of insect structure and physiology, especially of the modes of feeding; a knowledge of their life histories, adaptations to environmental conditions, including seasonal conditions and changes in weather; a knowledge of relationships to man, to domestic and wild animals, to plants of every sort, and to parasitic and predatory organisms in all the animal groups. The principles of insect control involve also a knowledge of plants and plant disease, a thorough knowledge of chemistry, especially of the chemistry of poisonous substances, of oils, sulphur, and lime; a knowledge of the principles of human health; a knowledge of machinery and its operation, of laws and legal procedures, and of their utilization in the solution of municipal, state, and national problems; lastly, a knowledge of farming and farm practices. Happily the necessary knowledge can be organized under a few relatively simple headings. Nevertheless, the field of insect control remains vast and complex and is steadily becoming more so.

Insect mouth parts and methods of feeding. For control purposes most insects may be grouped into two classes: those which chew and swallow solid foods and those which pierce plant or animal tissues with needle-like beaks and suck blood or tissue juices from them. The chewing types of insects, such as grasshoppers, katydids, and crickets, true or otherwise, caterpillars, and beetles, if they are typical herbivores, may be controlled by spraying or dusting stomach poisons on their food plants. Chewing insects which are not herbivores require other control measures. Piercing and sucking insects, especially the true bugs which make up the orders Hemiptera and Homoptera, are killed by the use of contact poisons or fumigants.

In addition to these principal classes of feeders there are certain minor classes. Insects like ants, for example, and yellowjackets, which lap up exposed liquids, sometimes may be controlled by the use of poisoned sirups exposed in places where the ants or yellowjackets will find them.

In the case of certain chewing and sucking insects, peculiarities of structure and habit render them immune or largely so to stomach poisons or contact poisons when applied by the usual techniques. Among these insects are certain of the true weevils. A true weevil is distinguished by the fact that the front of its head is drawn out into a long and usually slender snout. For this reason weevils are often called snout-beetles. The mouth parts are of the chewing type typical of beetles, but very tiny. They are grouped on the tip of the weevil's snout. Some weevils eat considerable amounts of leafy plant-growth. Among these are the Alfalfa Weevil (*Phytonomus posticus*) and weevils of the genus *Lixus* which feed on smartweeds (*Polygonum* spp.) and Wormwood (*Artemisia* sp.). Such weevils can be killed by ordinary sprayings or dustings of stomach poisons. Other weevils, such as the Cotton-boll Weevil (*Anthonomus grandis*) and the Rose Snout-beetle (*Rhynchites bicolor*), usually cut only minute holes through the surface tissues of a plant, feeding mainly from below the surface. The amount of poison eaten by such a weevil is likely to be too small to affect it. Such insects, also, are usually too hard-shelled to be killed easily by contact poisons. Success is sometimes achieved by combining several types of control procedure, depending on each to do its share. The application of stomach poisons has a place among these but it never shows the high efficacy that it does with chewing insects that are surface feeders. According to Metcalf and Flint[1] the use of calcium arsenate dust in the control of the Cotton-boll Weevil saves an average of 300 to 400 pounds of seed cotton to the acre. This means from 100 to 130 pounds of cotton fiber. In exceptional cases, the saving from destruction by the weevil is as high as 1,000 pounds of seed cotton, or about 350 pounds of fiber. Such savings are enough to pay for the cost of dusting the cotton plants many times over, but they are small in comparison with the savings made when a leaf-eating insect such as the Cotton Leaf Worm (*Alabama argillacea*) is controlled by stomach poisons.

In the case of numerous insect pests, various special conditions, such as peculiarities of behavior, of habitat, or of relationship to man, render ineffective or impossible or inadvisable these general control methods. The clues to the proper procedure, therefore, must be sought elsewhere than in the manner of the insect's feeding alone.

Life cycles and their bearing on pest control. The nature of an insect's life cycle, or its relationship to its environment, often provides the solution to a control problem. For example, mosquitoes are difficult to control in the adult stage. Stomach poisons are excluded by the mosquito's method of feeding. The mosquitoes are too scattered for

[1] *Destructive and Useful Insects*, McGraw-Hill Book Company, Inc., New York, 1928.

the use of contact poisons to be feasible. By screening houses protection is given to all who stay indoors. Most of the mosquitoes' biting may be prevented for a few hours by rubbing exposed parts with oil of citronella or some other repellent. Such practices are unsatisfactory and are only partial solutions to the mosquito problem.

In its larval and pupal stages, however, the mosquito lives in the water (Fig. 65). Enormous populations are concentrated in marshes, ponds, and puddles. They are accessible and easy to kill. Small puddles may be filled, and ponds and marshes drained. If drainage is not feasible, small fishes that feed on the larvae and pupae may be introduced. If neither of these solutions is practicable, then some oil, preferably a light fuel oil, may be spread on the water. Periodically the larvae and pupae must come to the surface to breathe. Whenever they do so, the volatile components of the oil vaporize in their tracheal systems and quickly kill them. The killing is due generally to direct and immediate respiratory poisoning; not to suffocation as is commonly believed.

Suffocation of mosquito larvae and pupae, no matter to what it is due, takes place slowly, especially so in the case of the larvae, which possess gills in addition to respiratory siphons. These gills enable the larvae to secure some oxygen directly from the water even when the respiratory siphons are clogged. Actually, when light oils are used for mosquito control, the larvae and pupae do not live long enough to suffocate. They die within a few minutes after the oil has been applied.

The life cycle of the common House-fly (*Musca domestica*) indicates that with this insect, too, the maximum as well as the most economical control can be had by striking at the immature stages. By cleaning stables daily, or nearly so, and spreading the manure so that it will dry quickly, or by digging it into the soil promptly, most of the breeding opportunities of the House-fly are destroyed. Thus we have relatively few flies.

Considerations based on human health. Insects which feed on dried fruits, nuts, and cereals that are destined to be eaten by man obviously are not subject to control by stomach poisons. The same is true of insects which consume various poultry and stock feeds. To control such insects the products concerned may be stored at low temperatures or in actual refrigeration, they may be heated to temperatures sufficiently high to kill any insect eggs or larvae they may contain, or they may be fumigated with substances such as carbon tetrachloride which eventually completely evaporate and leave no poisonous residue.

It has been found in recent years that even fruits like apples and pears, which do not absorb poison into their tissues and are not themselves injured by a coating of poison, are not always safe to eat unless very thoroughly washed. A certain amount of arsenical residue often remains on them; and the person who eats them without first cleaning them thoroughly may accumulate enough arsenic in his body to impair his health. Such fruits are now regularly washed in special solutions before being marketed. It has, moreover, been deemed advisable to fix legal limits to the amount of poisonous residue which may be present on fruits and other products when they reach the markets. These limits are based on physiological studies of the tolerance of the human body to the poisons used.

Knowledge of the danger from poisonous residue has led to an active search for new poisons, substances effective against insects but harmless to plants, to man, and to his domestic animals under the conditions of application. Many compounds derived from plants, such as nicotine from tobacco, rotenone from *Derris*, a South American plant, and pyrethrin from *Pyrethrum*, a plant of the chrysanthemum group, have been tested, found useful, and adapted to control practices. Numerous derivatives of petroleum also have been tested. Some of these are now being generally used. In general, the oils have proved to be very valuable. A few inorganic or mineral poisons other than arsenic compounds have been shown to have definite value. The best known of these are the compounds of fluorine such as sodium fluoride and sodium fluosilicate. These are much less poisonous to man than the arsenicals. No substance has as yet been found that is quite as effective in killing insects as the arsenicals, but one may be found in the future.

Miscellaneous considerations bearing on control procedures. Insects which run about a great deal, inflicting damage here and there, and insects of very secretive habits sometimes require special procedures to effect their control. This is especially true of household insects. A small amount of actual feeding on their part may seriously affect human well-being. Even slight contamination of produce with their fecal discharges in certain cases greatly reduces the value of the products damaged. Among this heterogeneous miscellany are the

Silverfish (Fig. 170), cockroaches, clothes-moths, carpet beetles, ants, fleas (Figs. 140 and 169), and bedbugs.

The Silverfish feeds on bookbindings, wallpaper, clothing, curtains, and other dry materials containing starches, dextrins, and sugars. Cockroaches consume anything edible which they can find in kitchens, pantries, storerooms, and bathrooms. The feeding habits

(*Photograph by Lester Brubaker.*)

FIG. 170.—PRIMITIVE SILVERFISHES DESTROY A NOTICE POSTED ON A COLLEGE BULLETIN BOARD. These interesting and graceful members of the bristle-tail order, Thysanura, mostly remain concealed by day and come forth to feed at night. They have a penchant for dry substances that contain starches, sugars, and other carbohydrates. Hence papers that contain starchy sizing materials, wallpapers, bookbindings, and various woven fabrics are much to their liking. Relatively uncommon in most places, they occasionally become numerous locally and do much damage in homes and business establishments.

of ants are well known. All these insects may be controlled by liberally sprinkling powdered sodium fluoride on floors, shelves, and water pipes which serve as runways for the insects. The cockroaches and the ants get the poison as a result of their toilet operations. They groom themselves frequently, scraping all dust and foreign matter from their bodies by means of their legs. These, as well as their antennae, are then drawn through their mouths. Sometimes, instead of using pure sodium fluoride, a mixture of sodium fluoride 12 parts to flour 100 parts is employed.

Root-feeding insects, because of their inaccessibility, constitute another group of pests which cannot be controlled practically with insect poisons. Recourse is had, therefore, to cultural practices. The Northern Corn Root-worm (*Diabrotica longicornis*), the grubs of which eat only corn roots, can be controlled by crop rotation. Other root-feeders, such as the white grubs, larvae of various species of June-beetles of the genera *Phyllophaga* and *Lachnosterna* (Family Scarabaeidae), which feed on the roots of pasture grasses, corn, potatoes, and strawberries, are controlled to some extent by early fall plowing. This exposes many of the grubs so that they may be eaten by birds or killed by heat or cold. More efficacious still is the practice of pasturing hogs in infested fields. The hogs root out and eat the great majority of the grubs.

Materials and techniques.[1] The various methods of insect pest control fall logically into five main classes: chemical control, cultural control, physical or mechanical control, biological control, and legal control.

I. *Chemical Control.* The materials used to kill insect pests, or to lessen their activities and thus reduce the damage they do, are classified here according to their functions in the control program. In other words, they are classified according to how they act on the insects or according to what their application is expected to accomplish.

A. *The materials used.*

1. *Insecticides.* These are substances which actually kill insects. They fall more or less definitely into three classes. Several insecticides possess properties which place them in more than one class. That is to say, such insecticides may kill insects in more ways than one.

a. *Stomach poisons.* These are used against insects which chew and swallow solid food. There are three subclasses of stomach poisons.

(1) *Compounds of arsenic.* These, the most effective of all insecticides, are dangerous

[1] In preparing this synopsis of insect control the authors not only have drawn on personal experience but have made liberal use of recent books and technical papers, especially of the writings of Metcalf and Flint, Essig, Sweetman, Herms, Doane, Van Dyke, Chamberlin, and Burke. The reader is referred to the excellent books by these authors for a fuller treatment of the subject. (See Bibliography for titles.)

to human beings and to livestock; and their use on fruits, vegetables, and other crops destined for consumption by man or livestock is being discouraged. Their use on other crops probably will be continued indefinitely.

(2) *Nonarsenical inorganic (mineral) poisons.* These consist mainly of compounds of sodium and calcium with fluorine. Examples are sodium fluoride and sodium fluosilicate. These also are dangerous to man though much less so than the arsenicals.

(3) *Organic poisons.* The only one extensively used consists of the dried and powdered roots of hellebore plants (*Veratrum album* and *Veratrum viridis*). Hellebore is expensive but is suitable for use on fruits and vegetables as its poisonous principle shortly evaporates. It is only mildly toxic to the higher vertebrates. *Derris* in a powder form, and liquid extracts made from *Derris* are also used to some extent as stomach poisons.

b. Contact poisons. These are regularly used against piercing and sucking insects, and against certain of chewing insects whenever circumstances make them preferable to stomach poisons. They, also, fall into three subclasses.

(1) *Poisons which burn the integument and tissues of the pest insect.* Examples: sulphur and lime applied as powders, soap and water suspensions, "lime-sulphur" and related sprays consisting of chemical compounds of sulphur with calcium, sodium, potassium, and barium. Used for the control of many species of scale insects and mites.

(2) *Poisons which react chemically with the tissues and, therefore, kill by a true poisoning.* In

this subclass belong tobacco extracts, nicotine solutions and dusts, pyrethrum powder, and powdered *Derris* root. These, especially the nicotine preparations, are used extensively in the control of delicate

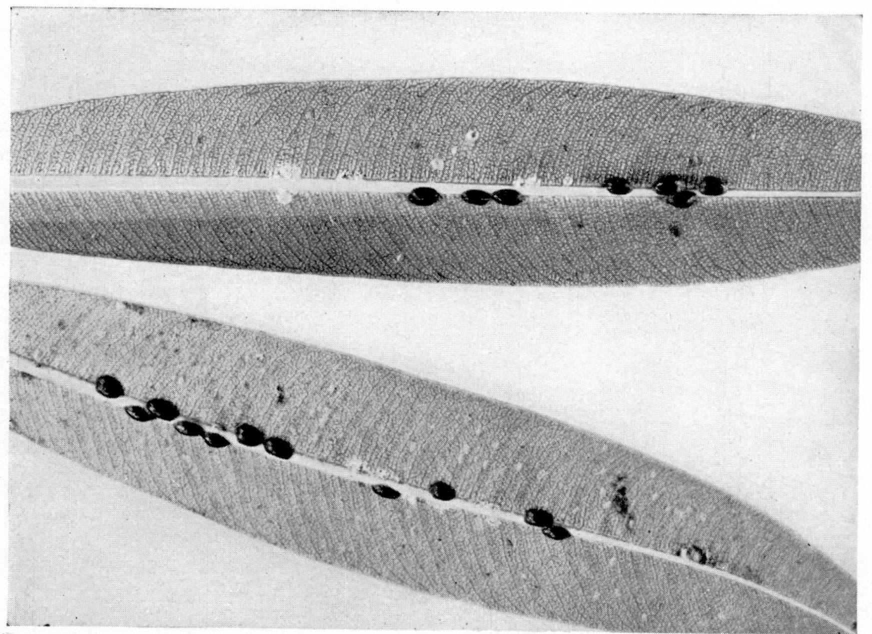

FIG. 171.—AMONG THE CREATURES INJURIOUS TO THE PLANTS GROWN BY MAN ARE THOSE STRANGEST OF CREATURES, THE SCALE-INSECTS.

With the exception of the males of most species, scale-insects have no wings. As they grow they insert their long thread-like mouth parts into the food plant, never again to withdraw them, and remain fixed in one spot for life. Many kinds lose their legs; many, also, cover themselves with shields of wax. Throughout their lives they suck the juices of the plants on which they live and, at maturity, lay their numerous, and usually pinkish, eggs beneath their own shriveling bodies, or in specially constructed egg sacs. The scale insects on these oleander leaves have no common name. Technically they are known as *Sassetia nigra* and are closely related to the Black Scale (*Sassetia oleae*).

insects such as aphids and thrips. Pyrethrum and *Derris* are also used extensively against household insects such as fleas, cockroaches, and Silverfish.

(3) *Oils*. Several kinds of oils are now used extensively in the control of scale-insects, aphids, thrips, and mites. Their action is undoubtedly complex. It probably

includes contact poisoning of the type described under (2), respiratory poisoning, and suffocation.

c. *Respiratory poisons and suffocating agents.* Strictly respiratory poisons usually are taken into the tracheae in a vapor form, and exert their poisonous effect when they are absorbed into the tissues from the tracheoles. Respiratory poisons, when applied in a gaseous condition, are termed *fumigants.* Suffocating agents simply clog the spiracles and slowly kill the insects by cutting off the oxygen supply. A single insecticide may act both as a respiratory poison and as a suffocating agent. The principal insecticides in this class follow:

(1) *Hydrocyanic acid gas.* Probably the most powerful respiratory poison known. It is a fumigant. It may be generated in several ways. When large quantities are needed it is generated commonly by dropping calcium cyanide or sodium cyanide into earthenware pots of dilute sulphuric acid, or by pouring a solution of calcium or sodium cyanide into dilute sulphuric acid. It is available in the pure form also, but compressed to a liquid state and shipped in steel cylinders. The gas is **exceedingly dangerous** to human beings as well as to all other types of animal life. It should be used only by highly trained persons under rigidly controlled conditions. Hydrocyanic acid gas is used to fumigate homes, ships, warehouses, and industrial plants to kill all sorts of household insects and those that infest stored products. It is used also to fumigate trees and shrubbery. In the latter case the gas is generated beneath closely woven canvas tents which are placed over the trees and shrubs.

Calcium cyanide in the form of a dust will give off hydrocyanic acid gas without being treated with acid. It is sometimes dusted onto plants in the open to kill insects which succumb quickly. Otherwise it is blown under tents over trees and shrubs or spread in a ⅛-inch deep layer on sheets of paper in the rooms of buildings.

(2) *Carbon bisulphide*, a heavy, oily liquid, evaporates on exposure to the air, to form a heavy, vile-smelling, highly poisonous, and inflammable gas. This gas is the most useful fumigant where deep penetration is needed. It is much used for fumigating buildings, grain in bins, and soils. It is effective against all types of insect life. The only real danger in its use is from fire.

(3) *Sulphur dioxide*, a gas generated by burning special types of sulphur, is a fairly effective fumigant but has certain drawbacks. It corrodes metals, destroys the germinating power of seeds, and changes the baking qualities of flour. It is used regularly to fumigate certain types of fruits prior to drying them.

(4) *Nicotine*, obtained from tobacco, is available in pure form as a liquid. It is vaporized for greenhouse or home fumigation by heating. Papers soaked in nicotine also are available. These are burned to liberate the nicotine. Dusts made of sulphur, lime, or mixtures of these and other carriers, to which nicotine has been added, are frequently used. The pure nicotine and nicotine papers are used for indoor fumigation. The dusts are used either indoors or outdoors. When dusted

onto vegetation the nicotine vapor given off is very effective against aphids, thrips, and other small or delicate insects.

(5) *Paradichlorobenzene*, a crystalline material, and *orthodichlorobenzene*, a liquid at ordinary temperatures, both vaporize on exposure to air. Paradichlorobenzene is used in the eradication of borers around the trunks of trees, an ounce of it being spread in a circular ditch a few inches deep around a tree base, close to but not against the trunk or roots. It is also used to "demoth" closets by putting it in a container attached to a vacuum cleaner, and blowing the vapors given off into the closet. Orthodichlorobenzene is used to paint floors and other woods infested with powder-post beetles.

(6) *Carbon tetrachloride*, *ethylene dichloride*, *chloropicrin (tear gas)*, *and nitrobenzene* are also used to some extent as fumigants.

(7) *Various oils*, such as the light fuel oils used in mosquito control, function mainly as respiratory poisons. Heavier oils act chiefly as suffocating agents.

(8) *The volatile substances given off by pyrethrum*, *Derris root*, and other organic insecticides work in part as fumigants.

(9) *Other substances*, *such as the soaps* used in sprays, undoubtedly act to some extent as suffocating agents because they clog the spiracles.

2. *Attrahents*. These are substances put in poison baits or in traps to attract insects to the baits or traps. Molasses and sirups are common attrahents in poisoned baits used in controlling ants, flies, or moths of various species. Milk as an attrahent is added to sweetened water and formalin to attract House-flies, the formalin killing them. Ground oranges and lemons, as well as

molasses, serve as attrahents in poisoned bran mash used to kill grasshoppers, sow-bugs, and pill-bugs, snails, and slugs. Moths, such as the Oriental Fruit Moth (*Laspeyresia molesta*) and the Codling Moth (*Carpocapsa pomonella*) are lured to bait pans of molasses, water, and poison by various attrahents. Among these amyl acetate and ethyl alcohol have been used.

3. *Repellents.* These, as the name implies, are substances which repel insects, usually by means of the odors given off. The insects simply are deterred from making their attacks; they are not killed. The various fly sprays put on the market in recent years are among the better known repellents. Oil of citronella, also, is a repellent that has long been known. Rubbed on a person's face and hands, or sprinkled around his pillow, oil of citronella will protect from the bites of mosquitoes. Bordeaux mixture has a repellent effect on many insects. Naphthalene, of which moth balls are made, is a well-known repellent. Creosote is a repellent used in termite control. Timbers that have been impregnated with creosote to a depth of a quarter of an inch or more, remain immune to termite attack for many years.
4. In addition to the active ingredients which act as insecticides, sprays and dusts usually contain other substances.
   a. Vehicles. The actual control of any insect pest is accomplished by a relatively small amount of insecticide. Only a few pounds to an acre of crop may be enough. Small amounts, for mechanical reasons, cannot be economically or uniformly distributed over large areas. The insecticides, therefore, are mixed with some other substance which is inexpensive, such as water, in order to get a quantity of material large enough to handle. These additional materials are called *vehicles*, or *carriers*. Lime, sulphur, and clay are used as vehicles to carry volatile insecticides such as nicotine and cyanide compounds.

b. Diluents. Pure insecticides of many kinds if put directly onto the plant tissues often cause "burning" or chemical injury. To prevent "burning," the insecticide must be diluted. The substance with which it is diluted is called a *diluent.* Any vehicle or carrier serves also as a diluent.

c. Spreaders. Insecticides which tend to cling to plant tissues in compact drops instead of covering the plant surface must be combined with *spreaders.* Soaps are used as spreaders in sprays containing nicotine. Lime acts as a spreader in Bordeaux mixture.

d. Adhesives. Insecticides, such as the arsenicals, if put on just with water are easily washed off by rains or are blown off or knocked off by winds and the beating together of branches. *Adhesives* are therefore added to the spray mixtures. Common adhesives are blood albumen, obtained from slaughterhouses, and casein from milk. Most spreaders act also as adhesives.

e. Emulsifiers. Insecticidal oils are applied in two ways. They are blown into fine mists or are mixed with water to make an emulsion. The mixture of oil and water is churned rapidly and forced through a pump at high pressure. This treatment breaks the oil into very minute droplets and distributes these through the water. Oils and water alone, however, will not make a permanent emulsion. A third substance known as an *emulsifier*, is added to the spray mixture. This forms a thin layer around each droplet of oil and prevents the oil from separating out of the water. The best-known and most widely used emulsifiers are soaps. Casein compounds also are good emulsifiers.

B. *The physical state of insecticides when applied.* Insecticides are applied in six different forms: as aqueous sprays, emulsions, dusts, mists, gases, and poisoned baits. Certain techniques employ a combination of two of these forms.

1. *Aqueous sprays* are used for insecticides which are soluble in water or which must be made up in water to distribute most effectively. The most widely used aqueous sprays are nicotine-soap sprays, lead arsenate, Bordeaux mixture, and lime-sulphur sprays. Both stomach poisons and contact poisons are distributed in the form of aqueous sprays.
2. *Emulsions*. As already stated, oils are applied in the form of emulsions. Oils act primarily as respiratory poisons or as contact poisons. Stomach poisons may, however, be added to oil emulsions if the value of the emulsion is not destroyed or lessened thereby.
3. *Dusts*. Many solid substances finely ground and mixed with a powdered diluent are most economically applied as dusts. They are blown into the air and allowed to settle on the plants. Dusting often results in more uniform distribution than any other method of application. It permits a great reduction in the amount of insecticide required. During recent years the dusting of field crops and orchards by airplane has proved practical and effective. The insecticides applied as dusts include sulphur, *Derris*, pyrethrum, sodium fluosilicate, cryolite, calcium cyanide, and calcium arsenate. Some of these function as stomach poisons, some as contact poisons, and some (calcium cyanide or any of the above if nicotine has been added) because they liberate poisonous gases, act as carriers for respiratory poisons.
4. *Mists* are produced by blowing liquid sprays through specially made blowers or nozzles under high pressure. They have come into use in very recent years and are proving to be highly successful. Oil emulsions and certain aqueous sprays, particularly those containing nicotine, may be applied as mists. Mists function chiefly to distribute contact poisons and are used against scale-insects, mites, aphids, thrips, and other small pests.
5. *Gases*. These are without exception respiratory poisons. They are applied as fumigants and as such have already been discussed adequately.

6. *Poisoned baits.* These are used in the control of grasshoppers, cutworms, ants, flies, sow-bugs, millipedes, snails, and slugs. All the above except the ants are controlled by the use of a poisoned bran mash. A widely used and highly successful mash for home use is made as follows: Mix, while dry, 1½ pounds of lead arsenate with 16 pounds of bran. Grind 6 small oranges or 6 lemons in a meat chopper. Add these and one quart of molasses to a gallon of water. Then add this mixture to the poisoned bran and mix thoroughly. Add more water as needed to produce a moist, but not wet, flaky mash which can be scattered readily by hand. Scatter this thinly over infested ground. Scatter it in the early morning if it is for grasshoppers; in the late afternoon if it is intended for the other pests listed. Under field conditions the bait is a little less concentrated: 1 pound of the arsenical to 25 pounds of bran being considered enough. It is also distributed more thinly, about 10 pounds to the acre being sufficient, except in very heavily infested land.

   Ants are killed by poisoned sirups set out in cans or other small containers, at the bases of trees and around house foundations where they will be found by the ants. Formulae for these sirups may be had for the asking at almost any county or state agricultural commissioner's office. Many commercial ant poisons, however, are entirely successful. The average person would do well to purchase a commercial preparation and simply follow the directions accompanying it.

   Poisoned baits for flies usually are watery rather than sirupy in nature. They are but little used now in comparison with a few years ago. A common means of dispensing fly poisons is to saturate thin blotting paper with a poison solution, dry the papers, and sell them. The dried papers are then cut into small pieces and these are put in a shallow dish of water to regenerate the poisonous solution.

II. *Cultural control.* Under this heading are included various agricultural practices which tend to prevent or discourage the development of insect pests. Whenever effective, they are more economical than chemical control for they require little or no expense or equipment besides that required for the normal care of a crop.

A. Clean culture. This consists of collecting and burning orchard litter and of plowing or disking under grain stubble and the remains of other field crops. It also includes cleaning weeds from fence rows and roadsides—in fact, keeping farms generally clean. Clean culture eliminates the materials in which pests such as the Shothole Borer breed. It eliminates also the hibernation quarters of pests like the Squash-bug.

B. Trap crops. These consist of crop plants in limited quantity sown or set out so as to develop before a main crop develops. Pest insects are attracted to them whereupon the trap crop plants are destroyed by burning or by spraying with oil. Cull onions planted around the edges of onion fields and in occasional rows through them come up quickly and attract the adults of the Onion Maggot (*Hylemyia antiqua*), a serious pest of onions in Northern United States and Canada. Straggling cabbage plants left in the field after the harvesting of a crop, and others set out very early in the spring, serve to trap Harlequin Cabbage-bugs (*Murgantia histrionica*) (Fig. 124) in both spring and fall. The only reasonably successful control of the Harlequin Cabbage-bug is through the use of trap crops combined with hand picking.

C. Crop rotation. This is an effective means of reducing pest damage in the case of insects which attack only one or a few crops. It is valueless against a general feeder. The Northern Corn Root-worm (*Diabrotica longicornis*), whose larvae feed only on corn roots, can be controlled easily and effectively by growing corn only every other year. The same is true of the Larger Cornstalk Borer (*Diatraea zeacolella*). Other insects which can be controlled by crop rotation are the Wheat Midge (*Thecodiplosis mosellana*), the Western Wheat-stem Saw-fly (*Cephus cinctus*), the Clover-root Curculio (*Sitona flavescens*), and the Tobacco Splitworm, or Potato Tuber Moth (*Phthorimaea operculella*).

D. Variation in the timing of farming operations. If fall wheat planting is delayed until the majority of Hessian-flies (*Phytophaga destructor*) have emerged, laid their eggs in other plants, and died—usually a delay of only a few days being sufficient—infestation can be greatly reduced and wheat yields increased accordingly. Early planting of cotton reduces the amount of damage by the Cotton-boll Weevil (*Anthonomus grandis*), for this leads to early setting of cotton bolls before the weevils are active or numerous.

Cutting a crop of alfalfa hay a few days early when grasshoppers or caterpillars of the Alfalfa Butterfly (*Eurymus eurytheme*) (Fig. 135) are abundant, and removing the hay from the field as quickly as possible, will reduce the amount of loss from the rapidly accelerating appetites of these growing insects.

Fall or winter plowing aids in the control of many insect pests. Fall plowing destroys many of the pupae of the Tobacco and Tomato Horn-worms (*Protoparce quinquemaculata* and *P. sexta*) (Figs. 27, 51, and 87), and the overwintering larvae of the Pea Moth (*Laspeyresia nigricana*).

III. *Physical or Mechanical Control*. This type of control includes a variety of practices in which some purely physical agency not directly related to crop handling is the means of destroying the insects. A few of the many techniques employed in physical control follow.

A. *Hand picking*. No more effective control method is known in certain cases. When insects are large and relatively scarce early in the season, hand picking is quite effective. It is an important part of the control of the Harlequin Cabbage-bug (*Murgantia histrionica*) and the only control known for the New York Weevil (*Ithycerus noveboracensis*) which eats the buds and young twigs of young apple trees.

B. *Jarring*. Fruit trees and shade trees infested with certain insects may be protected somewhat by spreading a sheet of canvas beneath a tree and jarring the tree to knock the insects off. Jarring is valuable in reducing damage due to the Green June-beetle (*Cotinus nitida*). The damage to grape vines caused by the Grape Flea-beetle (*Haltica chalybea*) may be reduced in a similar manner when only a few vines need protection, but the method is not practicable under field conditions. In this case the canvas used should be wet with oil to secure prompt killing of the beetles before they can take flight. The senior author and his wife have used jarring successfully to protect ornamental shrubs and more delicate plants from the feeding of hordes of Grass Plant Bugs (*Irbisia* spp.) which came into the garden when the wild herbage in surrounding fields dried up at the end of the spring rainy season in California. In this case an insect net was used to catch the bugs.

(*Photograph by Lester Brubaker.*)

FIG. 172.—MEALY-BUGS, THE ONLY SCALE-INSECTS WHICH REMAIN ACTIVE THROUGHOUT THEIR LIVES, CROWD BETWEEN OVERLAPPING DEAD LEAF BASES TO FEED ON THE JUICY STEM OF A BEGONIA PLANT.

Because of their juice-sucking habits, mealy-bugs, like other scale-insects and other members of the order Homoptera, cannot be killed by stomach poisons. They can be controlled by fumigation and by oil sprays which penetrate the protective coating of white wax with which they are adorned.

C. *Hosing with water.* This is sometimes effective in ridding greenhouse plants of aphids (Figs. 39 and 145) or mealy-bugs (Fig. 172).

D. *Traps.* Within recent years highly efficient electrically operated light traps have been devised. One type, developed by Professor William B. Herms and his associates, of the University of California, is lighted by neon tubes which can be changed to vary the color and the intensity of the light given off according to the insects to be caught. Surrounding the tubes is a grill of wires set close together and carrying an electric current. Alternate wires are positive and negative. As the insects fly to the light of the trap and pass between or come in contact with the wires they are electrocuted. Other and simpler but less effective light traps, which have long been used, consist of lights suspended above pans of water coated with oil. These catch any insects which fall into the oil. Older and better known types of traps are the various kinds of flytraps and bait traps used in work against the Codling Moth (*Carpocapsa pomonella*). These consist of pans filled with a sirupy liquid made especially attractive by the addition of some attrahent such as amyl acetate. The insects attracted to the baits are caught in the liquid as they attempt to feed.

E. *Hopperdozers and similar devices*. A typical hopperdozer consists of a shallow trough about 15 feet long, 3 feet wide, and 4 inches deep, mounted on skids. A vertical shield of oilcloth, metal, or boards, and about 3½ feet high, is fastened to the back of the trough. The trough is partly filled with water covered with kerosene or some other light oil. The hopperdozer is pulled back and forth across an infested field. As the grasshoppers, disturbed by the dozer, fly or jump upward they strike the screen at the back and fall into the oil-covered water.

Hoppercatchers differ in that a sheet of metal replaces the trough at the bottom and serves to guide the hoppers back to a screened box behind the vertical screen. The hoppers are thus caught alive. After a catch they are taken out, sacked and dried, and used for chicken or hog feed.

F. *Metal fences and ditches*. Wingless insects of poor jumping ability, such as the Mormon Cricket (*Anabrus simplex*) (Fig. 164) which has been so abundant and destructive in several Great Basin and Rocky Mountain states in recent years, are effectively stopped in their migrations by fences made of sheet metal. These need be only a few inches in height. The hungry crickets, having devoured much or all of the vegetation in a given area, migrate to adjoining uninfested territory. If a metal fence is installed the crickets are halted. Even so they eventually pile up in numbers sufficient to enable them to cross over the fence unless ditches, paralleling the fences, are dug. When one of these ditches fills with crickets, it is covered with earth and a new ditch dug.

G. *Heat and cold.* Cereal products, during the process of manufacture, are sometimes passed through heated rooms, or are carried by heated belts, to kill any eggs of stored-products insects, such as the Indian-meal Moth (*Plodia interpunctella*) or the Mediterranean Flour-moth (*Ephestia kuehniella*), which they may contain. The cereals are then promptly sealed in packages before additional infestation can occur.

Industrial establishments of many sorts, and occasionally private homes, are freed of all insect inhabitants by closing them and heating their interiors to temperatures between 120° and 150° Fahrenheit. The heat must be maintained within this range for several hours to be effective.

Grain elevators and storage warehouses in regions where winter temperatures go as low as 20° below zero Fahrenheit are sometimes freed of pests in the storage bins by opening the building to the outside air until the temperature inside has dropped to the outside level.

Simple refrigeration is depended on to protect hides and fur goods from pests in many modern establishments.

H. *Tanglefoot.* This sticky material, so well known for its value in capturing House-flies, has also a variety of uses in out-of doors insect control. Liquid tanglefoot painted on hopperdozers or comparable devices makes them effective in capturing leaf-hoppers and flea-beetles of various species. Bands of tanglefoot paper or belts of tree tanglefoot fastened or painted around the trunks of trees protect them from Spring and Fall Canker-worms (*Paleacrita vernata* and *Alsophila pometria*) and from tussock-moth caterpillars (*Hemerocampa*, various species). The females of all these insects are wingless, and the spread of the species, therefore, is accomplished by the caterpillars. If the caterpillars are jarred from the trees at the same time that tanglefoot is used, the latter is even more effective.

I. Constructional methods. The control of insects in stored products of every sort can be made more nearly complete and, in the long run, less expensive by the proper construction of storage bins and cases. Tightly built bins and cases effectively keep out the majority of pest insects. In museums tight construction is essential. The hundreds of thousands of insect specimens in many museums would last but a relatively short while were it not for the pestproof construction of the drawers, boxes, and cases in which they are stored.

Construction as a means of insect pest control has gained its greatest recognition in connection with the termite problem. A building, so constructed that it will resist termite attacks and with moderate care remain completely free of termites indefinitely, will possess the following features. It will rest on concrete or masonry foundations throughout. The concrete will be fine-grained and well tamped to eliminate the possibility of communicating air pockets (flaws). A brick or stone foundation will have a two-inch cap of fine-grained concrete. All sills, stringers, sleepers, and floor joists will be made of timbers impregnated with hot creosote under high pressure. Wooden sills resting on the concrete will be no closer than fourteen inches to the ground. If the building is stucco covered, the stucco will be brought down well over the foundation and great care will be taken completely to seal the stucco against the foundation. Wherever wooden rustic boards or other wall materials extend down in front of the foundation to form an apron, this apron will be built out from the foundation so as to leave an air space behind it. The apron, furthermore, will not extend downward all the way to the soil. All concrete forms and scrap lumber will be cleaned out from beneath the building and the ground leveled and raked smooth. An abundance of ventilating openings will be built into the walls below the floor level. The entire space beneath the floors will be built in free communication so as to maintain maximum air movement and thus to discourage the wood-destroying fungi which are the companions and handmaidens of termites. If the maximum protection is desired, termite shields of sheet metal will be laid between the foundations and the sills. These will project outward from both sides of the foundation for at least four inches to make it difficult for termites to build earthen tubes over the foundation and reach the floor timbers as they otherwise often do.

The above measures may sound extreme or be actually excessive in sections where termite damage is rare, but in at least two-thirds of the United States they are merely cheap insurance. They rarely add more than three per cent to the cost of a building. This amount frequently is exceeded by the cost of a single repair job due to termite damage following poor construction.

IV. *Biological Control.* In a state of primeval nature, as was pointed out in the early part of this chapter, all insects and other organisms are subject to more or less biological control by predators and parasites of many kinds and by various fungus and bacterial diseases, the result being the well-known "balance of nature." In Figs. 173 to 177 there is presented evidence of such biological control.

In utilizing biological factors as a part of applied control, man attempts one or the other of two things, depending on the manner in which the insect concerned acquired its status as a pest. If the normal balance of nature has not been disturbed but man wishes to reduce the amount of insect feeding to below that normal to the situation, he attempts to shift the natural equilibrium so that it will favor his crops, his livestock, or himself more than it now does. If an insect pest has been created by upsetting the balance of nature in any of the ways earlier described, then man attempts to restore the balance or to establish a new one. The various activities that are involved in biological control are here outlined.

A. *The use of resistant varieties.* Certain plant varieties are known to be much more resistant than others to the attacks of particular insects. Whenever such sufficiently resistant varieties are available they offer the simplest and least expensive means of insect control, for they eliminate, to a large extent, the necessity for other types of control.

On the other hand, it is often true that resistant varieties are lacking in other desirable qualities. It then becomes advisable to cross the resistant ones with varieties having good qualities generally, in the hope of securing progeny which combine in a single variety both pest resistance and the qualities required by market demands for the product. In conducting breeding experiments, resistant varieties are studied anatomically and physiologically to learn why they are resistant, for such knowledge is of value in planning the experiments and deciding which crosses to attempt. Examples follow.

Owing to hardness of the husk, the walnut varieties, Placentia and Seedling, are more resistant to attacks by the Walnut-husk Fly (*Rhagoletis completa*) than are many other walnut varieties. Certain varieties of wheat which have a relatively high ash or silica content in the stems are more resistant to the Hessian-fly (*Phytophaga destructor*) than other varieties. The more acid varieties of apples escape much of the infestation by the Apple Maggot (*Rhagoletis pomonella*) to which the sweeter varieties are subject.

B. *The use of bacterial, fungus, protozoal, and virus diseases.* Insects suffer from various diseases caused by the attacks of other organisms. Nearly everyone has seen House-flies and related species that have been killed by the fly fungus (*Empusa muscae*). With their abdomens swollen by the growth of the fungus, the dead flies cling to wood surfaces or glass. Between the dark abdominal sclerites are broad bands of grayish or yellowish intersegmental membranes. All around each fly is a sort of halo or aura of fungus spores adhering to the wood or glass on which the fly rests. Similar fungus diseases affect caterpillars, grasshoppers, and many other insects.

It is the hope of entomologists and agriculturists that techniques may be developed which will permit the manipulation of disease-producing organisms so that an epidemic of some disease or other may be generated when an insect outbreak threatens. So far the results have not been especially promising. In certain cases a high degree of insect control has been achieved; in others, none at all.

C. *The introduction of predatory and parasitic insects.* This method has to date brought many notable successes and promises to bring more. The explanation of its greater success as

(*Photograph by Lester Brubaker.*)

FIG. 173.—A MIXED COLONY OF SCALE-INSECTS TELLS A COMPLEX AND INTERESTING STORY. The large, fluted, white masses are the cottony, cushion-like, egg cocoons from which the Cottony-cushion Scale (*Icerya purchasi*) gets its name. They are made of innumerable minute threads of white wax produced by glands on the undersurface of the abdomen. Each cushion contains several hundred eggs. Nearly mature female scales with hair-fringed bodies, but before they have begun to form egg cushions, are to be seen in the upper right-hand corner of the figure. The two gaping, black exit holes in the large scale below and to right of center proclaim it to be a dead scale that has been killed by a tiny parasitic fly (*Cryptochaetum iceryae*) whose maggots feed on the scale's interior. Just to the left of this scale is a mealy-bug-like ladybird larva. At the lower left the scene is occupied by roundish, slightly convex Greedy Scales (*Aspidiotus rapax*), large and small; and a few elongate Oyster Shell Scales (*Lepidosaphes ulmi*). Two Argentine Ants in search of honeydew complete the picture.

compared with the use of bacterial, fungus, and protozoal diseases seems to be that the activities of predatory and parasitic insects are less sharply restricted by weather conditions than are the disease-producing organisms. For example, the development of an epidemic of a fungus disease requires that the relative humidity of the air be high. If the relative humidity drops below the critical level, the fungus ceases to be active. A ladybird beetle, by comparison, continues to eat aphids whether the weather be humid or dry.

The outstanding example of pest control through the importation of parasites and predators is the oft-cited case of the Cottony-cushion Scale (*Icerya purchasi*) (Fig. 173) in California. This scale-insect was accidentally introduced

FIG. 174.—A PARASITIC WASP LARVA OF THE FAMILY BRACONIDAE SPINS ITS COCOON BESIDE THE DYING SMALL CATERPILLAR WHICH WAS, UNTIL A FEW MOMENTS BEFORE, THE UNWILLING HOST OF THE WASP LARVA.

Inside the now dying caterpillar the wasp larva grew, feeding first on the tissue fluids of its host and later on the tissues themselves. Then the braconid bored its way out of the caterpillar to spin its cocoon and transform to an adult wasp. Braconid wasps play an important role in the biological control of many vegetarian insects.

into Menlo Park, California, about 1868. By 1883 it had multiplied tremendously and spread over much of the fruit-growing portion of the state. By 1888 it had killed outright hundreds of thousands of citrus trees. The doom of the citrus industry seemed at hand. In that year Albert Koebele was sent to Australia, believed to be the native home of the insect, to search for parasites and predators. He found there a minute parasitic fly (*Cryptochaetum iceryae*) and the Vedalia Ladybird (*Rodolia cardinalis*). These he found to be attacking the scale. Large numbers of both insects were shipped to the State Insectary at Sacramento, California, and from the few which arrived alive large stocks were reared. When many thousands were available they were distributed over the state and were liberated in the infested citrus groves and orchards.

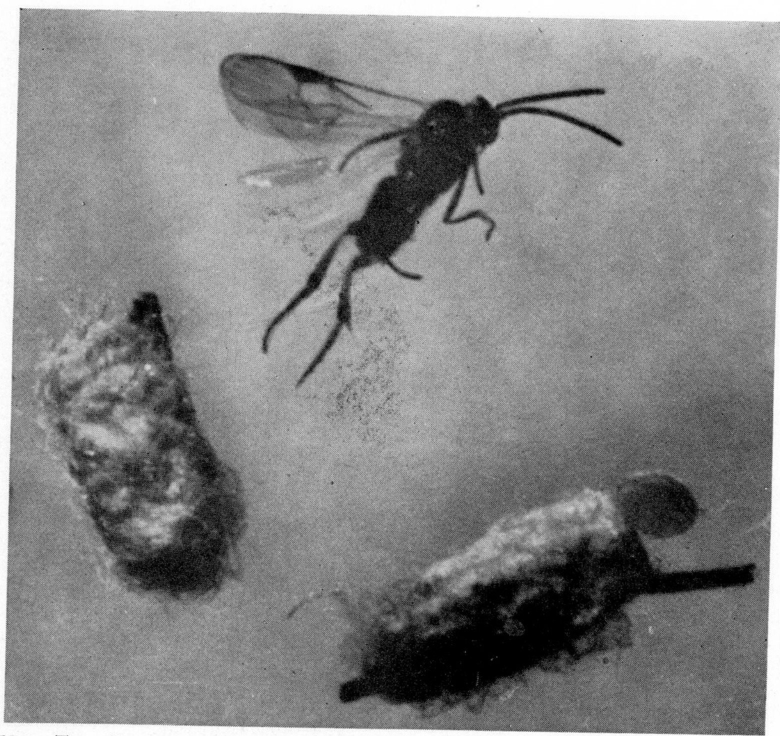

Fig. 175.—Two Cocoons of Braconid Wasps, and a Wasp That Emerged from One of Them. At maturity this little braconid wasp cut a circular lid out of one end of the cocoon at the lower right.

Both the *Cryptochaetum* fly and the Vedalia Ladybird adapted themselves to California conditions as well as the Cottony-cushion Scale had done before them. They made short work of the scale-insects. By 1890 all fear for the fruit industry had disappeared. Since that time the Cottony-cushion Scale, except for an occasional local outbreak in a district where the *Cryptochaetum* and the Vedalia have died out for lack of food, the scale has been rare. It has been so rare, in fact, that the average orchardist has never seen one. The local outbreaks referred to are quickly subdued by shipments of *Cryptochaetum* and the Vedalia sent out from Sacramento, or obtained elsewhere in the state.

No other case of biological control by the use of parasites and predators has been so phenomenally successful as that of the Cottony-cushion Scale. Successes have been suffi-

FIG. 176.—THIS CATERPILLAR PLAYED HOST TO SEVERAL PARASITES.
Sometimes a caterpillar will yield up not one but many parasite larvae, each of which spins its cocoon close by or even on its dead host. Twenty-three cocoons proclaim the fact that twenty-three parasite larvae derived their sustenance from the tissues of this caterpillar. Small wonder, then, that the caterpillar lacks vitality to continue living.

ciently extensive and frequent, however, to have established the method as a regular part of the pest control program of nearly every state and country.

In this country both the abundance and the rate of spread of the Gypsy Moth (*Porthetria dispar*) have been greatly reduced by the importation of numerous parasites and predators from Europe and Asia. Prominent among these in its effectiveness has been the large and handsome ground-beetle (*Calosoma sycophanta*). During its larval and adult life each of these beetles will consume the equivalent of nearly 300 full-grown Gypsy Moth caterpillars.

Successes such as these are gratifying but they do not signify that biological control through the use of parasites and predators is free from problems and difficulties. Predatory insects as well as vegetarians are subject to parasites, and parasites are subject to hyperparasites. Since the introduction of hyperparasites would nullify the good accomplished by primary parasites, great caution must be exercised to avoid their introduction. In fact, the desired predators and primary parasites must be reared for several generations under careful observation to make sure they are free from parasitism before being shipped to a new country.

FIG. 177.—THE WOOLLY BEAR CATERPILLAR AND ONE OF ITS PARASITES ILLUSTRATE ONE PHASE IN THE BALANCE OF NATURE.

One of nature's methods of keeping a check on insect numbers is by the use of parasites. Thus woolly bears conceivably might overrun the land if some of them were not destroyed in this fashion. The parasite here is a tachinid fly. On the left is a healthy woolly bear. Next is a dead woolly bear, with its body distorted by the squirming larvae of the parasites within. The woolly bear on the right has been opened to show two of the parasite larvae. On the extreme right a parasite larva is shown above; below it, a puparium of the parasite. Inset are two adult tachinid flies.

V. *Legal Control.* Legal measures exert their influence indirectly but they are at present an important part of any well-worked-out pest control program. Legal controls take several forms.

A. *Nuisance legislation.* Many districts and some states now have laws placing the responsibility for pest control on property owners. If an owner fails to control the pests and his property becomes a reservoir of pests from which other places are infested he may be declared to be maintaining a nuisance. He may then be required to control the pests, or the county or state may bring them under control and assess the landowner for the cost of the control work.

B. *Crop standardization laws*, stating that no produce may be marketed unless it measures up to established standards of quality, stimulate farmers and fruitgrowers to control insect pests. Infested produce nearly always fails to be of standard quality.

C. *Embargoes on imports*. Many out-of-state and foreign agricultural products, the importation of which might lead to the introduction of new and dangerous pests, are denied entry into the states concerned or into the country as a whole. Several fruits are thus excluded from the United States because they are likely to be infested with larvae of the Mediterranean Fruit-fly (*Ceratitis capitata*).

D. *Inspection and quarantine*. Products not actually excluded are subjected to inspection at points of entry. If badly infested, they are destroyed. In some cases they may be fumigated or given other needed treatment at the shipper's expense before being released ot be marketed.

E. *Pest abatement districts* are established under special legislation to further the control of particular pests. For example, such legislation in many sections provides for a tax levy on all property owners to provide the money needed for projects in the control of mosquitoes and other pests which present community problems rather than individual problems.

F. *Building codes and regulations*. Many states and communities now have building regulations requiring that all new buildings of a permanent character shall embody features of termite-resistant construction (see pp. 337 and 338). Such regulations eventually will largely eliminate extensive damage by termites.

G. *Examination and licensing of pest control companies*. Certain states now require that individuals and corporations which engage in pest control as a business shall be licensed as pest control operators; and that each person engaged in pest control, whether privately or as an official of a corporation, shall be required to pass a comprehensive examination to test his fitness to engage in pest control before being issued a license. The laws setting up these requirements also provide for punishments to be meted out to violators.

H. *Limitations on governmental aids.* The latest development in legal measures aimed at pest control is embodied in the regulations governing loans made by the Federal Housing Administration. Before a building is accepted as the security for a loan it must be inspected by a competent investigator and demonstrated to be pest free; or the construction work covered by the loan must begin with the elimination of termites, wood-destroying fungi, etc., and repair of the damage which they have occasioned.

CONCLUSION

The expanding field of insect control is requiring the attention of an ever-increasing number of well-trained men and women. Probably no other field in the range of biological endeavor, with the exception of medicine and bacteriology, offers so much promise to the young biologist of today. Investigators of every sort are needed, as well as field men to put into effect the findings of the investigators. The authors commend the field of entomology to the modern youth of ambition and ability who is looking anxiously to the future.

CHAPTER XVII

WHERE TO LOOK FOR INSECTS

INSECTS occur wherever living things are found except in the depths of the sea. No other class of animals is so widely distributed. They occur where one would think no animal could possibly live, such as the surface of snowbanks, the most stagnant of pools, the hottest of deserts, and even in puddles of oil! They are found below the ground, on the ground, on the surface of water, in the water, on every conceivable part of a plant, in the air to great heights, on living animals, in living animals, in dead animals, in everything that may be derived from animals; and, though insects are predominantly terrestrial, a few occur far out at sea!

From this it will be seen that he who would collect insects need never lack for a collecting ground. And the wise young collector will do well to start by taking any and all insects that he may find. In no other way can he gain the wide knowledge of this great class that he should have before he specializes on any one portion. Soft larval forms he will preserve in a ten per cent formalin solution, or in rubbing alcohol, which can be bought at any drugstore; firmer insects will be spread, dried, and pinned in boxes. And, above all things, records of place and date of capture will be made. Names will be searched for.

Let us start on a collecting trip from home. We shall go through the house, through the back yard, through an orchard, along a dusty road, up a small grass-covered, rock-strewn hill, into a bit of woodland, then into a wooded canyon that has a brook, and then visit a small pond. We shall have a sturdy collecting net, a killing bottle, a box (a cigar box will do) with a number of sheets of heavy paper, a trowel, some small vials and pillboxes. Most of these can be carried in a small knapsack, or in a belt with pockets that any clever boy can make.

At home. First of all, search Gyp, your dog. He is a most unusual dog if he doesn't have a representative of an annoying and impressive insect order—the order of fleas. And if Gyp has fleas, you may be sure that a careful search through the dust of his kennel will show tiny, squirming, dusty maggots, the larvae of the fleas (Fig. 140). Down in your basement you may spot a shining Silverfish (Fig. 170) as it slides into a crevice. There was a time when almost any home would show more insects than these, but the modern home is much too clean and well kept to have bedbugs, House-flies, or mosquitoes inside. But no house can fail to attract a clothes-moth, and our keen-eyed student will certainly see these tiny insects as they fly

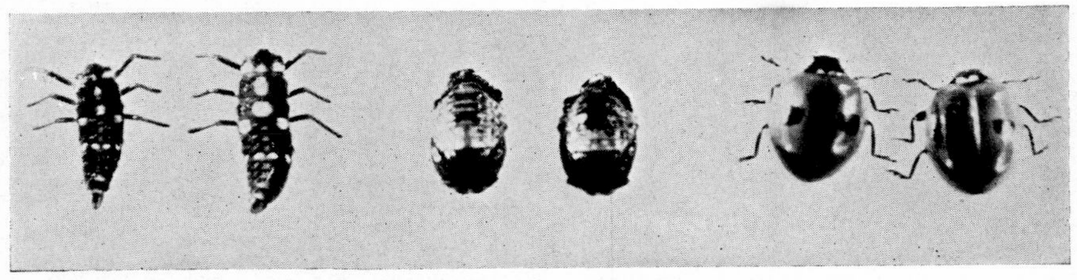

FIG. 178.—THE ROSES OF YOUR BACK YARD MAY SHOW THE COMPLETE LIFE HISTORY OF A LADYBIRD BEETLE.

Here on the left are two ladybird larvae; in the center, two pupae; and at the right, two adult beetles. The ladybird beetle is in your back yard to eat aphids, and there you should find it.

about at night in search of furs or woolens. You will know them because they are one of the smallest of moths and have an uncanny habit of darting into dark nooks and closets because, unlike nearly all other moths, they avoid the light and seek the dark. Nature has taught them through the ages that the thing their larvae eat will be hid away in dark places. If Mother pulls forth, some day, a woolen garment and cries, "The moths have eaten it," ask her to let you see it. Carefully pick up the little bundles of woolen lint on the garment and carefully pluck the fibers apart. In their midst you may find a tiny white caterpillar, the larva of a clothes-moth, a wolf indeed in sheep's clothing.

The back yard is a small universe of nature interest. If you really do justice to the insects there you may never get up the small hill with its grass cover and stones. Lift first the board that lies beneath the sprinkler tap. A small army of many-legged creatures is disturbed! Pill-bugs and sow-bugs are there by dozens. They are crustaceans, not insects, so today we shall ignore them. The slimy slugs we also overlook. But beetles, beetles on long, loosely jointed legs, we snatch up and plop into the killing bottle. Look closely. Isn't there a small short-legged insect there with a pair of forceps at the posterior end of its body? If so, you have an earwig for your bottle (Fig. 128).

Pull apart that pile of rotting leaf mold. If it is wet enough, fly maggots will be there. Their pale, writhing bodies, legless and seemingly headless, cannot be mistaken. Put one or two into a small

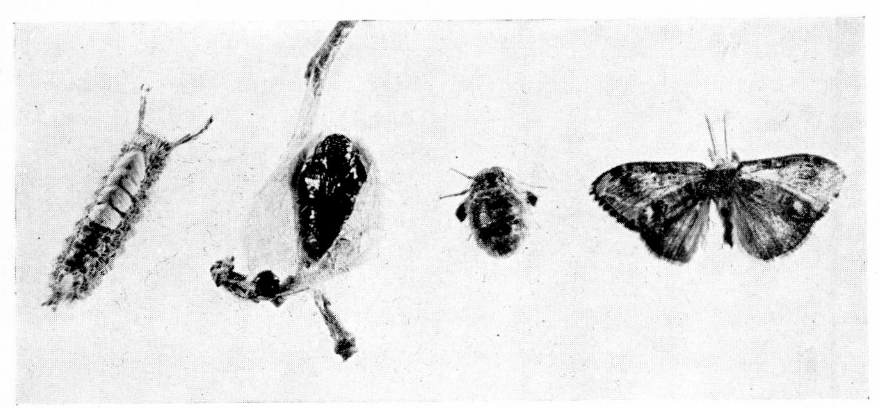

FIG. 179.—YOUR SHADE TREES, IN THE SUMMERTIME, MAY SHOW THE COMPLETE LIFE HISTORY OF THE TUSSOCK-MOTH.

The gaudy, bristling caterpillar with a toothbrush back will bring an exclamation, but when you search further and find a pursy-bodied, stump-winged female on an empty cocoon, it will bring more than an exclamation. Here the larva, or caterpillar, is shown at the left; next is an open cocoon showing a pupa; next a female with her little stubs for wings; and lastly the male.

vial of formalin or alcohol. Pick up several more, along with a handful of the moist debris in which they live. Place debris, maggots, and all, into a pillbox. You will want to watch those living maggots from time to time on succeeding days, for they will undergo a complete life history before your eyes, without any attention whatsoever on your part. From legless, nearly headless maggots they will change to stiff, brownish cases in which the pupae form; from pupae the adult flies will come. The whole process will require only a few days, but a few days from lowly maggots to one of the most highly developed adults of the entire insect world! In late spring, if your eaves' drains have not been cleaned, there will be the maggots of the long-legged crane-fly. Clean out the drain, but save some of the crane-fly maggots in their damp leaf mold. Shortly you will have a series showing the whole life history for your collection. Figures 14 and 71 were made from crane-fly maggots secured in just this way.

Now with the trowel do a little digging. Within the ground are many insects. Many of them will be too small for an amateur insect collector, but some big, fat beetle grubs may turn up. They will go into the alcohol, unless you wish to rear them too.

The possibilities of that back yard are almost unlimited! Turn over some clods among the chrysanthemums. You may find that Black Cricket that sang "chee, chee, chee" beneath your bedroom window. You may find the black songster and his mate. At the base of that small flower or plant that was cut off in the night you may uncover a big fat cutworm curled up in a daytime retreat. If you hadn't stopped that cutworm, it would have been a moth some day.

But that grassy hill with its stones is still far away, and we haven't lifted our eyes above the back-yard ground! Turn next to the plants in the flower garden. If flowers are blooming, flies and bees, ants and butterflies will be searching out their nectar. Here swing your net and use the killing bottle. Don't put too many in that bottle. The insects will damage each other. As soon as one is dead remove it, fold it in a paper envelope,[1] and transfer it to the cigar box for safe keeping until you return from the grassy hill, the woodland, and the pond.

Now, if your rosebushes haven't been sprayed recently their upper stems will have plant-lice, or aphids. Search here, insect collector! See pursy, small green bodies that almost cover the upper stems. Note empty, molted shells at lower levels; and among them see some aphids with wings (Fig. 39), the forms that will move on to start a line of aphids on other rosebushes. Your gardener, of course, knows how to protect the rosebushes from aphids. But long before there were gardeners, nature had worked out a scheme that helps to keep aphids in check. Do you notice among those aphids some lady-bird beetles? They are there to feed on aphids. And the larvae of the ladybird beetles may be there doing the same thing (Fig. 178). Feeding on aphids, too, may be the large-jawed but small larvae of the lacewing-fly. And, most exciting of all, beneath a rose leaf may be the eggs from which come those larval lacewing-flies (Fig. 60).

[1] Or, if it is a beetle, drop it into a tube made of stiff paper. Your box will have paper strips of various sizes from which you will make on the spot a tube of a size suitable for the insect you are papering. Figure 194 shows how to fold these tubes and envelopes.

Among these same aphids may be observed a curious fly maggot that, like the young lacewing-fly and the young ladybird beetles, is there to make its living by eating aphids. This maggot is the larva of *Syrphus*, a bee-like fly. These maggots thrust their pointed head end into the soft body of an aphid and swing it about as they extract its juices.

And ants, ants, ants! A continuous stream of them probably marches up and down the rose stem. They are eating not aphids but the "honey-dew," that peculiar excretion that aphids produce and ants are fond of (Fig. 145).

In the evening, after you return from the orchard, the hill, the woodland, with its brook and pond, the sun may have set. Then, if it is summer or autumn, a rapid "chur, chur, chur, chur" will lead you to a Snowy Tree Cricket among the geraniums or other flowers.

If you inspect the shade or fruit trees of your garden you may discover, crawling over the bark of the tree, a gaudy, bristling caterpillar with white-and-black hair-tufts arranged in striking patterns over a vivid red, blue, and yellow spotted body. This is the caterpillar of a tussock-moth. It will not be necessary to attempt to rear this caterpillar, for close inspection will show, in the crevices of the bark, small brown cocoons that other tussock caterpillars have made. Some of these will not contain living insects, but will have been parasitized by other insects; and the larva or the pupa within the cocoon will be dead and dry. But from some of the others wingless female moths will emerge. These females will mate, lay their eggs in a felty mass upon the empty cocoon, and die there without leaving. The males have wings, however, and long antennae, the sense organs of which help them to find the females (Fig. 179).

The garden isn't half inspected, but gardens can wait; they are always just behind the house. And grassy hill and wooded dell and little pond are calling.

The orchard is next. A well-kept orchard has few insects, except for flies and bees in blossomtime. But the weeds along the margins and at the bases of the trees will show some six-legged crawlers for the collector's bottles. Ants there always are, and tiny beetles crawl over the soil. Here and there among the branches may be the web houses of a colony of tent-caterpillars.

The dusty road. To reach the hill it will be necessary to make a short journey along a dusty road. Two insects will tempt your net: one, the Carolina Locust, will leap into the air before you to show its beautiful black-and-white wings that strike each other with a crackle like the clacking of castanets. The other will be an adult tiger-beetle that runs with amazing speed over the dust and leaps into the air to fly suddenly a few feet beyond your reach. It will try your insect-catching ability to the utmost before you finally bag it.

When horses were more frequent travelers along the dusty road, you might have found tumble-bugs or dung-beetles industriously rolling pellets of manure.

In the rank weeds along this road one will find the long-horned grasshoppers. Their singing wings will be a constant accompaniment of the heat of July or August.

The hill? What's on a hill? First of all, sweep your net back and forth among the grasses. You will bag an astonishing assortment of bees and flies, crane-flies, grasshoppers, plant-bugs, and beetles. Into the killing bottle with them! If it is spring, and wild flowers bloom, then Checker-spot Butterflies will dart from blossom to blossom. Unless you are an expert with that net, they will show you up. If buttercups are blooming among the tall grasses on the lower portions of the hill, the blossoms will disclose the coal-black, long-legged dance-flies.

Now turn several stones. Sooner or later, if you are turning stones in the Far West, a big black beetle will walk stiff-leggedly and slowly away, with abdomen turned toward the sky. This is a darkling-beetle bombarding (Fig. 85). Pick the beetle up and expect a bad odor on the fingers. That is nothing; you are an insect collector.

The bombarding darkling-beetle bottled, look then beneath the rock for the mud nests of mud-dauber wasps. Each cell of the nest will have a load of paralyzed spiders, and may have a wasp egg at the bottom. If the wasp egg has hatched, the spiders may have been eaten, and the cell will have a larval wasp or one that has grown and pupated. In any case, the old cocoon of the pupal wasp will still remain, even though the wasp has grown and gone. Beneath the stone there may be the nest of a papermaking wasp, *Polistes*. If that is true, it will not be necessary to look long, for the wasps will tell you that their nest is near.

Sit on the rock to get your breath. If you are in the Far West, a great, scintillating wasp with henna-colored wings may alight on the ground and busily prospect here and there. It is *Pepsis*, the

Tarantula Hawk. Now that you have her in the net, be careful; get *Pepsis* into the jar without touching her. She has an ugly sting. And speaking of ugly stings, here is a warning about that big, reddish ant that is running here and there in the dust at the base of a stone. It is no ant at all, but a mutillid, a wingless wasp, with a potent sting. Catch and handle it with that in mind. And as you sit, grass-

FIG. 180.—IF YOU SIFT THE DIRT IN THOSE LITTLE PITS AT THE BASE OF A TREE, YOU WILL FIND THE TINY DUSTY DEMON THAT IS THE DOODLE-BUG.

The doodle-bug is the larval ant-lion. Ant-lions are ant-lions because they build those pits which cause ants to tumble down into the big jaws that await them just beneath the dust. To learn the rest of the doodle-bug's life history see Figs. 115 and 116.

hoppers will vault from the ground and clack their upper wings together as they hover in aerial song.

And now our woodland! No single journey can get all the insects of any garden, of any hill, of any woodland. Insects vary from season to season and are always too numerous to do in a day: that's one big reason why insects fascinate. As you approach the woodland, if it be late summer, you will hear the song of the cicadas (Fig. 98) high in the trees; and on the trails, brilliant tiger-beetles will scurry.

First of all, beat the shrubs with the net. It's a sturdy net, you know. Hold the bag down and strike upwards against the twigs and leaves. Many, many insects tumble down: big insects, little insects, young insects, grown insects.

The first broad-leaved plants, whether they be herbs or shrubs or trees, will show the evidence of insects that work in the thinnest homes in the world. These are the leaf-miners that spend their growing days working between walls that are closer together than the thickness of a leaf. More than that, these miners may spend their early lives within a portion of one side of a leaf that is only a few microscopic cells deep. Leaf-miners are of many kinds. You will most likely find some that make blotches on one side of a leaf; others that make a long serpentine mine with a tiny beginning that increases in width and winds around and around as the larva that makes it grows in a kingdom that is paper-thin (Fig. 100).

Some of the oaks at the fringe of the woods may have "oak apples," those curious balls that minute insects cause the oaks to make (Fig. 40). In the center of each "apple" a tiny insect larva may be found. Wild roses, too, will have galls of several sorts.

Look carefully in the dust at the base of a tree for those fascinating pits of the doodle-bugs. Doodle-bugs are ant-lions, and ants are forever going up and down trees to ant cows and other pastures aloft. What better place for a dooble-bug that likes ant juices than at the base of a tree? Blow softly a little dust into the funnel of the doodle-bug. The doodle-bug reacts as if an ant were tumbling down, and flips its head to bring down more dust and cause the ant to tumble faster. Your breathing when you say the "Doodle-bug, Doodle-bug" poem, that is supposed to bring out the doodle-bug, blows down a little dust in a similar fashion, and the doodle-bug responds. The doodle-bug lives in the dust at the bottom of the pit with only the big mandibles protruding (Fig. 180). Scoop up this dust and you will have the doodle-bug. Take him home, dust and all, and he will make a new funnel for you.

And here is a fallen log. What a treasure mine is a fallen log! If it is winter, the bark you peel away may show a hibernating yellowjacket queen. Her antennae will be pulled back and her wings tucked under for the big "sleep" that precedes her nest building in the spring (Fig. 158). Beneath that bark will be, in winter, many other hibernating insects. Round-headed beetle larvae will be there, too, and squirming crane-fly maggots; and carpenter ants may have established a populous colony. Dig into the rotten wood with the trowel. Tunnels may lead to a big white larva of the Pine Sawyer (Figs. 25 and 73), one of the boring beetles. And if you dig a little deeper, the runways of those pale, light-shunning, wood-eating termites, may be disclosed. Now turn over the log—and work!

The pond. The day is too short! You leave the log with regret (of course you turned it back into place for another insect crop) and here at last is the pond. What can one do with a pond? Many,

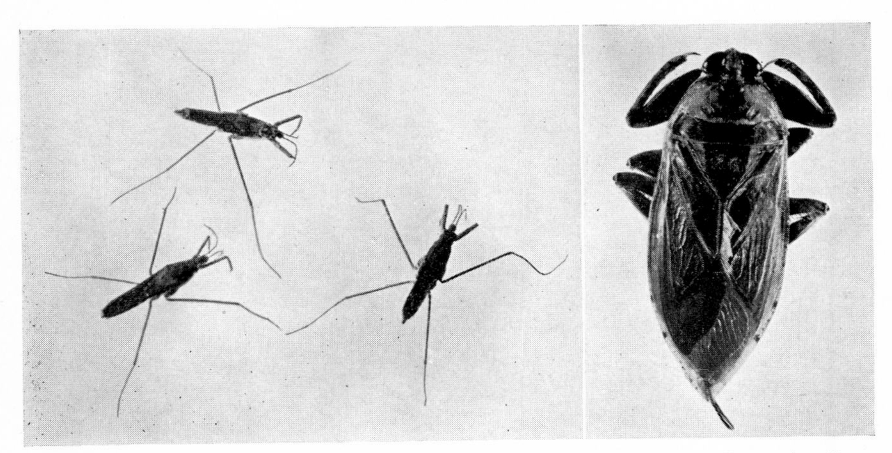

FIG. 181.—ON WATERS THAT ARE SLACK, LONG-LEGGED *Gerris* STRIDES; WHERE WATERS ARE QUIET AND DEEP, THE GIANT WATER-BUG LURKS.

Gerris (left) is the water-strider that will be on every quiet pool or eddy, waiting to grasp with its front legs any hapless insect that falls to the water's surface. The Giant Water-bug hides below the surface ready to grasp, also with front legs, an insect, a tadpole, or a small fish.

many things. So many, in fact, that the sun will be casting long shadows over its surface before all the things are done.

First there is *Gerris*, the Strider, marching over the surface (Fig. 181). *Gerris* is a true bug and, when on land, apparently a clumsy one. But before you have *Gerris* in your bottle you will have a new respect for water-striders. Don't make the mistake of putting *Gerris* in a bottle of water if you want to get him home alive. *Gerris* lives on the *top* of the water and not *in* it.

And whirligig-beetles! They don't stride over the top of the water, but swim on the surface film. They have two pairs of eyes, one pair to see above water and one pair to see below. And when they are alarmed, they dive to the bottom. To get them you must use your net as a seine—and be quick!

The swing of your net through the water should get mosquito wrigglers, midge larvae, and, in the late winter, that interesting aquatic larva, the Mosquito Destroyer, or Phantom Larva. You will miss seeing the Mosquito Destroyer unless you look closely, even though it is larger than a mosquito wriggler, for it is as transparent as glass and has only two small black floats on its anterior end to show you where it is. That net swing should get water-boatmen

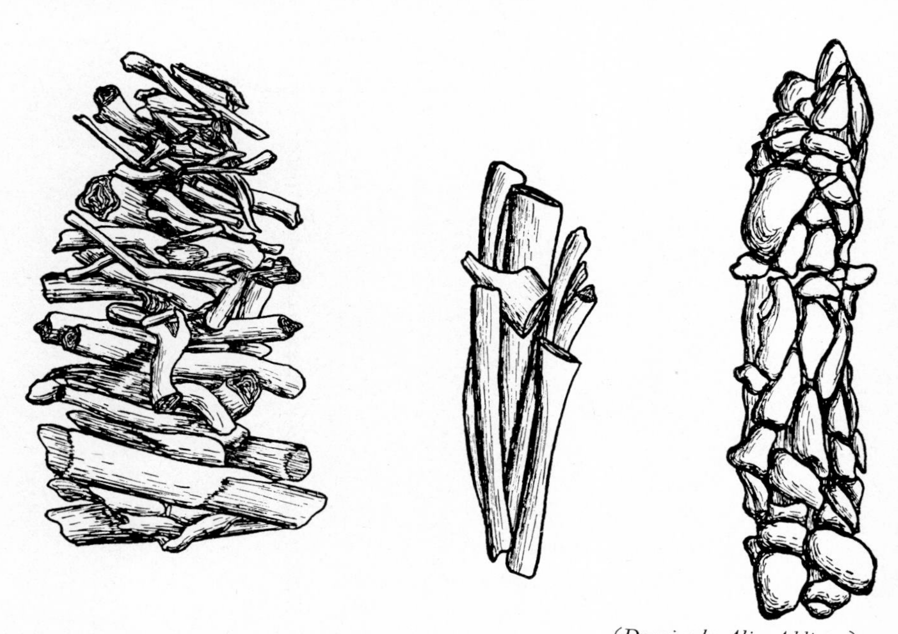

(*Drawing by Alice Addicott.*)

FIG. 182.—ON THE CLEAR BOTTOM OF FLOWING STREAMS CADDIS-FLY HOUSES MAY SEEM TO WALK. The houses "walk," of course, only when the caddis-fly larva that lives inside thrusts out its legs and walks. Caddis-fly houses are of many kinds. Can you find as many kinds as are shown here?

(Fig. 75), back-swimmers (Fig. 105), and water-bugs (Fig. 104), diving-beetles, and those water-tigers, the larvae of the diving-beetles. Don't put them all together. The water-bugs and back-swimmers will kill all the rest. And water-bugs and back-swimmers can give you painful stings with their beaks too; so handle them with care.

Next sweep the underwater vegetation. Lugubrious dragon-fly naiads will result (Figs. 53 and 80). Last, scrape up a little of the bottom mud and let it trickle over the bank. Another dragon-fly naiad, a sprawling, flattened type, quite unlike those that live upon the vegetation, may come forth.

The brook! Where it goes dashing over a bed of small boulders, pause; turn over a stone, snatch up a stone-fly naiad (Fig. 119) as it slithers away in the wetness. Where the water flows slowly over a sandy bottom, look for the cases of caddis-flies (Fig. 182). In this same quiet eddy, *Gerris*, the Strider, is again at home. The pond was merely sampled, and these few insects give merely a sample from the brook; but our day is done. Promise yourself that some day that pond and brook will receive more attention.

Homeward now! On the way you may pass a dead animal—a dog or cat or bird. Well, hold your nose, but don't pass it by. Take a stick and turn it over. A writhing mass of blow-fly larvae will show up. They are not so desirable, but their brown puparia may be here and there upon the ground. If so, they will shortly give you adult blow-flies. Look again; carrion-beetles may run scurrying away. They provide another insect for the killing bottle.

Home again! What a day! Already from the back yard come the first notes from the Black Cricket and the Snowy Tree Cricket. But the day is not yet done. The maggots and larvae must be supplied with new homes in cans and jars that have lids with holes for air. The doodle-bug must have a pan of dust. The aquatic insects must be separated—carnivores from herbivores, boatmen and mosquito wrigglers together, back-swimmers, dragon-fly naiads, and water-bugs by themselves. The containers that hold the aquatic insects must not have too many insects in proportion to the amount of water. Stone-flies and caddis-flies you cannot hope to keep alive for long unless the conditions of the brook can be duplicated, and that means a stream of running water. In any case, an example of each should be preserved for the collection, in formalin or alcohol; these insects shrivel badly when dried. Before they harden, spread the wings of moths, butterflies, and grasshoppers on your spreading board.

Take a deep breath. Vow that you will do your best to look up all their names. To do so will take you on another trip—a trip into books.

CHAPTER XVIII

REARING INSECTS

It is thrilling to find caterpillars and grasshoppers, moths and butterflies, beetles and dragon-flies out-of-doors and to study them in their natural habitats, but if the thrill must end with what may be seen in the field, much of the pleasure and value of insect study will be lost. Field trips of necessity are short, and contacts with insects in the field, therefore, brief in duration—too brief to be satisfying. Of course, specimens can be brought back and preserved in alcohol or mounted in cases for display and study, and much may be learned thereby, but the enthusiastic student wants to watch his caterpillars devour leaves, and his mantids capture and eat their prey. He wants to see his Mole Crickets and Jerusalem Crickets burrow into the soil. He wants the exciting experience of watching a caddis-fly, a moth, or a butterfly emerge from its pupal skeleton and become a colorful, flying marvel before his very eyes. And so he must bring back some of his treasures alive and keep them at home or in the schoolroom where he can observe them day after day. In order to satisfy these desires, suitable equipment must be taken into the field and care must be given to captive insects after they have been brought home.

SOME GENERAL CONSIDERATIONS

It is frequently said that in order to rear insects successfully it is necessary to provide them with surroundings as nearly as possible like those to which they are accustomed. This statement is only partially true. It is not necessary to supply caged insects with a miniature garden or field; nor is it necessary to duplicate a bit of woodland indoors to rear insects satisfactorily. Moreover, it is often undesirable to do so. They have been brought back that they may be observed. They should not, therefore, be supplied with too normal an environment lest they find so many opportunities for concealment as to defeat the purpose in keeping them. Certain conditions, however, must be supplied. Captive specimens must have sufficient food of the right kind, enough but not too much water, and their cages must be well ventilated.

The food supply. Providing the proper food for captive insects is generally, though not always, a relatively easy matter. Herbivorous insects, such as caterpillars and leaf-beetles, are found as a rule on the plant on which they feed, but sometimes the problem is more difficult. For example, what should one feed to grasshoppers or to caterpillars which were not actually on plants but were taken in a field where several kinds of plants were growing? It is a common belief that grasshoppers will eat anything green, and certain widely distributed species will. There are some kinds, on the other hand, that may be found in almost any community, which will accept only a limited number of plants. Lacking these, they will starve rather than so much as nibble anything else. In such cases the hoppers, or other insects which behave similarly, must be supplied with a bit of each of the kinds of plants present in the field where they were collected, and carefully observed until it is discovered which ones they will take.

If picked leaves are supplied to herbivorous insects, these should be renewed frequently and the uneaten parts removed. Wilted or partially dried leaves are deficient in water and may retard growth and development. Accumulations of old leaves become moldy and sometimes lead to outbreaks of disease. Young insects, especially those just hatched from eggs, should be given the most tender parts of their food plants.

Aquatic vegetarians are more likely to feed on algae than on anything else. Some, however, eat decomposing sticks, fallen tree leaves, and other detritus. If the water in which such insects are kept contains these materials, taken preferably from the place where the insects were collected, no other food will be necessary in most cases. Borers in dry or decaying woods may be reared simply by putting some of the wood containing the insects into suitable containers such as are described later on in this chapter. Larvae which feed on ripening seeds, such as those of sunflowers and thistles, may be brought to maturity indoors if ripening flower heads are picked. It is often advisable to put the stems of these into water until the insects emerge.

Gall-insects can be reared only if the galls are mature or nearly so when picked. If one wishes to rear leaf-miners, he should pick branches bearing infested leaves and put these into jars of water in suitable cages until the insects emerge.

Insects which eat nectar and honeydew, such as moths, butterflies, bees, wasps, and various flies, may be kept quite successfully if they are given sirup or molasses mixed with enough water to thin it to an easily flowing state. Dip a piece of cloth or paper towel into the mixture and suspend this in the cage with the specimens.

Predatory insects present comparable problems concerning a food supply. Some, like most aquatic predators, are rather general feeders and will feed on any insect or other small creature which they can capture and hold, but many kinds show preferences. Dragon-fly and damsel-fly naiads should be fed the smaller and softer-bodied prey, such as mosquito larvae and small tadpoles; diving-beetles, back-swimmers, and Giant Water-bugs will feed readily on larger and more hard-shelled prey. Terrestrial predators, especially those found under bark or in rotting wood, are more difficult to care for but the trial-and-error method of discovering their food preferences will eventually lead to success.

Certain types of insects are difficult to keep successfully for any length of time unless one has special equipment. Examples are such aquatic insects as live in rapidly running water and strain out microscopic food from the water. Neither adequate food nor sufficient oxygen can be supplied to these insects. Insects, such as bark-beetles, which live in the cambium layer of trees, are difficult to rear. After the wood is cut the cambium soon dies. Besides, the small pieces one must put in a cage dry out too rapidly to permit the insects to mature. Specimens that are nearly full grown when collected, however, will complete their development.

Water. The water supply for caged insects is fully as important as the food supply, but is often neglected. A large percentage of the insects which die when brought indoors, or which fail to transform to the adult stage, do so because of an insufficient water supply. This is especially true of pupae. Caterpillars, and other insects living on green food, need not be given water if their food is succulent, plentiful, and frequently replenished. All insects, such as flies, bees, and wasps, which lap up liquid foods from surfaces, must be supplied with drinking water. When it proves necessary to give water to caterpillars and other leaf-eaters, the water may be sprinkled on the plants given them. Flies, bees, wasps, and butterflies may be given water in the same way they are given food, that is, by saturating a piece of cloth or paper toweling and putting this in the cage. Care should be used not to supply too much water, however. The bottom and sides of the cage should never be wet or drippy, for the insects should not have so much water about that they become soiled. Moreover, too much water encourages the development of molds and of bacterial diseases which will kill the insects. Plant-lice (Fig. 39), cicadas (Figs. 19 and 98), and all other bugs which feed on plant juices sucked from beneath the surface of the plants do not need to be supplied with water so long as they are given succulent plant material frequently. They get their water supply along with their food. The plants supplied should have their stems placed in water, however, or the insects quickly suck them dry of their available juices.

In addition to making sure that a supply of drinking water is available, the matter of atmospheric moisture must be looked after. The air of schoolrooms and of homes generally is much drier than the air out-of-doors. Consequently the schoolroom and home are difficult places for insects to live. When the humidity of the air is too low, many caterpillars and pupae fail to produce butterflies and moths simply because they dry up. All delicate insects should be kept in cages composed partly of glass, such as the lamp-chimney cage and the wide-mouthed jar cage shown in Fig. 184 or in cages of the cellophane-fronted shoe-box type shown in Fig. 183. They may be kept in the glass "live cage" described farther on in this chapter. In any of these cages it is an easy matter to supply the needed moisture. A dish of damp earth in the bottom of the cage, or a damp (not wet) piece of paper toweling will suffice; or succulent plant food put into the cage will give off enough moisture to dampen the air properly. Chrysalids should be suspended in cages in which the air is thus moistened, or they may be laid on damp (but never wet) earth, or they may be laid on a piece of screen placed over a dish of water and kept out of the sun in a cool place.

Ventilation. All cages and other containers in which insects are to be reared or observed indoors must be ventilated if insect study is to be successful. The best way to provide for ventilation is to have a part of the cages covered with gauze or screening (Figs. 184, 185, 187, and 188). The cellophane-fronted shoe-box cage needs no gauze or screening, as the cellophane is sufficiently porous to permit the needed ventilation. The benefits derived from ventilation are twofold. Ventilation prevents the air in the cages from getting foul through the

(*Photograph by Lester Brubaker.*)

FIG. 183.—AN ADMIRABLE CAGE FOR MANY INSECTS, ESPECIALLY FOR JUICE-SUCKING OR NECTAR-EATING TYPES, CAN BE MADE OF A SHOE BOX, RUBBER BANDS, AND A LITTLE CELLOPHANE.

Many herbivores, also, may be kept in such a cage, but large and strong-jawed species are likely to chew out. Ventilation holes are superfluous, as ordinary commercial cellophane is sufficiently porous to permit all the movement of air that is needed. The jar holding the plants which serve as food is filled with sand as well as water to safeguard against the drowning of specimens.

development of objectionable odors, and it discourages or prevents the growth of mold by automatically keeping the humidity below the point needed by the molds, though not too low for the insects. Regulation of the humidity by proper ventilation also tends to prevent the outbreak of disease in the cages.

Nothing has been said so far about the supply of oxygen to captive insects for the reason that it is the least important of the problems concerned with the successful keeping of insects. Insects need little oxygen as compared with warm-blooded animals. The numerous holes which the average person punches in the lid of a jar in which he puts a beetle, a butterfly, or a caterpillar are entirely unnecessary. If the lid of a jar is loosened ever so little, or if one tiny hole is punched through it, an adequate supply of oxygen is assured. Most insects can survive several days in a tightly closed jar or bottle, so far as oxygen supply alone is concerned. They may die from lack of food or because of some other factor, but rarely from lack of oxygen. Of course, the holes punched in a jar lid provide the much-needed ventilation already discussed, but that is a matter which relates more to humidity than to oxygen.

COLLECTING EQUIPMENT

Jars. When making an excursion into the field, one should go well supplied with containers in which to bring back his catches. Small glass jars, such as mayonnaise and mustard jars, are excellent as temporary containers for all sorts of insects. These will hold aquatic species or ground-dwellers and burrowers as well as flying kinds. Jars for aquatics, when covered with lids, must not be filled full of water. There should be an air space above the water. If facilities are available for transporting aquatics in large open containers, such as large jars, wide-mouthed bottles, or pails, the water may be prevented from splashing and spilling by putting a liberal supply of some coarse water plant in each jar. In the absence of these, a handful of weeds or leafy twigs may be used. As soon as the schoolroom or home is reached, the weeds or twigs or excess water plants may be taken out.

Boxes. All sorts of tin, pasteboard, and wooden boxes are useful. Caution should be exercised in the use of cigar boxes, as enough nicotine is absorbed by the wood to kill many soft-bodied insects. Sturdy species, such as most beetles, may be carried in cigar boxes without being endangered. Paper bags also may be employed.

The improvised paper tube. It sometimes happens that one finds a desirable specimen at a time when he is without a suitable jar or box to put it in. In such an emergency a successful container may be improvised from an oblong piece of paper of almost any sort. A piece of newspaper, a letter one may have in his pocket, even the back of an envelope will do. The method of making the container is illustrated in Fig. 194. First, roll the paper into a tube a half-inch or more in diameter, depending on the size of the specimen to be carried and the size of the paper available. Next, flatten one end of the tube. Then fold the corners of the flattened end diagonally, one in one direction, the other in the opposite direction. This will make the flattened end pointed in outline. Then fold the pointed end over and crimp it to prevent the folds from coming undone. Now drop the specimen into the tube through the open end. Finally, flatten and fold the other end of the tube in exactly the same way you did the first, so as to enclose the specimen, but flatten it at right angles to the way in which the first end was flattened. By flattening and folding the two ends in opposite directions, the tube will be braced and the central part kept expanded so as to form a chamber that will hold the specimen without crushing. If one expects to do much collecting and rearing of insects, it is worth while to carry one or more pieces of suitable paper with him all the time. Cards made of stiff paper of about the weight of ordinary drawing paper and four by six inches in size make ideal tubes for carrying most specimens picked up at unexpected moments.

REARING CAGES

The lamp-chimney cage. This type of cage (Fig. 184) is of the simplest construction, and is among the most successful of inexpensive cages. Fill a flower pot (4- or 6-inch size) with damp sand or soil. In this, set out a small specimen of the food plant. If the food plant is large, or is not suitable for potting, put a branch of it in a small can or bottle and fill the can or bottle with sand saturated with water. The coarser the sand the better. Then bury the can or bottle in the pot of soil. The water in the sand will keep the food plant fresh. The sand will prevent the insects from drowning. Next, place over the plant an ordinary old-fashioned glass lamp chimney. Press it well down against the soil so that no crevices or holes will be left through which specimens might escape. Then drop in the insects for which the cage is prepared. Finally, tie a piece of muslin, mosquito netting, or gauze over the top, and the cage is complete. This type of cage can be cleaned readily as it is only necessary to lift the chimney, take out the old food material and litter, put in new food, and replace the chimney.

The wide-mouthed jar cage (Fig. 184). This is the most inexpensive of all improvised cages. All that is needed is a wide-mouthed bottle or jar (any kind will do), a little gauze or other cloth, and a piece of string. In most cases it is desirable to put an inch or so of damp earth in the jar before putting in the specimens, but judgment should be

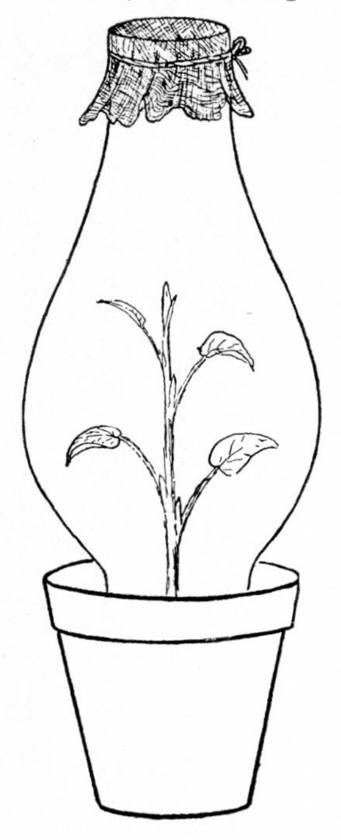

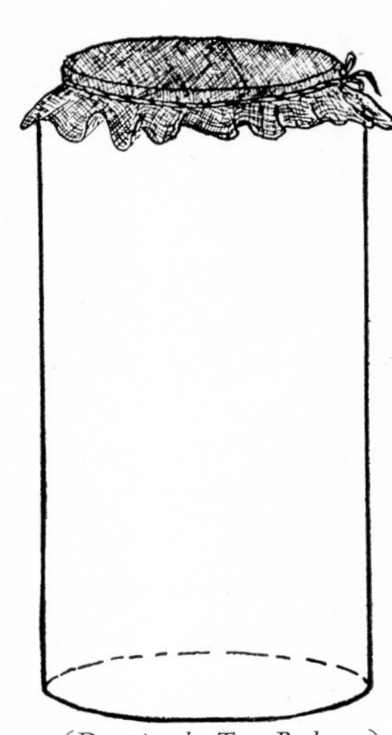

(*Drawing by Tom Rodgers.*)

FIG. 184.—INSECT CAGES MADE OF A LAMP CHIMNEY AND A WIDE-MOUTHED JAR.

Here are simple insect cages made of materials so inexpensive that any young student or any schoolroom may easily acquire them. The lamp-chimney cage serves well for such climbing insects as caterpillars and grasshoppers. The wide-mouthed jar provides a home for ground-inhabiting species, such as ground beetles and crickets. Burrowing insects that might be lost in the lamp-chimney cage should be kept in the jar.

used in deciding this matter. This cage is not so easy to care for as the lamp-chimney cage, but it is better for some insects. Ground-inhabiting species, especially those which burrow, can be observed more easily in this kind of a cage.

The cereal-box cage (Fig. 187). Another type of inexpensive cage is the cereal-box cage. It is made of an empty cereal box and a piece of window screen. The stiff pasteboard cartons in which ice cream is sometimes packed are suitable also. The figure shows a cylindrical box, but an oblong one can be used. The box should have a lid; if this is lacking, a piece of gauze or cheesecloth may be tied over the top in its place. To make one of these cages, cut two oblong holes, like that shown in the figure, on opposite sides of the box. Then cut a piece of wire screening large enough to fit just inside the box. In a cylindrical box the screen will form a roll; in an oblong box it will have to be bent for the corners. In any case, the tension in the screen will keep it against the sides of the box. Such a cage is a good home for caterpillars, grasshoppers, and other large insects.

The cellophane and shoe-box cage (Fig. 183). For many insects this is an ideal cage. Large and strong-jawed caterpillars, beetles, and grasshoppers, however, will chew their way out. The materials required are a shoe box (or other oblong, pasteboard box), a sheet of cellophane (plain, not colored), some glue or mucilage, and rubber bands or a piece of string. Cut out the bottom and the lid of the shoe box to within a half inch of the sides. Then cut two pieces of cellophane, one to fit inside the bottom of the shoe box, one in the lid. Next, spread mucilage over the inner surfaces of the rims which remain on the bottom and the lid of the box. Do not put the mucilage on the cellophane. Next lay the pieces of cellophane in place and press the edges down firmly against the mucilage. Finally, install the specimens and secure the lid with rubber bands or string.

The glass live cage. Still another cage that is inexpensive and easy to make is the glass live cage. The materials needed for this cage are the following: a supply of adhesive tape, 1½ inches wide, three oblong pieces of glass, an oblong piece of wire screening a trifle larger than one of the pieces of glass, and two square pieces of glass. The square pieces of glass should have the same dimension as the short edge of one of the oblong pieces. The necessary glass may be cut from old windowpanes or purchased for a few cents at any hardware store. To make the cage, cut the adhesive tape into strips; with these, fasten the pieces of glass together to form an oblong box open on top. The oblong pieces of glass will form the bottom and sides of the box, the square pieces will form the ends. The edges where the pieces of glass meet should be well taped both inside and out. To make the lid, hinge the piece of screening to the glass box along one edge by means of tape. Finally, tape the free edges of the lid to give it strength and to prevent the screen from fraying.

The wooden frame box cage (Fig. 185). If facilities are available, it may be worth while to make a more durable cage than any of the preceding. A wooden box cage will last for many years if given good care. The materials needed are some pieces of a soft wood, such as redwood or white pine, wire screening, tacks, nails, a pair of small hinges, a

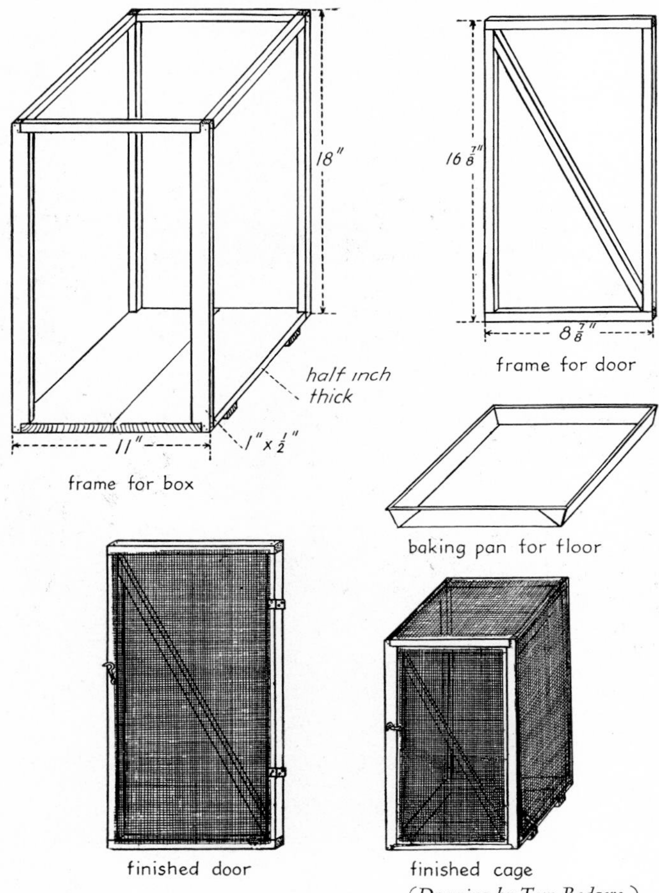

(*Drawing by Tom Rodgers.*)

FIG. 185.—A BOX TYPE INSECT CAGE.

Here is a sturdy cage for that ambitious student of insects who wants the thrill that comes to the butterfly farmer. It will provide a home for many caterpillars or other large insects. The pan, filled with earth, will give burrowers a normal place to pupate. Needed moisture may be supplied either by keeping the earth in the pan damp (not wet) or by putting a saucer of wet sand in the cage. This cage can be improved by making one or two sides of glass instead of screen.

hook and eye, and a cheap baking pan like that shown in the figure. A saw, a hammer, a ruler, and tin shears will be needed as tools.

Make the frame for the cage as shown in the figure. The size should be determined by the size of the baking pan, for the cage should be so made that when completed there will be just room enough for the baking pan on the floor of the cage. Cleats should be nailed across the bottom of the floor of the cage to keep it from warping.

When completed, the baking pan should be placed on the floor of the cage and filled with damp earth. This will help to maintain the necessary moisture supply for the air in the cage. It will also provide earth into which those larvae which pupate beneath the surface of

FIG. 186.—THIS IS THE BUTTERFLY FARMER'S REWARD.
These Mourning Cloak Butterflies were reared in a box-type cage similar to that in Fig. 185. They are shown clinging to the removable top of the cage shortly after emerging from their pupal skeletons.

the soil may burrow. This cage is excellent for keeping all kinds of caterpillars, grasshoppers, katydids, and other large plant-eating species. It is a good cage in which to store pupae and cocoons also. The only objection to the cage is that the screen is a little difficult to see through. This objection can be eliminated if one side is made of glass.

Wide-mouthed jar for small aquatics (Fig. 187). The usefulness of wide-mouthed jars does not end with their use as simple cages for caterpillars. They make excellent aquaria for small water insects as well. To use a jar as an aquarium, fill it half or two-thirds full of water, put in a small wisp of some aquatic plant, such as the plants

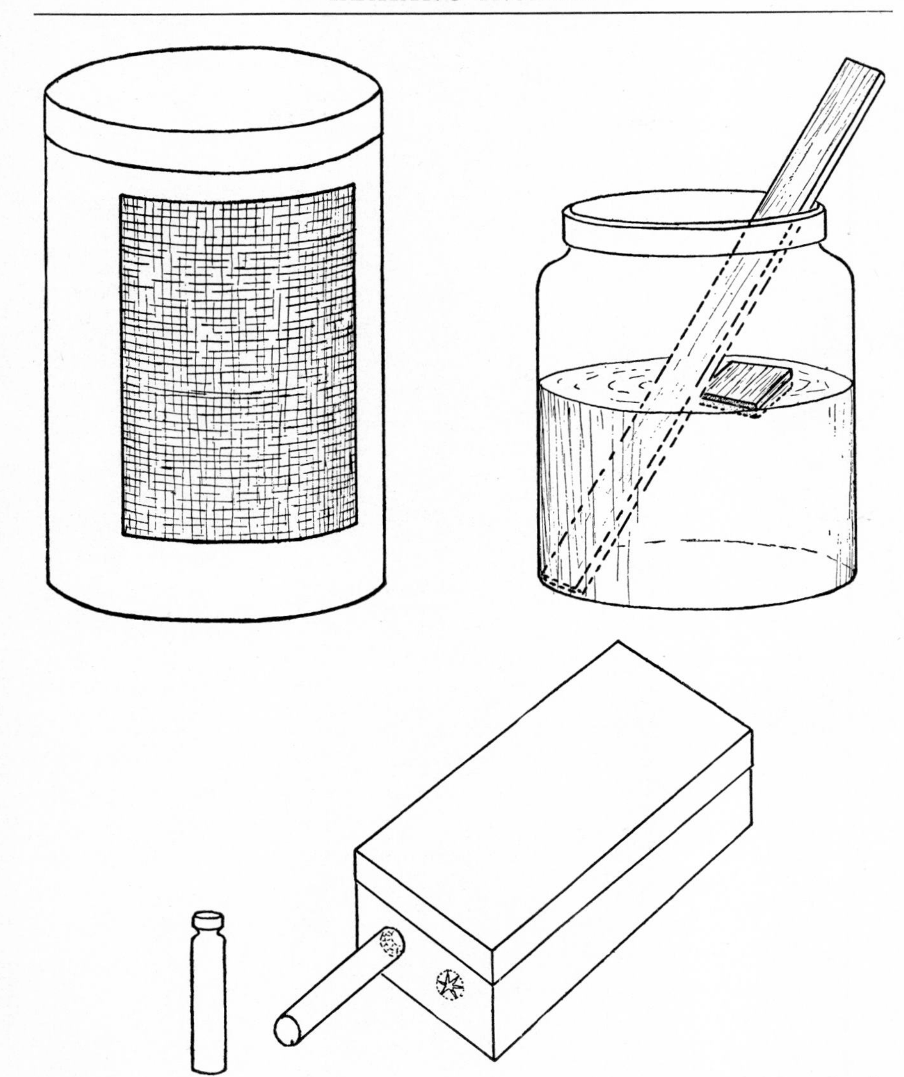

(*Drawing by Tom Rodgers.*)

FIG. 187.—SOME SIMPLE, IMPROVISED INSECT CAGES.

Insects that do not jump or fly can be kept in the cereal-box cage; watch them by removing the lid. Place galls or parasitized insects in the shoe-box cage, and many surprises will be yours as gallmakers and tiny parasites come to the light that the vial provides. The stick in the jar aquarium will let aquatic naiads come out of the water when the time has come for the adults to emerge.

commonly used in goldfish bowls, or any one of the coarser, more wiry algae found growing in horse troughs and creeks. (Do not use *Spirogyra*, the slippery alga known as "water silk," as it does not thrive indoors and it is so fine that the insects in the jar get entangled in it.) Then drop in a small wooden block or chip and stand a stick slantwise in the jar. Then put in the insects.

The water plants keep the water fresh by renewing the oxygen supply. The chips and the sticks provide supports which enable the insects to crawl out of the water when the time comes for them to transform to the adult stage. If one desires to keep adult insects so that they, too, may be observed, the stick in the jar should not project above the top of the jar and a piece of cheesecloth should be tied over the opening.

Cautions: The greatest loss of specimens in aquaria is the result of overcrowding. A pint jar should not contain more than six water-beetles a half inch in length, or other insects of comparable size. If larger insects are kept, the number should be reduced. If smaller ones are kept, the number may be increased. Judgment and experience will guide one in determining how many to keep in a jar. If predatory species are used, it may be necessary to keep only one in a jar, as they will kill and eat one another.

The aquarium cage (Fig. 188). If one possesses an aquarium of oblong shape it may be converted into an excellent cage for the rearing of the larger aquatic insects, such as dragon-flies, damsel-flies, stone-flies, and May-flies. The only necessary addition is a wooden frame covered with wire screening as shown in the figure. The frame must be of the same dimensions as the top of the aquarium so as to fit neatly. Pieces of tin may be nailed to the corners of the frame, as shown in the figure, to hold the frame in place and prevent its slipping off the aquarium. Into the aquarium may then be put sand and stones, water plants, and insects. Also, there should be floating chips and slanting sticks or other objects which project above the water surface, on which the larvae and nymphs may crawl when ready to transform.

Shoe-box cage for parasites and gall-insects (Fig. 187). One of the disappointing experiences connected with rearing insects is that many of the larvae and pupae fail to produce adult insects for us; occasionally as many as nine out of ten caterpillars shrivel, die, and turn brown instead of transforming into butterflies and moths. The disappointment which this failure brings, however, may be turned into profit. It may be made to form the basis of other nature lessons fully as exciting as the rearing of caterpillars, for the failure of so many insects to transform is due to their being parasitized by other and smaller insects, as was explained in the chapter on "Insect Foods and Feeding Habits." Now, these parasites may be reared too. And what is more amazing than to see a caterpillar which should become a moth or butterfly suddenly sicken and die, but in its dying give birth to twenty or thirty or even a hundred other insects of a totally differ-

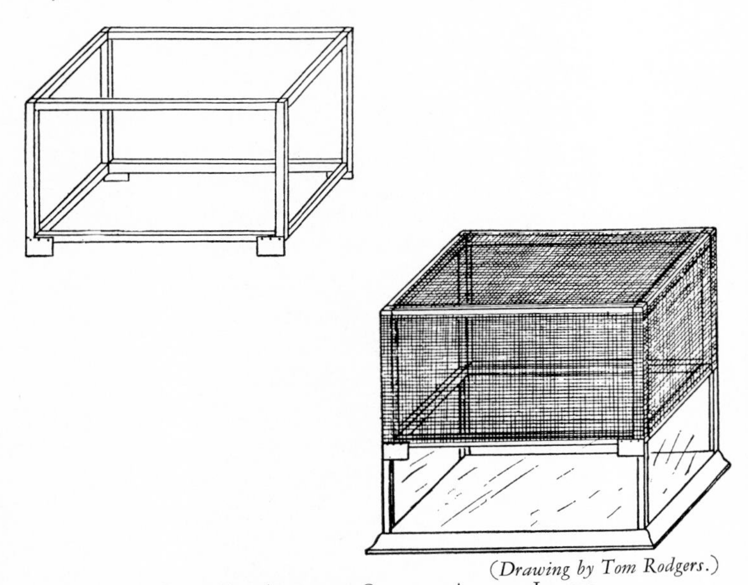

(*Drawing by Tom Rodgers.*)

FIG. 188.—AQUARIUM CAGE FOR AQUATIC INSECTS.

The aquarium cover shown here will capture the adult insects as they emerge from their naiad skeletons; otherwise they will fly away.

ent kind (Fig. 176)? Therefore, when your specimens become sickly or enfeebled and you suspect parasitism, put them into a shoe-box cage, made as shown in Fig. 187, and watch for results. To be sure, you will not always get parasites; but when you do you will be amply repaid for your trouble. As fast as the parasites emerge in the dark interior of the shoe box, they will be attracted by the spots of light in the ends of the box where the glass vials are inserted and they will fly or crawl into the vials, where they may be observed and from which they may be collected. Some of the parasites will be fuzzy or bristly tachina flies (Fig. 177), distant relatives of the common House-fly but not carriers of human disease like the House-fly. Other parasites will be tiny wasps, which often are resplendent with brilliant colors. Many of the wasps will be only dull black or brown, but others will be shimmering green or blue or gold. Some of these parasites are among the most beautiful of insects.

Sometimes parasitized insects can be recognized long before they sicken. Parasitic flies often lay their eggs on the surface of caterpillars. When one of these caterpillars is found, the eggshells of the parasite may be seen clinging to the caterpillar's skin. Parasitic wasps usually puncture the skin of the insects they parasitize and lay their eggs inside. The punctures then heal, but they sometimes leave small blackish blemishes which can be recognized and which mark an insect as parasitized. Occasionally one finds a parasitized caterpillar which has already died and which has a large number of tiny oval or cigar-shaped cocoons clinging to it (Fig. 176). These are cocoons spun by the parasites. Any specimens such as those just described may be kept in a shoe-box cage to secure the parasites.

There is another group of insects for the rearing of which the shoe-box cage is ideal. These are the gall-insects. Many tiny wasps and flies lay their eggs in the tissues of plants, with the result that knobs or growths, which look like swellings, develop around the eggs or around the larvae which hatch from the eggs. These growths are called *galls* (Fig. 40). They may be found on a great variety of plants, but more kinds are found on oak trees and roses than on any other plants. These galls may be collected as they mature and placed in the shoe-box cages. When the gall-insects emerge, they will fly or crawl into the vials where they may be observed.

An artificial termite nest. Few insects have attracted more popular attention in recent years than termites (see Chapter XIV) and none is more easily kept and observed. A termite nest like that shown in Fig. 189 can be made by anyone. Simply proceed as follows: Procure two equal-sized panes of glass. Those from a discarded window will do admirably. Wash them clean and dry them. Place one on a table. Then get some thin slats of wood, preferably old weathered pieces, about ¼ inch thick if the nest is to hold damp-wood termites or dry-wood termites, and ⅛ inch thick if the nest is for subterranean termites. All should be of the same thickness. Pieces from old fruit or vegetable crates are ideal. Lay them lengthwise on the glass on the table with spaces ¼ to ½ inch wide (but not more) between them. The side slats should extend the full length of the glass and be flush with its edges. The inner ones should be broken in one or two places so as to produce crosswise passageways connecting the lengthwise spaces between the slats. Next, lay the second pane of glass on top

FIG. 189.—AN ARTIFICIAL NEST THAT HOUSES A TERMITE COLONY AND PERMITS OBSERVATION OF TERMITE ACTIVITIES.

Thin pine boards, not over one-fourth of an inch in thickness, between two panes of glass held by metal clamps, and set in a galvanized tank of moist earth or sand and provided with a removable pasteboard cover, constitute the assemblage. Quarter-inch spaces between the boards provide room to receive the termites when the nest is set up. A little water added occasionally to the tank of earth or sand is all the care needed. In this nest the center strip consisted of three pieces, the middle one of partially decayed wood. Termites will not leave such a nest.

of the slats. Then fasten the whole assembly together. This may be done in various ways. The nest assembly may be tied at each end with stout twine which has been dipped into melted wax previously to guard against decay. It may be bound with adhesive tape or tire tape which extends around the glass panes close to the edges but not on the edges (the edges of the slats should be left exposed), or it may be held with metal clips as shown in the figure. When the nest assembly has been bound together, stand it on end in a metal pan about four inches deep (an oil can, washed clean of oil, or a sirup can, cut open, will do) and fill in around it with sand or soil, packed down. The nest is now ready to receive the termites.

Next, hunt up a colony of termites out-of-doors. They can be found in dead stumps and fallen branches, or in and beneath old lumber that has rested on the ground for a long time. Cut open or break open the wood containing the termites and shake them out into a large can or jar. Put a few small pieces of wood in the jar for them to cling to. Several hundred should be collected if the termites are subterranean species; a hundred of the large damp-wood species will suffice. To put them into the nest, pick them out of the jar or can and drop them into the spaces between the wood slats at the top. A funnel with the end of the spout flattened so as to fit just between the panes of glass will simplify the job. (An improvised paper funnel is entirely satisfactory.) Drop the termites into the funnel; then thump the funnel to knock the termites down into the nest.

The final additions to complete the nest are two. Make a jacket of heavy paper or thin pasteboard to slip over the nest assembly and fit down against the sand or soil at its base. This will keep out the light and it may be lifted off when the termites are to be observed. Then pour in enough water to moisten thoroughly, but not make muddy, the soil around the nest base. The termites will never leave the nest. They will accept the spaces between the wooden parts as home, close the upper ends of the spaces to shut out the dry air, and burrow into the wood in the manner typical of their species. Such a nest, barring the advent of disease, will last for many months. In it eggs will be laid, young will grow up, and the various castes of termites develop (see Fig. 160). The only care needed will be to add a little water occasionally when the sand or soil dries out. All the normal activities of a termite colony may be observed through the glass, and the colony will be not only instructive, but a never-ending fascination as well.

Artificial ant nests (Fig. 190). Ants are among the most interesting of insects, yet they are rarely kept for study. They are relatively easy to keep, too, though not so easy as termites, for captive ants must be fed frequently and given real care. They repay their keeper well, however, for the care which they require.

The simplest of all artificial ant nests is a tall jar about two-thirds full of earth for the ants to burrow in. Such a nest provides only limited opportunities for observation. A more satisfactory nest is the type shown in Fig. 190*a*. It consists of a wooden frame holding two panes of glass about a half inch apart. The panes of glass are held in grooves cut into the side and bottom bars of the frame. If tools are

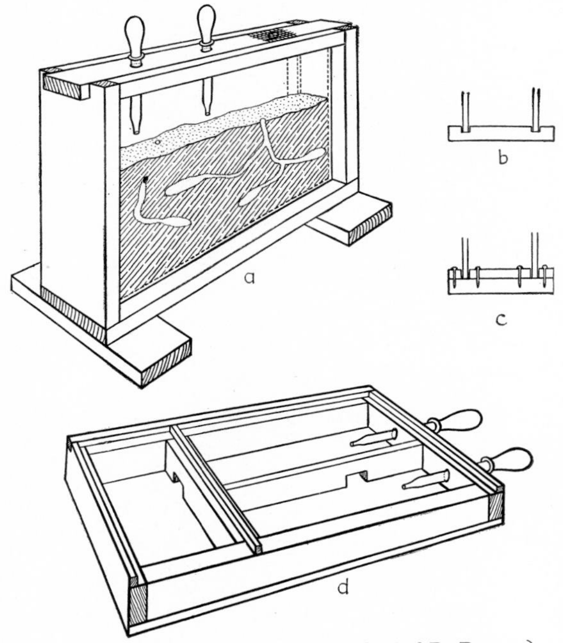

(*Drawing by Carl D. Duncan.*)

Fig. 190.—Artificial Ant Nests.

Though by no means so easy to keep and care for as are termites, ants may be kept for a considerable time with little difficulty in nests like the ones shown here. One medicine dropper and sponge are used to supply water, the other to supply food.

not available for making the grooves, a substitute type of construction, as shown at *c* in the figure may be employed. The space between the panes is filled three-fourths full of soil unless one wishes to keep carpenter ants (wood ants). In this case the space should be filled loosely with pieces of wood, preferably partially decayed wood of medium dryness. The top bar of the frame is removable, allowing the ants to be put in. This bar has three holes bored in it. Over one hole is tacked a small piece of wire screen. This hole provides ventilation. The other two holes are fitted with medicine droppers. Through one of these water is given to the ants, the other is for food. The only objection to this type of nest is that the ants have but little space aboveground in which to wander around. This lack can be remedied somewhat by loosely piling a few sticks or blocks in the space above the soil, but the lack of room is still objectionable.

A third type of artificial ant nest is that shown in Fig. 190*d*. It is commonly called a "Fielde nest," because it was invented by a Miss Fielde. Fielde nests, with instructions for their operation and care may be purchased from almost any biological supply house. But with a little care a nest of this type may be constructed at home. Such a nest consists of three connecting compartments covered with pieces of clear glass. One compartment (the one at the left in the figure) has a second piece of glass, a red one, on top of the white piece. This compartment is the brood compartment. Ants appear to be insensitive to red light and beneath the red glass they behave exactly as if they were in the darkness of a nest in the soil, yet they can be seen. The other two compartments are fitted with medicine droppers through which food and water, respectively, are given to the ants. A Fielde nest provides no soil in which the ants may dig, so it, too, is open to certain objections. It is, in fact, the most artificial of the three types. On the other hand, it permits observations of the ants at all times.

Most common species of ants may be fed a mixture of honey or corn sirup and water to which a little egg white has been added. The mixture should be thin enough to flow readily. To vary the diet a dead fly, grasshopper, or other insect should be put in the nest occasionally. If the ants belong to one of the small species called "grease ants" because of their fondness for cured meats, a bit of bacon may be fed now and then. If agricultural ants are kept, seeds in some variety must be given. These should be in the main the seeds of weeds and garden flowers such as the ants may be observed to collect out-of-doors.

Ants are so common that directions for securing a colony for the nest seems unnecessary.

CHAPTER XIX

HOW TO COLLECT AND PRESERVE INSECT SPECIMENS

The collecting net. One of the indispensable aids in the collection of insect specimens is a good collecting net. The net shown in Fig. 191 is inexpensive, easy to make, and for the needs of the general student in many ways superior to the heavier manufactured nets that are on the market. The following materials are needed: a piece of springy wire about 1/8 inch in diameter and 9 feet long; a smooth rounded stick, 3 feet long; a piece of curtain scrim or other net-like well-woven fabric, 22 by 38 inches; a strip of strong muslin 5 by 38 inches; several feet of stout twine; 3 or 4 feet of tire tape; a small drill; a pair of pliers; a crayon or a piece of colored chalk; thread and a needle. For the handle, a dowel stick 5/8 or 3/4 inch in diameter is about ideal. It is thick enough to hold securely. A larger stick is too heavy. Cheesecloth and mosquito netting are not suitable for the net. They are not durable enough. Moreover, the simple manner in which they are woven results in their being pulled out of shape and snagged easily.

To make the net, first cut a deep groove across one end of the stick (see *c* of the figure). Through the stick, in the same direction as the groove, drill two holes a little larger than the diameter of the wire. Drill one of these holes 2½ inches, the other 3½ inches from the grooved end of the stick.

Bend the middle part of the wire to make a circular loop 1 foot across (*a* of figure). To hold the loop wrap a small piece of tire tape around the wire where the two ends cross. Then wind each free end of the wire around the wire of the loop until the free ends meet (*b* of figure). They should meet at a point directly opposite the first crossing (the one wrapped with tape).

Fit the loop on the end of the stick as shown in *d* of the figure. Bend each free end of the wire so that it will run down the stick and fit snugly against the stick. Bend one end again and push it through the first hole in the stick. Pull it through so it fits tightly, and bend the projecting end up on the other side of the stick. Bend

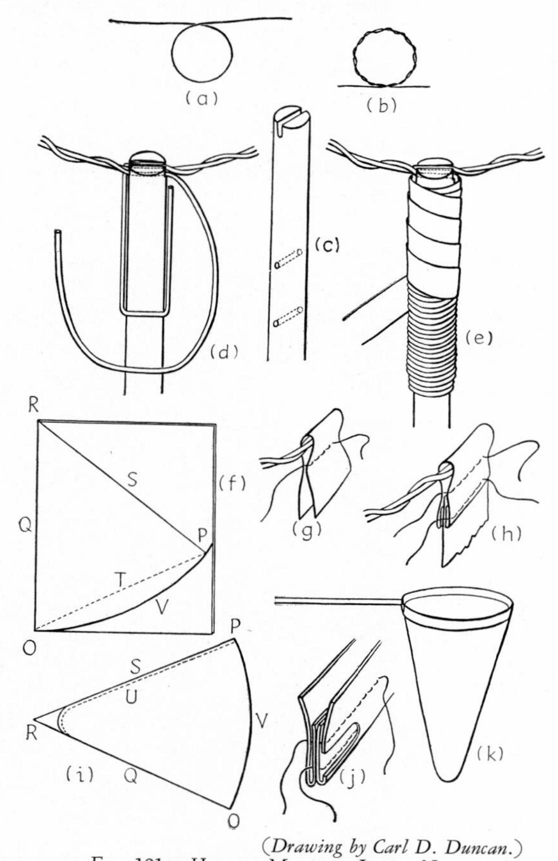

(*Drawing by Carl D. Duncan.*)

FIG. 191.—HOW TO MAKE AN INSECT NET.

With simple materials and easy procedure, every young entomologist may have his own net. Complete directions for making this net are given.

the other end of the wire in the same manner, putting it through the second hole in the stick. Cut off any excess wire about ½ inch back from the grooved end of the stick. Wrap the stick and the ends of the wire securely with twine. Plenty of twine should be used to ensure that the wires will not break loose or become caught on other objects. Finally, wrap tire tape over the twine (*e* of figure).

Fold the piece of scrim, of which the bag of the net is to be made, so that the two 22-inch ends will be together (*f* of figure).

Tie the crayon to one end of a piece of twine. Then, using one end (*R*) of the fold (*Q*) as a center, and 22 inches of string as a radius, draw the curved line *V*. Next, mark point *P* on line *V* so that *T* is 19 inches long. Then, draw line *S*. It will be 22 inches long. Now cut out the body of the net, cutting along lines *S* and *V* (*i* of figure). Pin the folded cloth at *P* and at two or three places on line *S* so it will not slip in handling. Then on a sewing machine, or by hand, stitch along line *U*, ½ inch in from line *S*, but do not stitch all the way to *R*. Instead, stitch around the curve in line *U* to the fold (*Q*). This will leave ½ inch of material beyond the stitching. Turn the net inside out, flatten along the seam and stitch again, this time ⅛ inch inside the seam (*j* of figure). This will make a French seam and prevent any ripping. Then trim off the excess material in the edges that project inward from the seam.

Next, fold the strip of muslin over the loop of wire and, with needle and thread, fasten it in place as shown at *g* in the figure, allowing plenty of room for the muslin to slip on the wire loop. Finally, slip the raw edge of the scrim which forms the net between the edges of the muslin strip, turn in the edges of the strip, and sew the three together securely (*h* of figure). The last two operations will have to be done by hand. The net is now ready for use (*k*).

It is one thing to possess a net; it is another to know how to use it. Much can be learned only by experience, but some of the essentials can be learned from instruction. As a general rule, do not run after insects with your net. It is rarely worth while. A few butterflies, which otherwise might be lost, may be caught in this manner, but in general you will only wear yourself out. Far greater success results from the use of strategy. Study the habits of would-be captures; note where they alight; or take them while they are feeding.

Not all insects can be captured with the same maneuvers. If insects are feeding on flowers or are resting on foliage it is better usually to swing the net sidewise. With certain insects, such as the spider-wasps of the family Pompilidae, the net, when possible, should be swung upward as well as sidewise, for these wasps seek to avoid capture by going down. So do certain butterflies and many beetles. Most wasps, bees, flies, and butterflies, however, escape by rising. In capturing wasps, tiger-beetles, butterflies, and other insects which alight on the ground or on low herbage, and which fly readily, approach them with the net held before you with one hand and with the tip of the bag held up with the other. Then bring the net down quickly over the specimen in a striking motion, releasing the tip of the bag as you strike. Then, holding the net ring against the ground, lift the tip of the net so that the insect will crawl or fly upward into the bag. Once a specimen is in the bag of the net, no matter how it was caught, swing the net quickly through the air to force the specimen to the bottom and then with a quick twist of the wrist fold the bag of the net over the ring so as to hold the specimen inside.

Specimens which are sturdy enough to stand handling without damage, and which do not bite or sting, may be taken out of the net by hand. Most beetles, bugs, grasshoppers, and dragon-flies may be handled in this way. Others are best taken by slipping a killing bottle up inside the net and catching the specimens directly. If one has several specimens in a net at one time and is fearful of losing some while taking others, he may slip the tip of the net containing the specimens in the killing bottle; cover the bottle for a minute till the specimens are stupefied, then take the net out, open it, and pick out the specimens. Active, delicate specimens, and those which sting severely, may be treated in the same manner.

Two other matters deserve mention. Numerous insects may be collected from low-growing herbage by swinging the net back and forth through the tops of grasses, weeds, and flowers. This method is called *sweeping*. It yields an astounding number and variety of insects. The foliage of trees and shrubbery may be worked over in a comparable manner, but the action must be more vigorous. It is, therefore, called *beating*. Another type of beating is accomplished by holding the net upside down beneath the branches of trees and shrubbery and beating the latter with a stout stick. As insects are jarred loose they fall into the net.

If one can afford them, it is desirable to have nets of several types and sizes: one for general use, one for beating, one for use in the water, etc. Lacking these, a single stout net may be used for all purposes.

The killing bottle. Some of the insects collected should be brought back alive for observation, but some should be killed for preservation. It is not necessary to kill insects in order to study them. There are many things that cannot be learned when the insect is dead. On the other hand, live insects oftentimes will not permit the handling and close scrutiny necessary if one is to identify them and learn how their bodies are constructed. Furthermore, it is usually desirable to keep a collection of the insects captured so as to learn how many kinds live in one's neighborhood and how the various kinds differ from each other. Specimens to be killed for preservation should be

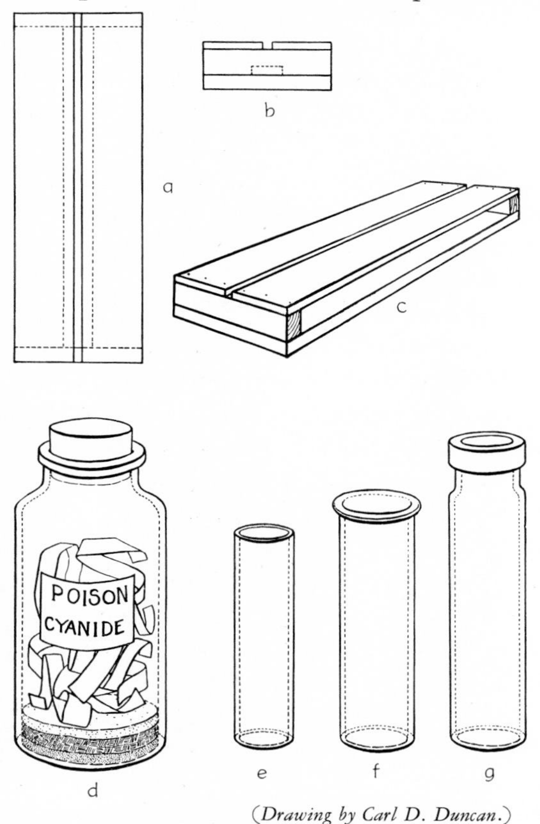

(*Drawing by Carl D. Duncan.*)

FIG. 192.—SPREADING BOARD AND KILLING BOTTLES.

These are necessary equipment for every bug collector. Instructions for making them are given on pages 382 and 383.

killed as soon as collected, or as soon as possible thereafter. In any case, killing bottles are needed.

It is desirable to have several killing bottles (Fig. 192), at least two large ones and a small one. One of the large bottles (pint size) should be used only for butterflies and moths. The numerous wing scales which these insects lose in the jar cling to other kinds of insects and make them untidy in appearance. One large bottle should be used for large insects other than butterflies and moths. The small bottle, used for tiny insects, should be made of a vial with a neck or a lip (*f* or *g* of the figure), else it may split open when the cork is put in. If only a shell vial (one with neither lip nor neck, *e* of figure) is available, bind the top of the vial with adhesive tape. All killing bottles should have tightly fitting stoppers or screw lids. To conserve the killing agent, the bottles should be kept *tightly* closed except when specimens are being put in.

Several killing agents are used. The best known because the most effective is cyanide. A killing bottle using cyanide is called a *cyanide bottle*. The cyanide that is used is obtained as either sodium cyanide or potassium cyanide. These substances may be obtained at most drugstores. Potassium cyanide and sodium cyanide are **extremely poisonous,** a piece no larger than a pinhead being sufficient to cause death. Moreover, the poison is so quick in its action that death nearly always results before there is time to administer an antidote. **Be very careful,** therefore, **in handling them. Do not leave them where anyone else can accidentally get them, and under no circumstances allow children to handle them.** It will be necessary to sign a "poison register" at the drugstore where they are purchased. Some druggists will not sell them at all, and in such cases it will be necessary to have the druggist make the bottles. If cyanide or a cyanide bottle cannot be had from a local druggist, one may be purchased from any of the biological supply companies. It is better for most persons to buy ready-made bottles anyway, rather than risk handling the cyanide.

To make a cyanide bottle of pint size, put a tablespoonful of granular sodium or potassium cyanide in the bottom of the bottle. If only lump cyanide is available wrap a lump in two or more thicknesses of cloth and crush it by pounding. Then use an appropriate amount of the crushed cyanide. Be sure the cloth used is free from holes and strong so that it will not break during the pounding. A flying chip of cyanide that lands in one's eye or goes up the nose is just as fatal as if it were swallowed. Over the cyanide in the jar put a layer of sawdust ¼ inch or a little more in depth. Pack the sawdust lightly. Then mix dry plaster of Paris with enough water to make a paste which will just pour readily. Pour this in until it is ¼ or ⅜ inch deep over the sawdust. Jar the bottle so that the paste will spread evenly and settle to a smooth surface. If bubbles are present, break them. There must be no holes through the plaster. Let the bottle stand open until the plaster is dry. Then stopper tightly. In making smaller jars use proportionately smaller amounts of material. When a bottle is finished, put a label on it marked conspicuously with the words CYANIDE, POISON.

Wash your hands carefully before getting them near your face. Wash all utensils and equipment thoroughly. Any leftover cyanide should be buried deeply or put into a jar under a running faucet until it has been completely dissolved and washed down the drain. Such a bottle containing cyanide should be watched continuously until it is emptied and no danger remains. Guard against anyone else picking it up unwittingly to use while it still contains cyanide.

A much safer killing agent is the liquid, ethyl acetate. A bottle in which ethyl acetate is to be used is made like the cyanide bottle, with two exceptions. First, only sawdust is used beneath the plaster of Paris. Second, a small stick should be held upright in the center of the bottle while the plaster of Paris paste is being poured in and until it sets. The stick should then be removed. It will leave a hole in the center of the plaster. When the plaster is dry, a teaspoonful or more of ethyl acetate should be dropped or poured through this hole to be absorbed by the sawdust beneath. The hole should then be closed lightly with a small wisp of cotton or a wad of absorbent paper. As often as the ethyl acetate evaporates out of the bottle it should be replenished.

To kill insects, place them in the killing bottle and close it. After about an hour (a longer time may be required for some hard-shelled beetles, a shorter one for flies and Hymenoptera) remove the specimens. If left too long (several days) the specimens may become brittle or they may discolor. Be careful not to crowd too many specimens into a bottle at one time. They will break one another, especially if some are fragile and others rough and powerful. A few narrow strips of crumpled paper toweling or other absorbent paper should be kept in a bottle at all times. They help to prevent breakage of specimens; they also absorb excess moisture given off by the specimens and prevent their getting wings and legs stuck together.

Some collectors of butterflies, moths, and dragon-flies prefer not to use a killing bottle at all. They carry two or three ounces of gasoline or benzine in a bottle equipped with a medicine dropper. A discarded "nose drops" bottle is excellent. A few drops of the gasoline or benzine are dropped through the net on each specimen. This kills the specimens almost instantly, whereupon they are removed from the net. In a few minutes all traces of the gasoline or benzine have evaporated. Beetle specialists likewise often dispense with the usual killing bottle. They drop their beetles directly into strong alcohol. Later the specimens are taken out of the alcohol and pinned.

Mounting insects on pins. One might think that any way to mount an insect would be permissible, but if one is to make the most of his collection he should mount his specimens according to approved methods.

It is worth while to procure specially made insect pins for mounting. These are longer and more slender than common pins. The better kinds are made of stainless steel, or they are heavily enameled to prevent rusting or corroding. They come in different sizes, which are numbered. The best sizes for most purposes are numbers 2 and 3, though it is advisable to have a few of number 5 for mounting very large specimens. Insect pins may be obtained from any of the biological supply houses. They cost from thirty to forty-five cents a hundred.

The larger insects are mounted by placing the pin directly through them. Definite rules for placing the pins have been established. A glance at Fig. 193 will show how the pins should be placed. In butterflies and moths the pin should pass through the center of the thorax. In dragon-flies and damsel-flies the pin should be set just in front of the forewing and a little to the right of the mid-line. These insects have but few areas in their body walls hard enough to provide support on a pin. Many collectors prefer to fold the wings together over a dragon-fly's back and pin it through the side. In the grasshoppers and other members of the order Orthoptera, the pin should be placed slightly to the right of the median line and toward the back of the hood-like prothorax. With soft-bodied specimens, such as some Orthoptera, it is often necessary to place an oblong piece of stiff paper on the pin beneath the specimen until it dries, to keep the abdomen from sagging. The hind legs of a grasshopper may be held up in the same manner until they are dry. In flies, and also in members of the order Hymenoptera, which includes the bees, wasps, and ants, the pin should be placed a little to the right of the center of the thorax. In beetles, the pin should pass through the right wing cover close to the mid-line and about a fourth of the way back. In

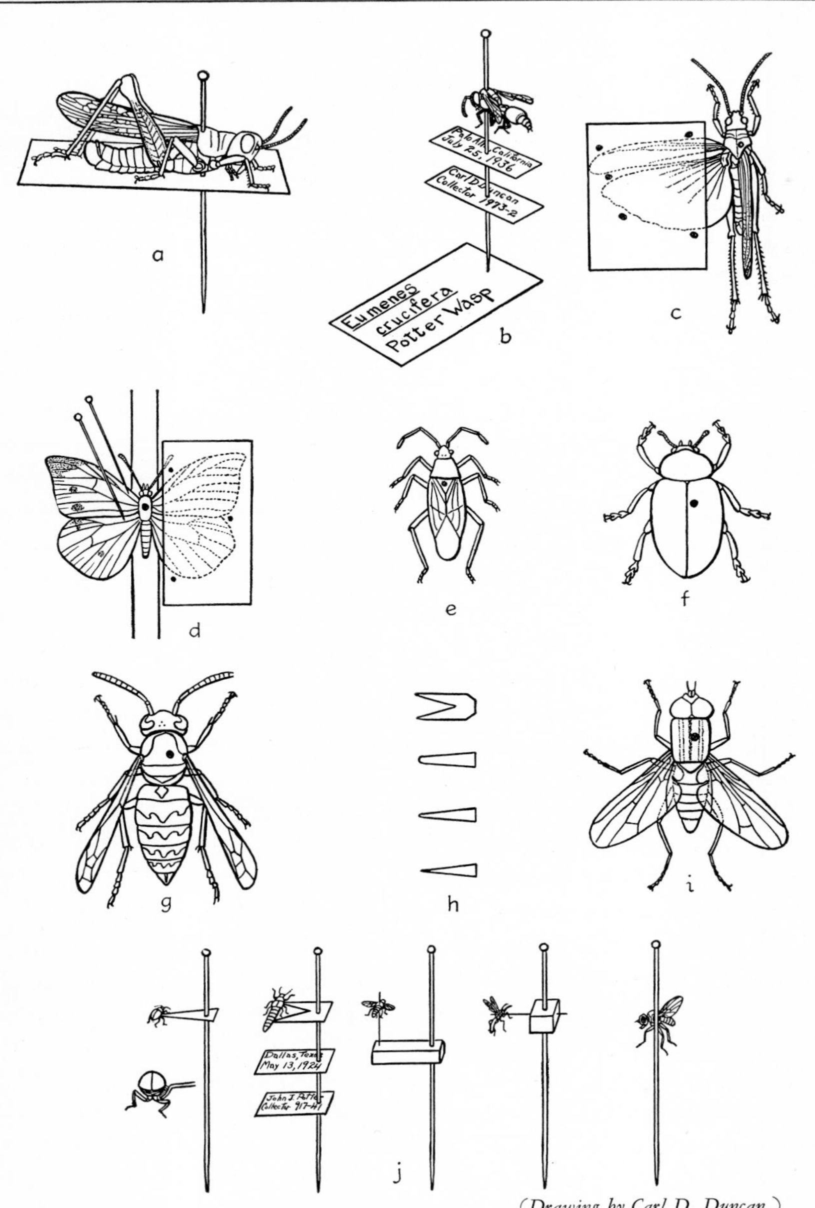

(Drawing by Carl D. Duncan.)

FIG. 193.—THERE IS A BEST WAY TO MOUNT EACH TYPE OF INSECT SPECIMEN.

This group of drawings illustrates the approved methods of mounting several types of insect specimens.

the "half-winged" insects of the order Hemiptera (the true bugs), the pin goes through the triangular scutellum at the base of the wings. It is desirable to have the backs of all specimens the same distance (about 3/8 inch) from the pinheads. This will facilitate handling. It will give the collection a neat, carefully prepared appearance.

Some insects are so small that they would be ruined if a pin were stuck through them. These may be mounted on the so-called *paper points* (really slender little triangles of stiff paper; see Fig. 193). Fasten each specimen to the end of a "point" with a very little glue or shellac. The pin passes through the other end of the "point." It is best, in fact, to put the "point" on the pin before gluing on the specimen. Another way of mounting very small specimens is to pin them by means of *micro-pins* (pins of a minute headless type; see figure) to little pieces of cork and then mount these on the larger insect pins. Some specialists on Diptera recommend gluing small flies directly to the side of an ordinary insect pin.

When mounting butterflies and moths it is desirable to spread the wings. Grasshoppers and beetles are sometimes mounted with the wings of one side spread. The method of spreading the wings will be explained in a later paragraph. After a specimen is mounted it should be labeled. On each pin there should be two labels which are pushed well up toward the specimen, not so far, however, as to touch it. The top label should bear, neatly printed or written in ink, the place (the nearest town or other place bearing an established geographic name) where the specimen was collected and the date; the second label should bear the name of the collector and a number referring to notes made on the specimen, if notes are kept. These labels should be as small as it is feasible to make them. A common size is 1/4 by 5/8 inch. At least one specimen of each species collected should bear a third and slightly larger label. This should be at the bottom of the pin. On it should be written the common name and the scientific name of the insect.

The spreading board. This device consists of two thin boards of soft wood set a short distance apart on a base as shown in Fig. 192. When the insect is pinned with its body in the space between the two boards, its wings may be stretched flat on the boards and held in place until dry.

The materials needed to make the spreading board shown in the figure are the following: two strips of smoothly surfaced soft wood

¼ by 2 by 12 inches for the top; one strip ½ by 4¼ by 12 inches for the bottom; two pieces ½ by 15/16 by 4¼ inches for the ends; a piece of soft, pressed cork or peat ¼ by 1 by 11 inches to receive the pins on which the specimens are mounted; some small nails or wire brads; glue; and a hammer.

The pressed cork or peat must be purchased from a biological supply company. Other materials may be used in its place if the cork or peat is not easily procurable. A strip of any of the pressed composition boards used in house construction may be used. The material must be soft enough that a pin can be thrust into it for a depth of ⅛ inch. If nothing else is available, a strip of soft corrugated pasteboard such as is used for making fillers and separators in cartons may be used. The pasteboard of which the cartons are made is not suitable; it is too hard. If the material substituted for the cork strip is thicker than ¼ inch, make the end blocks correspondingly thicker (*i.e.*, more than 15/16 inch). If the substitute material is thinner than ¼ inch, make the end blocks correspondingly thinner. When the spreading board is completed the distance from the upper surface of the top strips to the top of the cork strip should be just 15/16 inch.

To make the spreading board, first nail the bottom strip to the two end blocks. Then glue or nail the strip of cork down the middle of the bottom strip between the end blocks. Finally, nail the top strips to the end blocks. The top strips will be ¼ inch apart. The spreading board is now finished. A board made in this manner is suitable for moderate-sized butterflies and moths. For smaller specimens the top strips should be closer together. For the largest specimens wider strips will be required. A spreading board to accommodate several sizes of specimens may be made by putting the top strips ⅛ inch apart at one end and ½ inch apart at the other.

The specimens whose wings are to be spread should be placed on the board as soon as possible after they are killed, or at least while they are still soft and flexible. Set the pin which holds the body of the insect firmly in the middle of the cork strip. The place where the insect's wings join its body should be the merest trifle higher than the top of the board. Pull the wings forward by means of pins and fasten them in place with strips of paper as shown in Fig. 193. When properly mounted, the hind margin of the forewings of a butterfly or moth should form a straight line across the board; the hind wings should slightly underlap the forewings. Specimens should be left on the spreading board until completely dry. This will require from three or four days to two weeks, depending on the size of the specimen and the weather.

If specimens cannot be mounted when they are first collected, they may be stored until later and then relaxed for mounting. Butterflies,

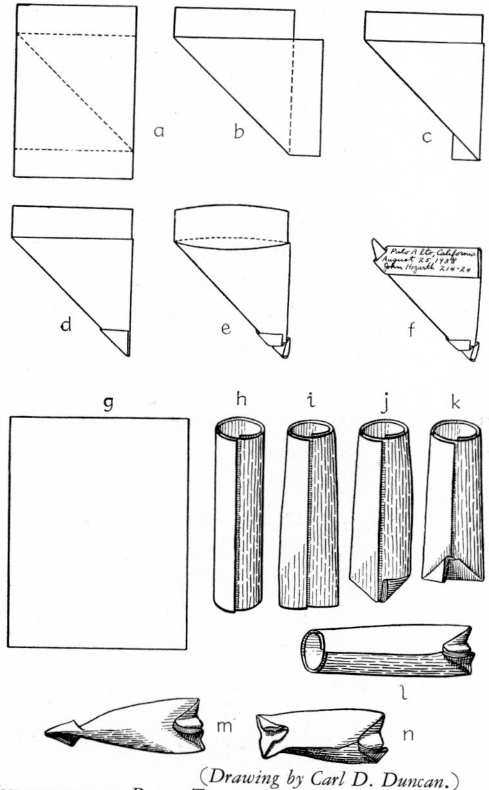

(*Drawing by Carl D. Duncan.*)

FIG. 194.—PAPER ENVELOPES AND PAPER TUBES TO SERVE AS TEMPORARY INSECT CONTAINERS. The intelligent collector will take a box of paper sheets with him into the field. Paper envelopes will hold butterflies, moths, and dragon-flies, protecting them against damage until they can be mounted. Paper tubes will hold almost any type of material, living or killed, until it can be better cared for at home.

and other insects whose wings may be folded flat, may be stored temporarily in paper envelopes made as shown in Fig. 194. Other specimens may be stored in paper tubes (shown in same figure) or in small pasteboard boxes. Do not put them in airtight tin boxes unless they are thoroughly dried out, or they will become moldy and decay.

To make envelopes for storing specimens use pieces of paper that are one and one-half times as long as they are wide. First fold one of the papers diagonally across the middle so that the projecting ends are of the same size. Then fold one of the ends around the edge of the paper against which it rests, and fold down the corner which still projects. Finally crimp the corner to hold it. Then write the collection data on the envelope, drop in the specimen, and close the envelope by folding the second projecting end as you did the first.

Before such stored specimens can be mounted they must be *relaxed*. Relaxing is merely softening them again. For this purpose a relaxing jar or box should be made. Secure a wide-mouthed jar of glass or other material, or a box of some noncorroding metal such as galvanized iron or zinc. Put in about an inch and a half of clean sand. Next pour in enough water to wet the sand thoroughly without making it sloppy. A teaspoonful of carbolic acid crystals or two teaspoonfuls of carbolic acid solution should also be mixed with the sand. If any of the acid gets on your hands while preparing the relaxing box, wash it off thoroughly and immediately to avoid the severe skin burning which it may cause. Finally, cover the sand with a piece of moistened blotting paper or toweling cut to fit the inside of the jar or box. Without removing the specimens from their paper or pasteboard containers put them into the relaxer, cover with a close-fitting lid, and leave for two or three days, or longer if necessary. They will absorb enough moisture to soften them, and the carbolic acid will prevent the growth of mildew which otherwise would develop and spoil them. Additional water may be added as needed. At long intervals it will be necessary to add more carbolic acid.

Cases for insect collections. All dealers in biological supplies carry cases of various sizes and construction in which to keep and display insect collections. If these can be afforded, it is best to buy them. In the absence of available funds, various kinds of boxes may be substituted. Any case intended to hold specimens permanently must be well made. The parts should fit tightly so as to exclude museum pests, the little scavenging beetles that feed on specimens. The bottom of the case or drawer should also have a lip on the inner side, over which the lid fits when the case is closed. Even then collections are not always safe from museum pests.

Satisfactory cases for temporary storage of specimens can be made of cigar boxes. Cut a piece of corrugated paper (if a soft kind can be obtained) that will just fit the bottom of the box. Glue this in. Or use any of the softer pressed wallboards. As cigar boxes are cheap (they may usually be had for the asking), it will be possible to make a separate box for each order of insects. The specimens should be arranged neatly in rows in the box. They should not be crowded, for space enough should be left for the labels to be seen easily. Labels bearing the names of the families of the specimens should also be put in the box. These should be fastened with separate pins, to the bottom of the box.

The cases in which specimens are kept, especially cigar-box cases, or others on which the lids fail to fit tightly, should be examined carefully at frequent intervals for museum pests. The pests may be kept out fairly easily, however, providing vigilance is never relaxed. Repellents are valuable in keeping pests away, but once they get in, the collection must be fumigated. Moth balls or naphthalene (of which moth balls are made) tied in little squares of cheesecloth and pinned in the corners of the cases will keep pests from entering but will not kill those already present. Beechwood creosote, a clear but odoriferous liquid, is an excellent repellent. A few drops on the bottom of a box of specimens will keep museum pests out for several months. Paradichlorobenzene (easily pronounced if divided thus, para-dichloro-benzene), a crystalline solid, combines the properties of repellent and fumigant. It is among the commonest of the so-called *demothing* materials used in connection with a vacuum cleaner to kill clothes-moths in a closet. It is also the standard insecticide used against the Peach Tree Borer (see page 327). Paradichlorobenzene deters pests from entering a specimen box and if used in sufficient quantity or in a tightly closed box it quickly kills any pests that may be present. A half-teaspoonful to a cigar box is enough, but the box must be tightly closed. The only objection to paradichlorobenzene is that it evaporates rapidly, and its vapors do not cling to a container as do those of naphthalene.

If a collection gets badly infested, the only safe thing to do is to fumigate with carbon bisulphide. This is a vile-smelling, poisonous, and highly inflammable liquid. The vapors are explosive, so it should never be used near a fire in any kind of enclosed space. Put the specimen boxes with the lids propped slightly open into a metal tank or a large, tightly built wooden box with an equally tight-fitting lid. Then pour a quantity of carbon bisulphide in a pan or low vessel and set it in the fumigating box. Set it as high in the box as possible as the vapors are heavy and sink to the bottom. Leave covered for two days or more. Then remove the lid, allow the vapors to become dissipated, and remove the specimen boxes.

REFERENCES

A selected list of insect references is given herewith together with an indication of the fields to which they apply.

Insects in General

Comstock, John Henry. *An Introduction to Entomology*. Ithaca, N. Y., Comstock Publishing Company, 1936. 1044 pp., 1228 figs. This, the great classic of North American entomology, written by the dean of American entomologists, considers insects from manifold points of view.

Essig, E. O. *Insects of Western North America*. New York, The Macmillan Company, 1926. 1035 pp., 765 figs.

Imms, A. D. *A General Textbook of Entomology*. New York, E. P. Dutton & Company, 1924. 698 pp. 604 figs.

Metcalf, C. L., and W. P. Flint. *Fundamentals of Insect Life*. New York, McGraw-Hill Book Company, Inc., 1932. 581 pp., 315 figs.

More Popular Books Dealing with Insects

Bradley, J. Chester, and E. L. Palmer. *Insect Life*. New York, Boy Scouts of America, 1925. 214 pp., 155 figs. A Boy Scout merit badge manual and one of the best of that series.

Comstock, John Henry, Anna Botsford Comstock, and Glenn W. Herrick. *A Manual for the Study of Insects*. Ithaca, N. Y., Comstock Publishing Company, 1936. 401 pp., 633 figs. A book less detailed and less technical than *An Introduction to Entomology*.

Weed, Clarence. *Insect Ways*. New York, D. Appleton-Century Company, 1930. 325 pp., many figs. A book for the younger student and the average reader.

Wellhouse, Walter Housley. *How Insects Live*. New York, The Macmillan Company, 1926. 435 pp., 157 figs. An elementary entomology with most of the material built around the important species of various orders.

Identifying Insect Manuals

Many of the preceding books will be of assistance also in identifying insects, for they all discuss the various groups, give their characteristics, and describe typical and common forms. This is especially true of Comstock's *Introduction to Entomology* for it contains the most comprehensive keys for insect identification that are available to the general student.

Jaques, H. E. *How to Know the Insects*. Mt. Pleasant, Iowa, published by the author, 1937. 140 pp., 253 figs. A well-illustrared identifying manual for the beginning student.

Lutz, Frank E. *Fieldbook of Insects*. New York, G. P. Putnam's Sons, 1921. 562 pp., 101 plates (many colored), and hundreds of figs. This book gives "special reference to those of Northeastern United States."

Metcalf, Z. P., and C. L. Metcalf. *A Key to the Principal Orders and Families of Insects*. North Carolina State College and University of Illinois, published by the authors, 1928. 23 pp., more than 200 figs. A useful key for beginning students.

Needham, James G., and Paul R. Needham. *A Guide to the Study of Freshwater Biology*. Ithaca, N. Y., Comstock Publishing Company, 1938. 88 pp., 24 full plates, many figs.

MANUALS FOR SPECIAL GROUPS

Betten, Cornelius. *The Caddis-flies or Trichoptera of New York State*. Albany, N. Y., *Bull.* 292, New York State Museum, 1934. 576 pp., 67 plates, 61 figs. The only generally available work on caddis-flies known to the authors.

Blatchley, W. S. *Orthoptera of Northeastern America*. Indianapolis, Ind., The Nature Publishing Company, 1920. 784 pp., 246 figs. Useful over the whole United States.

Blatchley, W. S. *Heteroptera or True Bugs of Eastern North America*. Indianapolis, Ind., The Nature Publishing Company, 1926. 1116 pp., 12 plates, 215 figs. Useful over the whole United States.

Bradley, J. Chester. *A Manual of the Genera of Beetles of America North of Mexico*. Ithaca, N. Y., Daw, Illston, & Company, 1930. 360 pp. The only comprehensive key to American beetle genera.

Classen, Peter W. *Plecoptera Nymphs of America*. Springfield, Ill., Charles C. Thomas Company, 1931. 199 pp., 35 plates, 4 figs. The only general manual on the immature stone-flies that is available.

Comstock, John Adams. *Butterflies of California*. Exposition Park Museum, Los Angeles, published by the author, 1927. 334 pp., 63 color plates, 86 figs. Every California butterfly shown in full colors.

Comstock, John Henry, and Anna Botsford Comstock. *How to Know the Butterflies*. Ithaca, N. Y., Comstock Publishing Company, 1936. 311 pp., 45 color pages, 49 figs. One of the best.

Curran, C. H. *The Families and Genera of North American Diptera*. New York, N. Y., published by the author at the American Museum of Natural History, 1934. 512 pp., many figs. The only general manual of the Diptera that is available.

Duncan, Carl D. *A Contribution to the Biology of the North American Vespine Wasps*. Stanford University, California, Stanford University Publications, 1939. University Series, Biological Sciences, Vol. VIII, No. 11, 272 pp., 255 figs.

Holland, W. J. *The Butterfly Guide*. Garden City, N. Y., Doubleday, Doran & Company, Inc., 1920. 237 pp., 150 plates in color. A pocket manual.

Holland, W. J. *The Moth Book*. Garden City, N. Y., Doubleday, Doran & Company, 1922. 479 pp., 48 plates in color, 263 figs. A book dealing extensively with the moths of North America.

Holland, W. J. *The Butterfly Book*. Garden City, N. Y., Doubleday, Doran & Company, 1931. 382 pp., 48 plates in color, 183 figs. This book considers the butterflies of North America.

Kofoid, Charles A., S. F. Light, A. C. Horner, Merle Randall, W. B. Herms, and Earl E. Bowe. *Termites and Termite Control*. Berkeley, California, The University of California Press. 1934. 795 pp., 182 figs.

Matheson, Robert. *A Handbook of the Mosquitoes of North America*. Springfield, Ill., Charles C. Thomas Company, 1929. 268 pp., 26 plates, 24 figs.

Morgan, Ann Haven. *Field Book of Ponds and Streams*. New York, G. P. Putnam's Sons, 1930. 448 pp., 23 plates, 330 figs. Though this book considers many forms of life associated with streams, the emphasis is on insects.

Needham, James G., and P. W. Claasen. *A Monograph of the Plecoptera or Stone-flies of America North of Mexico*. Lafayette, Ind., Thomas Say Foundation, Entomological Society of America, 1925. 397 pp., 50 plates, 29 figs. The only general manual on the adults of this order that is available.

Needham, James G., Stuart W. Frost, and Beatrice H. Tothill. *Leaf-mining Insects*. Baltimore, Md., Williams and Wilkins Company, 1928. 351 pp., 91 figs. A comprehensive manual to this interesting group of insects.

Needham, James G., and Hortense Butler Heywood. *A Handbook of the Dragon-flies of North America*. Springfield, Ill., Charles C. Thomas Company, 1929. 380 pp., many figs.

Needham, James G., Jay R. Traver, and Yin-Chi Hsu. *The Biology of May-flies*. Ithaca, N. Y., Comstock Publishing Company, 1935. 759 pp., 42 plates, 168 figs.

Peckham, G. W., and E. G. Peckham. *Wasps, Social and Solitary*. Boston, Houghton Mifflin Company, 1905. 311 pp., many figs.

Phillips, Everett F. *Beekeeping*. New York, The Macmillan Company, 1928. 490 pp., 190 figs.

Plath, Otto Emil. *Bumblebees and Their Ways*. New York, The Macmillan Company, 1934. 201 pp., 20 figs.

Rau, Phil, and Nellie Rau. *Wasp Studies Afield*. Princeton, N. J., Princeton University Press, 1918. 372 pp., 69 figs.

Snyder, Thomas Elliott. *Our Enemy the Termite*. Ithaca, N. Y., Comstock Publishing Company, 1935. 196 pp., 56 figs.

Wheeler, William Morton. *Ants, Their Structure, Development and Behavior*. New York, Columbia University Press, 1910. 663 pp., 286 figs. The classic on the subject of ants.

Wheeler, William Morton. *Social Life Among Insects*. New York, Harcourt, Brace & Company, 1923. 375 pp., 113 figs.

Wheeler, William Morton. *Demons of the Dust*. New York, W. W. Norton & Company, 1930. 378 pp., 49 figs. Devoted to two insect groups, ant-lions and worm-lions.

Economic Entomology

Doane, R. W., E. C. Van Dyke, W. J. Chamberlin, and H. E. Burke. *Forest Insects*. New York, McGraw-Hill Book Company, Inc., 1936. 436 pp., 234 figs.

Doane, R. W. *Common Pests*. Springfield, Ill., Charles C. Thomas Company, 1932. 398 pp., 215 figs.

Ewing, Henry Ellsworth. *A Manual of External Parasites*. Springfield, Ill., Charles C. Thomas Company, 1929. 225 pp., 96 figs.

Felt, Ephraim Porter. *Manual of Tree and Shrub Insects*. New York, The Macmillan Company, 1924. 382 pp., 256 figs.

Herms, William B. *Medical and Veterinary Entomology*. New York, The Macmillan Company, 1923. 462 pp., 229 figs.

Herrick, Glenn W. *Manual of Injurious Insects*. New York, Henry Holt & Company, 1925. 489 pp., 458 figs.

Herrick, Glenn W. *Insects Injurious to the Household and Annoying to Man*. New York, The Macmillan Company, 1926. 478 pp., 152 figs.

Metcalf, C. L., and W. P. Flint. *Destructive and Useful Insects*. New York, McGraw-Hill Book Company, Inc., 1928. 918 pp., 561 figs.

Insect Books for the Younger Student

Comstock, John Henry. *Insect Life*. New York, D. Appleton-Century Company, Inc., 1905. 349 pp., 296 figs., 18 color plates. This book was written especially for the younger student.

Fabre, J. Henri. *Insect Adventures*. New York, Dodd, Mead & Company, Inc., 1929. 287 pp., pencil drawings. This collection of adventures is taken from *Souvenirs Entomologiques*.

Jenkins, Oliver P. *Interesting Neighbors*. Philadelphia, P. Blakiston's Son & Company, 1922. 248 pp., 81 figs. This book is not restricted entirely to insects, but a large part of it deals with them.

Needham, James G. *Elementary Lessons on Insects*. Springfield, Ill., Charles C. Thomas Company, 1928. 210 pp., 71 figs. Organized lessons for younger students, built about insect structure, development, and habits.

Patch, Edith M. *Hexapod Stories*. Boston, Little, Brown & Company, 1930. 170 pp., pen-and-ink drawings. No other book in this field will so intrigue the elementary child.

Special Article Treating of Insects

Klots, Alexander B. *Directions for Collecting and Preserving Insects*. Rochester, N. Y., Ward's Natural Science Establishment, 1932. 29 pp., 30 figs. A pamphlet for the young collector of insects.

INDEX

Bold-face type indicates illustration

A

Abdomen, 12, 22
Abedus, 80
(*See also* Giant Water-bug)
Abundance of insects, 3, 347
Achemon Sphinx Moth, 233
Acraea Moth, 299
larva of, 160
Adaptability of insects, 199–202
Adaptations of insects, 4, 189–190
Adhesives for insecticides, 329
Adipose tissue, 27
Aedeagus, 107
Air getting, 125–136
(*See also* Respiration)
Alabama argillacea (*see* Cotton Leaf Worm)
Alaptus psocidivorous, 85
Alates, termite, 282
Alfalfa Butterfly, **233**
control of, 333
Alfalfa Weevil, 318
Alimentary canal, 25
Alsophila pometria (*see* Canker-worm)
Alveoli, 128
Ambrosia beetles, 72
Anabrus simplex (*see* Mormon Cricket)
Anasa tristis (*see* Squash-bug)
Ancient insects, 68
Andricus californicus, 74–75
Angoumois Grain Moth, 312
Angular-winged Katydid, 174, 182
Anoplura, characteristics and life history of, 222–223
tabulation of, 244
Antennae, 12, 16–18, 109
Anthonomus grandis (*see* Cotton-boll Weevil)
Anthophilous insects, 73
Anthrenus scrophulariae and *piceus* (*see* Carpet Beetle)
Ant-lion, 39, 80, **213, 215,** 354
larvae of (*see* Doodle-bug)
Ants, 72
Argentine, 3, 254
army, 78
artificial nest for, 374–376, **375**
associates of, 90
Black Carpenter, **252**
control of, 331
exoskeleton of, 14
Formic, 166, 194
white, 278–279
(*See also* Hymenoptera)
Anus, 26
Aorta, 24
Aphelinus semiflavus, 86
Aphidius phorodontis, 86
Aphids, **73,** 90, 97, 121, **122,** 123, **254,** 350
(*See also* Homoptera)
Aphis, Green Peach, 86
Apple Maggot, 339
Aquarium cage, 370
Aquatics, complete, 151
incomplete, 149–151
Aqueous poison sprays, 330
Arachnida, characteristics of, 8
Aradidae, 72
Arsenicals, 320, 322–323
Artemisia, 318
Arthropods, characteristics of, 5–8
position in animal kingdom, 8
Asparagus Miner, 72
Aspidiotus rapax (*see* Greedy Scale)
Assassin bugs, 80
Attrahents, 327–328

B

Back-swimmers, 133, **200**
where to find, 356
Baits, poisoned, 331
for Codling Moths, 328
for cutworms, 331
for flies, 331
for grasshoppers, 331
for millipedes, 331
for slugs and snails, 331
for sow bugs, 331
Balance of Nature, 303, 338
Bark-beetles, galleries of, **198**
Bees, exoskeleton of, 14
mouth parts of, 96
solitary bee larvae, **117**
(*See also* Hymenoptera)
Beeswax, 298
Beet Leaf-hopper, 314
Beetle, **227**
ambrosia, 72
bark-, 77
bombardier, 165
carpet, 312
carrion, 88, 194, 357
Carrot, 312
click-, 310
Colorado Potato, 309–310
Confused Flour, 312
Convergent Ladybird, **251**
darkling-, **164,** 201–202, 352
dermestid, 87–89
diving-, 356
Drug-store, 312
Fimbriate June-, **228**
Grape Flea-, 333–334
Green June-, 333
hister-, 88
Japanese, 313
Ladybird, 341, **348,** 350
Larder, 312
meloid, 111
oil-, 167
Pine Sawyer, **51, 142, 145,** 355
Potato Flea, 312
Powder-post, 76, **77, 201**
Predacious Diving-, **150**
Prionus, 174
Red-shouldered Leaf-, 116
Rose Snout-, 318
Beetle, Saw-toothed Grain, 312
Scarabaeid, 90
snout-, 228
soldier, **110**
Striped Cucumber, 312
tiger-, **80,** 352–353
Tobacco, 312
Vedalia Ladybird, 80, 193
Water-scavenger, 133, **151**
water-tiger, 132–133
West Coast Ten-lined June-, 174, 176, **228**
whirligig-, 355
young of, 39
(*See also* Coleoptera)
Belostomatidae, 80
Benefit of small size of insects, 192–199
Big Four, 227
Biological control of insects, 338
Bird-lice (*see* Mallophaga)
Black Cricket (*see* Field Cricket)
Black-winged Locust, 183
Black-winged Stone-fly, 242
Blood of insects, 24, 128
Bloodworms, 135, 152
Blow-fly, 88
where to find, 357
Body regions of insects, 5
Bombardier beetles, 165
Bombylid Fly, 86
Bombyx mori (*see* Oriental Silk Moth)
Book-lice (*see* Corrodentia)
Bordeaux Mixture, 330
Borer, European Corn, 72
flat-headed, 76
Larger Cornstalk, 332
round-headed, 76
Shot-hole, 306–307
Spotted Tree, **145**
Bostrichidae, 201
Bot-fly, Cattle, 83
Horse, 83
Sheep, 84
Box Elder Bug, 224, 245
Braconid Wasp, 58, **341, 342**
Brain of insect, 29
Bristle-tail, 22
(*See also* Thysanura)
Brochymena sulcata, 80
Brownie-bug, 226
Buds, leg, 48
wing, 48

Bug, assassin, 80
  Box Elder, 224, 245
  Common Milkweed, **223**
  Grass Plant, 334
  Harlequin Cabbage-, 72–73, **222,** 224, 245, 312, 332, 333
  Milkweed, **35,** 73, **223**
  Rubber-neck, **38, 212**
  Spotted Milkweed, 73
  Squash-, 72, 224, 245, 312
  Sulcate Rough Shield-, 80
  Tarnished Plant, 224
  true, 72, 93–94
    (*See also* Hemiptera)
  tumble-, 5
Bumblebee, 255
Burke, H. E., 322
Bursa copulatrix, 107
Butterfly, Alfalfa, **233,** 312, 333
  Buckeye, **15**
  Cabbage, 71
  Checker-spot, 352
  Monarch, 5, 85, 167, **234, 235,** 247
  Mourning Cloak, 247, **368**
  swallowtail, **56–59, 61–63**
  Viceroy, 170
  Western Parsley, 55–65
    (*See also* Lepidoptera)

C

Cabbage-bug, Harlequin, 72–73, **222,** 224, 245, 312, 332
    control of, 333
Cabbage Butterfly, 71
Cabbage Worm, Imported, 303
Caddis-fly, 38, **230–232, 356**
    (*See also* Trichoptera)
Cages for insects, **362, 365, 367–369, 371, 373, 375**
  aquarium type, 370
  box type, 366, 367
  cereal-box type, **369**
  jar type, 365, 368–369
  lamp-chimney type, 364
  shoe-box type, 366, 370–371
California Camel Cricket, **207**
California Embiids, **221**
California Oak Moth, **306, 307, 308**
California Timemas, 110
Calliphora erythrocephala and *vomitoria*, 316
Calosoma sycophanta, 343
Cambium-eaters, 77
Camel Cricket, 50, **207**
Campodeids, 240
Canker-worms, control of, 336
Carabidae, 79, 165
Carbon bisulphide as insecticide, 326
Cardo, 19
Care of living insects, 357–363
Carnivores, 67, 77–88, 101
Carolina Locust, where to find, 352
Carpenter Moth, 75–76
Carpet Beetle, 312
Carpocapsa pomonella (*see* Codling Moth)
Carrion beetles, 88, 194, 312, 357
Case-making Clothes-moth, 312
Castes, of termites, 281–286
  of wasps, 258–259
Caterpillars, 32
  Monarch, **52**
  sphinx, **167**
  tent-, 251
  Woolly Bear, 85, **160, 344**
Cecidomyiidae, 123–124
Centipede, 6, 8
    (*See also* Chilopoda)
Cephus cinctus (*see* Western Wheat-stem Saw-fly)
Cerci, 22
Cereal Psocid, 243
Chalcidoidea, 84
Chamberlin, W. J., 322
Characteristics of insects, 5–8
Checker-spot Butterfly, 352
Chilopoda, characteristics of, 8
Chironomidae, 135
Chitin, 5, 10
Chrysalis, 32
    (*See also* Pupa)
Chrysanthemum Leaf Miner, 72
Chrysomelidae, 133, 134
Cicada, 42, 96, 97, 183–186, **184, 224**
  Periodic, 253
  Watch-winding, 185
    (*See also* Homoptera)
Claspers, 107
Click-beetles, 310
Clothes-moth, 89, 348
  Case-making, 312
Clover-root Curculio, 332
Clypeus, 19
Cochineal, 298

Cochliomyia macellaria (*see* Screw-worm Fly)
Cockroaches, 69, 70, 321
Cocoon, spinning of, 26, 39
Codling Moth, 302–303, **313**
  control of, 335
Coleoptera, characteristics of, 226–228
  metamorphosis of, 37
  tabulation of, 246
  wings of, 21
    (*See also* Beetles)
Collecting insects, 377–390
  cases for, 389
  equipment for, 347, 363–364, 377–390, **378, 388**
  hunting grounds for, 347–357
  killing bottles for, 380–382
  net for, 377–379
Collembola, 35
Colorado Potato Beetle, 309–310
Common Bean Weevil, 312
Common Damp-wood Termite, **76,** 241, 280
Common Dry-wood Termite, 241
Common Milkweed Bug, **223**
Common Yellowjacket, **257, 270, 277,** 278
Confused Flour Beetle, 312
Connectives, circumesophageal, 29
Contact Poisons, 323, 325
Containers for collecting insects, **388**
Control of insects, 298–346
  biological, 338
  by chemical methods, 322–331
  by cultural practices, 322
  by heat and cold, 336
  knowledge necessary for, 317–322
  by legal measures, 344–346
  by other methods, 340
    (*See also* Baits, poisoned)
Convergent Ladybird Beetle, **251**
Cooties, 222–223
Copulation, 101–111
Corethra, 135
Corn Ear-worm, 311, 312
Corrodentia, 218–220
  tabulation of, 243
Corsair, Western, **223**
Cotinus nitida (*see* Green June-beetle)
Cotton-boll Weevil, 310, 318
  control of, 333
Cotton Leaf Worm, 318
Cottony-cushion Scale, 80, 313, **340,** 341–343
Coxa, 20–21
Crabronid wasp, 39, 86
Crane-fly, **33,** 111, 120, **128, 140,** 141–142
  Giant, **236**
  where to find, 349–350
Cremaster, 62
Cricket, Black (*see* Field Cricket)
  California Camel, **207**
  camel, 50
  ears of, 10
  Field, 19, **43,** 70, 174, **177,** 178, 181–182, 350
  Jerusalem, 22, 50, 70, 162, 174, 176, **203,** 209, 358
  Mole, 358
  Mormon, **302,** 308, 335–336
  mouth parts of, 18
  Snowy Tree, 174, 177–182, **179,** 312, 351
  song of, 177–182
Crop, 25
Crop rotation, in insect control, 332
Crustacea, characteristics of, 8
Cryptochaetum iceryae, 340–343
Cultural control of insects, 331–333
Curculio, Clover-root, 332
Cuticle (*see* Exoskeleton)

D

Damsel-fly, **216**
  Black-wing, 242
  Ruby-spot, 222
    (*See also* Odonata)
Dance-fly, 111
Darkling-beetle, **164,** 201–202, 352
Dealated termites, 282
Dentate Eleodes, **164, 228**
Dermaptera, characteristics of, 226
  metamorphosis of, 35
  tabulation of, 245
    (*See also* Earwigs)
Dermestes lardarius (*see* Larder Beetle)
Dermestid beetle, 87–89
Dermestidae, 88
Derris, 323–324, 327, 330
Destiny of Man, Viewed in the Light of his Origin, 253
Destructive and Useful Insects, 310, 318
Development of young, 34–40, 113–116
Diabolical Yellowjacket, **259, 260**
Diabrotica vittata and *trivittata* (*see* Striped Cucumber Beetle)

Diabroticas, 71
Diaeretus rapae, 86
Diatraea zeacolella (*see* Larger Cornstalk Borer)
Diluents, 329
Diplolepis, 123
Diplopoda, characteristics of, 8
Diptera, 97
 characteristics and life history of, 233–237
 how to mount, 386
 metamorphosis of, 37
 tabulation of, 247
 wings of, 21
Direct development, 34–35
Disease borne by insects, 316
Dispersal flights of termites, 285–287
Diving-beetle, Predacious, **150**
 where to find, 356
Doane, R. W., 322
Dobson, Western, **212**
 larva of, **152,** 153
Dolichovespula, 258, 261, 264, 274, 276
Dolichovespula arenaria (*see* Diabolical Yellow-jacket)
Doodle-bug, 10, 102, 214, **353**
 (*See also* Ant-lion)
Dorsal vessel, 24
Dragon-fly, **45,** 68–69, 78–79, **102,** 111–112, 154, **215**
 eyes of, 17
 grasping labium of, **100–101**
 Green Darner, 242
 naiad of, **100, 101, 135, 155, 215**
 Ten-spot Dragon-fly, **157,** 242
 where to find, 356
 White-tail, 242
 (*See also* Odonata)
Drone-fly, 316
Drosophila, 87
Drug-store Beetle, 312
Duct, ejaculatory, 107
 salivary, 26
 sperm, 107
Dust of butterfly wing, 15
Dusts, as insecticides, 330
Dytiscidae, 79
Dytiscus, 80, 102

E

Ears, of insects, 10, **185,** 186
Earwig, European, **226,** 245
Earwig, where to find, 349
 (*See also* Dermaptera)
Ear-worm, Corn, **311,** 312
Ectoparasites, 82
Egg cell, 106
Eggs, 32, 114–124
 of Buck Moth, **114**
 of butterfly, 55
Eleodes, 164
Eleodes dentipes (*see* Dentate Eleodes)
Elimination of carbon dioxide, 125–126
Elytron, 21
Embiids, 211
 California, 221
Embioptera, characteristics of, 221
 tabulation of, 243
 (*See also* Embiids)
Emergence, of fly, 34
 of swallowtail, 64–65
Emulsifiers, 329
Emulsions, 330
Encyrtidae, 124
Endoparasites, 82–85
Enemies, of insects, 160
 of swallowtail, 58–60
Ephemerida, characteristics and life history of, 214–216
 metamorphosis of, 37
 tabulation of, 241
 (*See also* May-flies)
Ephestia kuehniella (*see* Mediterranean Flour Moth)
Ephydrid fly, larva of, 15
Epitrix cucumeris (*see* Potato Flea Beetle)
Ergates spiculatus (*see* Pine Sawyer Beetle)
Eristalis, 132
Eristalis tenax (*see* Drone-fly)
Esophagus, 25, 45
Essig, E. O., 322
European Corn Borer, 72
European Earwig, **226,** 245
Eurymus eurytheme (*see* Alfalfa Butterfly)
Eutettix tenellus (*see* Beet Leaf-hopper)
Evolution of insects, in connection with metamorphosis, 49–54
 and feeding habits, 67–69
 as pests, 304–316
Exoskeleton, of insects, 10–16
 strengthening of, 12–14
Eyes of insects, 12
 compound, 16–17

Eyes of insects, simple, 16–17
(*See also* Ocelli)

F

Facets of eyes, 17
Factors increasing number of insect pests, 305–317
Fannia canicularis (*see* Lesser House-fly)
Fannia scalaris (*see* Latrine-fly)
Fat body, 27
Feeders, general, 69–71
restricted, 71–72
Feelers (*see* Antennae)
Femur, 20–21
Ferris, G. F., 202
Fertilization, 106
internal, 107, 191–192
Field Cricket, 19, **43,** 70, 174, **177,** 181–182
mouth parts of, 18
song of, 177–178
where to find, 350
wing of, **178**
Fielde nest, 376
Filament, median, 22
Fimbriate June-beetle, **228**
Firebrat, 240
Fireflies, 109
Fish-flies, 241
Fish-moth (*see* Silverfish)
Fiske, John, 256
Fitness of insects, 188–204
due to adaptability, 199–202
due to persistence, 204
due to physical structure, 202–204
due to small size, 192
Flabellum, 97
Flat-headed borers, 76
Flea, 89, 98, **237**
Cat-, 248
Dog-, 248
Ground Squirrel-, 248
Human-, 248
male and female, **315**
Rat-, 248
where to find, 348
(*See also* Siphonaptera)
Flesh-flies, 83–84, 88, 121, 194
Flies, 32, 40–41
ability to fly, 33
bombylid, 86
Flies, caddis (*see* Trichoptera)
crane, **33,** 111, 120, **128, 140,** 141–142, **236,** 349–350
dance-, 111
as disease carriers, 316
drone-, 316
emergence of, 34
ephydrid, 15
fish-, 241
flesh-, 83–84, 88, 121, 194
growth of, 46
hanging-, **102, 229,** 230
Hessian-, 124, 313, 332–333, 339
horse-, 141–142
House-, 33, 88, 112, 116, 253, 316, 319, 336, 339, 371–372
lacewing-, **118, 213,** 214, 350
Latrine-, 316
Lesser House-, 316
May-, 22, 46, 68–69, 71, 88, **134,** 136, 151, 214, 216
robber, 236
saw-, 120, **238**
scorpion-, 229, 246
Screw-worm, 83, 316
snake-, 241
Stable-, 33, 88, 98, 316
stone-, 22, **36,** 39, **218, 219**
syrphid, 132, 236
tachina, **133,** 134, 236, **344,** 371–372
true (*see* Diptera)
Tsetse-, 314
Walnut-husk, 339
Flint, W. P., 204, 310, 318, 322
Fluorine, 323
Flying, 154–158
specializations for, 157–158
Food, for insects, 66–91
relationship of, to numbers, 70
for young, 113–121
Fork-tailed Bush Katydid, **168, 208**
Fragmentation of termite colonies, 283–284, 288
Fumigants, 325, 327
Fundamentals of Insect Life, 3, 204
Fungivores, 71

G

Galea, 20
Gall-insects, 74

Gall-wasp, 74, **75,** 123, 194, 354
Ganglion, 27–28
subesophageal, 28
supra-esophageal, 28
Gastric caeca, 26
General Textbook of Entomology, 124
Genitalia, 22
Geometridae, 172
Gerris, 355, 357
Giant Water-bug, **17,** 18, **44,** 80, **94, 102,** 103, **118**–119, 129, **199,** 224, **355**
Gills, 135–136
Girdle, of swallowtail, 60
Gizzard, 25, 45
Glands, labial, or salivary, 26
Glossa, 20
Glowworms, 109
Gnats, 236
Granary Weevil, 312
Grape Flea-beetle, control of, 333–334
Grass Plant Bugs, control of, 334
Grasshopper, **6, 11, 28, 29, 119,** 120, **203, 207**
description of body parts, 11–12
dissecting of, 25
ear of, **185**
internal structures of, 23
mouth parts of, 93
shield-backed, 182
Greedy Scale, **340**
Green Darner Dragon-fly, 242
Green June-beetle, control of, 333
Green Ladybugs, 71
Green Peach Aphis, 86
Growth, of insects, 16
of larvae, 57–58
Gryllus assimilis (*see* Field Cricket)
Gypsy Moth, 313, 343

H

Habitations of insects, 188–189
Half wings, 223
Halteres, 21, 236
Haltica chalybea (*see* Grape Flea-beetle)
Hamuli, 15, 21
Hanging-fly, **102, 229,** 230
Harlequin Cabbage-bug, 72–73, **222,** 224, 245, 312, 332
control of, 333
Head of insect, parts of, 12, 16–20
Heart of insect, 24
Heart of insect, ostia of, 24
pulsations of, 25
Heliothis obsoleta (*see* Corn-ear Worm)
Hellebore, 323
Hemelytron, 21
Hemerocampa (*see* Tussock-moth)
Hemiptera, 73, 97, 223–224
how to mount, 386
metamorphosis of, 35
tabulation of, 245
Herbivores, 72
Herms, William B., 322, 334
Hessian-fly, 124, 313, 339
control of, 332–333
Hippodamia convergens var. *ambigua* (*see* Convergent Ladybird Beetle)
Hister-beetles, 88
Homoptera, 73, 97
characteristics and life history of, 225–226
tabulation of, 245
Honeybee, 3, 4, 112, 297
fertilization of, 108
Honey-dew, 351
feeders on, 90–91
Hooks, as locomotor devices, 15
Hopperdozers, 335
Hornet, Brown, 257
Hornworm, Tobacco, **53**
control of, 333
Tomato, 312
Horse-fly, 141–142
Hosts, defined, 81
House-fly, 88, 112, 116, 253, 316, 336, 339, 371–372
control of, 319
Lesser, 316
puparium of, 33
Hum of bees, 175–176
Hydrocyanic acid gas, 325–326
Hydrophilidae, 133
Hylemyia antiqua (*see* Onion Maggot)
Hymenoptera, 20, 21, 37, 120, 124
characteristics and life history of, 238
tabulation of, 248
Hyperparasite, 83, 85–86
Hypopharynx, 20, 95

I

Icerya purchasi (*see* Cottony-cushion Scale)
Ichneumon wasps, 120–121

Ichneumonid wasp, **239**
Ichneumonoidea, 84
Imms, A. D., 124
Imported Cabbage Worm, 303
Indian-meal Moth, control of, 336
Insecta, characteristics of class, 8
Insecticides, 322–327
Insects, abundance of, 3
  characteristics of, 5–8
  compared to vertebrates, 9
  complex, 205
  defined, 5–8
  distribution of, 3–4
  fitness of, 188–204
  net for collecting, **378**
  simple, 205
  size of, 189–198
  strength of, 195–198
  structures of, 9–30
Internal braces of exoskeleton, 14
Internal gills, 135
Interrelationship of plants and animals, 304
Intestine, 26
Invaginations, 16
Irbisia (*see* Grass Plant Bugs)
Isoptera, 279
  description and life history of, 209–212
  metamorphosis of, 35
  tabulation of, 241
    (*See also* Termites)
Ithycerus noveboracensis (*see* New York Weevil)

J

Japanese Beetle, 313
Japygids, 240
Jerusalem Cricket, 22, 50, 70, 162, 174, 176, **203,** 209, 358
Juice-suckers, 72
June-beetle, Fimbriate, **228**
  West Coast Ten-lined, 174, 176, 228

K

Katydid, 170, **183, 207**
  Angular-winged, 174, 182
  ears of, 10, **185**
  Fork-tailed Bush, **168,** 170, 174, 181–182, **208**
  true, 182
Killing bottles, 380–383, **381**
Koebele, Albert, 341

L

Labellum, 97
Labial palpus, 20, 95
Labium, 20, 92, 100
Labrum, 19, 92
Lac insect, 226
Lacewing-fly, 117, **118, 213,** 214, 350
Lachnosterna, 322
Lacinia, 20
Ladybird beetle, 341, **348,** 350
  Convergent, **251**
  Vedalia, 80, 193, 341, 343
Larder Beetle, 312
Larger Corn-stalk Borer, 312, 332
Larvae, 32–33
Lasioderma serricorne (*see* Tobacco Beetle)
Laspeyresia molesta (*see* Oriental Fruit Moth)
Laspeyresia nigricana (*see* Pea Moth)
Latrine-fly, 316
Leaf-hopper, 9, 90
  Beet, 314
    (*See also* Homoptera)
Leaf-miner, 72
Leg, divisions of, 20–21
Legal control of insects, 344–346
Lepidoptera, characteristics and life history of, 232–233
  metamorphosis of, 37
  tabulation of, 247
    (*See also* Butterflies; Moths; Skippers)
Lepidosaphes ulmi (*see* Oyster Shell Scale)
Lepisma saccharina (*see* Silverfish)
Leptinotarsa decemlineata (*see* Colorado Potato Beetle)
Lesser House-fly, 316
Lethocerus, 80
Libellula pulchella (*see* Ten-spot Dragon-fly)
Lice, 98
  Bird- (*see* Mallophaga)
  Book- (*see* Corrodentia)
  Tree (*see* Anoplura)
Lignivores, 75–77
Ligula, 20
Ligyrus gibbosus (*see* Carrot Beetle)
Lime sulphur, 323
Lixus, 318
Locomotion, 137–158
  adaptations in, 145
  aerial, 154–158
  aquatic, 147–148

Locomotion, of gill-breathing insects, 152
telescopic, 141
terrestrial, 146–147
tubercles for, 143
of water surface-dwellers, 148
Locust, Black-winged, 183, 352
Carolina (*see* Black-winged)
Long-tailed Skipper, 247
Louse, biting, **220**
Body, 244
Common Hen, 243
Crab, 244
Head, 244
Lucilia caesar, 316
Lyctidae, **77,** 312

M

Machilids, 240
Maggot, 235
Apple, 339
Onion, 332
Wheat-stem, 312
where to find, 349
young of flies, 32
Mallophaga, 89–90
characteristics and life history of, 220
tabulation of, 243
(*See also* Lice)
Malpighian tubules, 10, 26–27
Mandible, 92
location of, 19
Mantids, 103
Mantis, Praying, **208**
Mantispids, 103, 241
March-flies, 88
Margarodes vitium, 202
Mating, 106, 109–110
Maxilla, 19, 92
Maxillary palpus, 95
May-flies, 46, 68–69, 71, 136, 151
gills of, 22
naiad of, **134**
(*See also* Ephemerida)
Mealy-bugs, **334**
Measuring-worm, **171, 172**
Mechanical control of insects, 333–338
Mecoptera, characteristics and life history of, 229
metamorphosis of, 37
tabulation of, 246
Mediterranean Flour Moth, 312
Mediterranean Fruit Fly, 345
Megarhyssa, 120, **239**
Meloid beetles, 111
Meloidae, 167
Membranes, 12
folded, 184
mirror, 184
timbal, 184
Mentum, 20
Meromyza americana (*see* Wheat-stem Maggot)
Mesothorax, 20
Metamorphosis, 31–54
advantage of, 227
complete, 37–41, 47–48
gradual, 35, 47
incomplete, 37, 47
indirect, 35
meaning and types of, 34
of swallowtail, 65
Metathorax, 20
Metcalf, C. L., 3, 204, 310, 318, 322
Micro-pins, 386
Micropyle, 114
Midge, 236
Wheat, 332
Milkweed bug, **35,** 73, **223**
Miner, 193
Asparagus, 72
stem-, 72
Mists as insecticides, 330
Mole Cricket, 358
Molt, 57–58
Molting, 41
in connection with growth, 41–45
in connection with metamorphosis, 47
fluid formed for, 41
Monarch Butterfly, 5, 85, 167, **234, 235,** 247
caterpillar of, **52**
Mormon Crickets, **302,** 308
control of, 335–336
Mosquito, 38, **96,** 98, 132, 194, 236
control of, 319
Destroyer of, 356
larva of, 152, **153,** 154
life history of, **130**
as malaria carrier, 314
mustaches of, 15
Moth, Achemon Sphinx, **233**
Acraea, **160, 299**
Angoumois Grain, 312

Moth, California Oak, **306, 307,** 308
  Carpenter, 75–76
  Clothes-, 89, 312, 348
  Codling, 302–303, **313,** 335
  Gypsy, 72, 313, 343
  Indian-meal, 336
  Mediterranean Flour, 312, 336
  Nevada Buck, **46, 47, 115, 161**
  Oriental Fruit, 328
  Oriental Silk, **67**
  Pea, 333
  Polyphemus, **40,** 247
  Potato Tuber, 312, 332
  sphinx, 39, 168
  Tobacco Sphinx, **99, 169,** 170
  Tomato-worm, 170
  tussock-, 39, 112, 336, **349,** 351
  White-lined Sphinx, 71, 247, **296**
Mounting insects, 384, **385,** 386
  equipment for, 384–390
Mourning Cloak Butterfly, 247, **368**
Mouth parts, **19, 93, 94, 96, 100, 153**
  adaptations of, 92–100
  adapted for chewing, 93–95
  for lapping, 95–96
  names of, 92–96
  for piercing and sucking, 94, 97–98
  primitive type, 94–95
  for siphoning, 98–99
  for sponging or rasping, 97
  variations of, 18
Murgantia histrionica (*see* Harlequin Cabbage-bug)
Musca domestica (*see* House-fly)
Muscles, 16, **29,** 138–145, **141**
  lever action of, 144–145
  method of working, 139–145
  shape and attachment of, 29–30
  strength of, 195, **196**–198
Mycetophilidae, 71
Mylabris obtectus (*see* Common Bean Weevil)
Myrmecophiles, 90
Myzus persicae, 86

N

Naiads, 37, 217
Nerve ring or nerve collar, 29
Nerve wings (*see* Neuroptera)
Nervous system, 4, 27, **28**
  connectives of, 27
Nervous system, relation to setae, 15
Net for collecting insects, 377–380
Neuroptera, 80
  characteristics and life history of, 212–214
  metamorphosis of, 37
  tabulation of, 241
Nevada Buck Moth, **47**
  caterpillars of, **46, 115, 161**
New York Weevil, control of, 333
Nicotine, 326, 327
Nits, 223
Northern Corn Root-worm, 322, 332
Notonectidae, 80
Nymphs, 36

O

Ocelli, 16, 17
Odonata, characteristics and life history of, 216–217
  metamorphosis of, 37
  tabulation of, 242
Oecanthus niveus (*see* Snowy Tree-cricket)
Oil-bettle, 167
Ommatidea of eyes, 17
Ommatidium, 18
Omnivores, 66, 70
Onion Maggot, 332
Onion Thrips, 244
Optic lobes, 28
Orange Psocid, 243
Orders of insects, 205–249
  tabulation of, 240–249
Organs, sex, 107
Oriental Fruit Moth, bait for, 328
Oriental Silk Moth, **67,** 71, 72
Orthodichlorobenzene, 327
Orthoptera, description and life history of, 206–209
  how to mount, 384
  metamorphosis of, 35–36
  tabulation of, 240
  wings of, 21
Oryzaephilus surinamensis (*see* Saw-toothed Grain Beetle)
Osmeteria, 60
Ovaries, 106–107
Oviducts, 107
Oviparous insects, 121
Ovipositor, 22, 119–121
Ox Warble, 83

Oxidation, 125
Oyster Shell Scale-insects, **225, 340**

P

Paedogenesis, 123–124
Palaeodictyoptera, 68–69
Paleacrita vernata (*see* Canker-worm)
Palpus, 95
  location of, 20
Paper points, 386
Paper tubes for collecting insects, 388
Papermaking of wasps, 263–264
Papilio, 165
Papilio zelicaon Lucas, 55
Paradichlorobenzene, 327
Paraglossa, 20
Parasites, 81–87, **343**
  definition of, 79
  how to rear, 85
  indirect, 86
  true, 82
Parasitism of swallowtail butterfly, 58–59
Parasitoids, 82
Parthenogenesis, 123
Pea Moth, control of, 333
Pear Thrips, 244
Pelopaeus cementarius, 116
Pelopaeus servillei, 116
Penis, 107
Pentatomidae, 80, 166
Pepsis, 352–353
Periodical Cicada, 253
Peripsocus californicus, 85
Peristalsis, 140
Persistence of insects, 4
Phantom larvae, 135
  (*See also* Mosquito Destroyer)
Phasmidae, 110
Phasmids, 240
Phormia regina, 316
Phryganidea californica (*see* California Oak Moth)
Phthorimaea operculella (*see* Potato Tuber Moth)
Phyllophaga, 322
Phytonomus posticus (*see* Alfalfa Weevil)
Phytophaga destructor (*see* Hessian Fly)
Pieris rapae (*see* Imported Cabbage-worm)
Pine Sawyer Beetle, **51, 142, 145**
  where to find, 355
Piophila casei (*see* Cheese Skipper)
Plant-lice, 3
Plecoptera, characteristics and life history of, 217–218
  metamorphosis of, 37
  tabulation of, 242
  (*See also* Stone-flies)
Pleural ridge, 13
  suture, 13–14
Plodia interpunctella (*see* Indian-meal Moth)
Podalonia wasps, 81
Poisons for killing insects, 322–333
  aqueous poison sprays, 330
  contact poisons, 98, 323–325
  spreaders for, 329
  stomach, 318–319, 322–323
Polistes, **273,** 352
Pollinization by insects, 294–297
Polyembryony, 124
Polygnotus minutus, 124
Polygonum, 318
Polyphemus Moth, **40,** 232, 247
Pompilidae, 379
Popillia japonica (*see* Japanese Beetle)
Porthetria dispar (*see* Gypsy Moth)
Potato Flea Beetle, 312
Potato Tuber Moth, 312, 332
Powder-post beetle, 76, **77, 201**
Praon simulans, 86
Predacious Diving-beetle, **150**
Predators, 79–81
Prementum, 20
Prepupa, 48, 61
Prionoxystus robiniae, 75–76
Prionus Beetle, 174, 176
Proctodeal food, 287–288
Products of insects, 297–298
Protection for insects, 60, 159–173
  from drying, 190
  for eggs, 114–124
  of yellowjackets, 271
  for young, 113–121
Prothorax, 14, 20
Protoparce quinquemaculata, 170
  (*See also* Tobacco Hornworm)
Protoparce sexta (*see* Tomato Hornworm)
Proventriculus, 25
Psocid, Cereal, 243
  Spotted, 243
  Ten-spotted, 85
  (*See also* Corrodentia)
Ptilinum, 32, 34

Pulsations, 141
Pupa, 32, 48
  significance of, 52–54
  of swallowtail, 63–64
Puparium, 33, 236
Pupation of swallowtail, 60–63
Pyrethrum, 320, 327

R

Ranatra, 80, **131,** 132
  (*See also* Water-scorpion)
Rearing insects, 358–376
  cages for, 361, 364–376
  food supply for, 359–360
  parasites of, 370–372
  ventilation for, 360–361
  water supply for, 361–362
Red-shouldered Leaf-beetle, 116
Reduplication, 14
Reduviidae, 80
Repellents, 328, 329
Reproduction, 104–124
  cells united in, 106
  control of, 106–107
  necessity for, 104–105
  organs of, 25
  of termites, 287–288
  of yellowjackets, 271–274
Reproductives, secondary, 283
  second-form, 283
  of termites, 281
  tertiary, 283
  third-form, 283
Respiration, 125–136, 190–191
  adaptations for, 135–136
  of aquatic insects, 129–136
  of gill-breathing insects, 151–152
Respiratory siphon, 132
Rhabdophaga strobiloides, 74
Rhagoletis completa (*see* Walnut-husk Fly)
Rhagoletis pomonella (*see* Apple Maggot)
Rhodites, 123
Rhodites bicolor, 74
Rhodolia cardinalis (*see* Ladybird beetle, Vedalia)
Rhynchites bicolor (*see* Rose Snout-beetle)
Robber-flies, 236
Root-eaters, 72
Rose Snout-beetle, 318
Round-headed beetle, larvae of, 354–355
Round-headed borers, 76
Rove-beetles, 88
Rubber-neck Bug, **38, 212**
Ruby-spot Damsel-fly, 242

S

Salivary glands, 20
Samia cecropia, 5
Sassetia nigra, 324
Sassetia oleae, 324
Saw-fly, 120, **238**
  Western Wheat-stem, 332
Saw-toothed Grain Beetle, 312
Saxinis saucia, 116
Scale-bugs (*see* Homoptera)
Scale-insects, 90, **324**
  Cottony-cushion, 80, 313, **340,** 341–343
  Greedy, **340**
  Oyster Shell, **225, 340**
Scarabaeid beetle, 90
Scarabaeidae, 322
Scavengers, 67, 87–90
Sclerites, 12, 14, 19
Scolytus rugulosus (*see* Shot-hole Borer)
Scorpion-flies, 229, 246
Screw-worm Fly, 83, 316
Seed-eaters, 73–74
Segments of insects, 12
Setae, 15–16
Sexes, attraction of, 108
Sheath wings, 227
Sheep-tick, 122–123
Shield-backed Grasshopper, 182
Shield-bug, Sulcate Rough, 80
Shot-hole Borer, 306–307
Sight, 109
Silk glands, 10
Silkworm, 297–298
Silphidae, 38, 88
Silverfish, 68, **206,** 312, **321,** 348
  growth of, 34
Siphonaptera, characteristics and life history of, 237–238
  metamorphosis of, 37
  tabulation of, 248
    (*See also* Flea)
Sitodrepa panicea (*see* Drug-store Beetle)
Sitona flavescens (*see* Clover-root Curculio)
Sitophilus granariae (*see* Granary Weevil)
Sitotroga cerealella, 312

Size of insects, 189–198
Skaters, 148
Skeleton, 10
  lining of, 45
  modifications of, **13**
  molting of, 41
    (*See also* Exoskeleton)
Skipper, Cheese, 87, 312
  Long-tailed, 247
  Western, **233,** 247
    (*See also* Lepidoptera)
Snake-flies, 241
Snout-beetle, 228
  Rose, 318
Snowy Tree Cricket, 174, 312, 351
  song of, 177–182
  wings of, **179, 180**
Social Life Among the Insects, 253
Social life of insects, 250–293
  development of, 252–256
  reasons for, 250–256
Sodium fluoride, 320, 321
Sodium fluosilicate, 320
Soldier beetles, **110**
Soldiers, termite, 281
Solitary bee larvae, **117**
Song of insects, 176–186
Sounds of insects, 109, 175–176
  devices for making, 178–186
Sow-bug, 5, 7, 8
Sperm cell, 106
Spermatheca, 107
Sphecidae, 81
Sphex nigricans, 81
Sphinx moth, 39, 168, 171, 247, 296
  caterpillar of, **167**
  Tobacco, **99, 169,** 170
Spiders, 5–8
Spiracles, 21–22, 128
Spittle-bugs, **163**
Splitworm, Tobacco, 332
Spotted Milkweed-bug, 73
Spotted Tree Borer, **145**
Spreaders, for insecticides, 329
Spreading board, 386–388
Spring-tails, growth of, 35
Squash-bug, 72, 224, 245, 312
Stable-fly, 33, 88, 98, 316
Staphylinidae, 88
Stenopelmatus longispina (*see* Jerusalem Cricket)
Sternum or sternite, 22
Stings, 22, 162–163
Stipes, location of, 20
Stomach, 26
Stomach poisons, 318–319, 322, 323
Stomodeal food, 287
Stomoxys calcitrans (*see* Stable-fly)
Stone-fly, **36,** 39, **218, 219**
  Black-winged, 242
  cerci of, 22
Strength of insects, 195–198
Striped Cucumber Beetle, 312
Structures, 9–30
  external, 9–22, **11, 19**
  internal, 22, **23,** 24–30
  specializations in, 50–54
Stylets, 97
Submentum, 20
Sulcate Rough Shield-bug, 80
Sulphur dioxide, 326
Suspensoria, 261
Suture, 12
Swallowtail butterfly, **56–59, 61–63**
  enemies of, 58–60
  life history of, 55–65
Synaphaeta guexi (*see* Spotted Tree Borer)
Syringe action of muscles, 139–144
Syrphid flies, 132, 236
Syrphus, 351

T

Tachina fly, 134, **344,** 371–372
  larva of, **133**
Tachinidae, 84
Taeniopoda picticornis, 175
Tanglefoot, for insect control, 336
Tanglefoot guns, 285
Tarantula, **7**
Tarantula Hawk, **239**
Tarnished Plant Bug, 224
Tarsus, 20–21, 147
Tassel-tails (*see* Thysanura)
Teeth of insects, 19
Tegmen, 21
Telea polyphemus, 40
Ten-spot Dragon-fly, **157,** 242
Tent-caterpillars, where to find, 351
Tentorium, development of, 14
Tergum, or tergite, 22
Termites, 4, 46, 50, 77, 112, 202, **210, 211**
  artificial nest for, 372–374

Termites, castes of, 281–285
Common Damp-wood, **76,** 241, 280
Common Dry-wood, 241
construction of buildings to prevent entry of, 337–338
defense of, 284–285
feeding habits of, 289–291
galleries of, **76,** 291–293
king and queen of, **282**
life history of, 278–293
nests of, 288, **373**
origin of, 279–280
soldiers of, 281
Western Subterranean, 241
(*See also* Isoptera)
Testes, 106, 107
Thecodiplosis mosellana (*see* Wheat Midge)
Thoracic structures, 20–21
Thorax, function of, 12
Thread-waisted Sand Wasp, 81, 87, **239**
strength of, 197
Thrips, Bean, 244
Cotton, 244
Sunflower, 244
Thysanoptera, characteristics and life history of, 221–222
tabulation of, 244
Thysanura, 35
characteristics and life history of, 205–206
tabulation of, 240
Tibia, 20–21
Tick, 7
Sheep-, 122–123
Tiger-beetle, **80,** 352–353
Timema californica, **108,** 110
Tinea pellionella (*see* Clothes-moth)
Tipula, 120
Tobacco Beetle, 312
Tobacco Hornworm, **53**
control of, 333
Tobacco Juice, 26
Tobacco Splitworm, 332
Tomato Hornworm, 312
Tomato-worm Moth, 170
Tracheae, 127–129, **128**
molting of lining of, 41
spiracular, 128
Tracheal system, 25
trunk, 128
Tracheoles, 128
Trap crops, 332
Traps for insects, light, 334–335
Tree-hopper, 90
Tribolium confusum (*see* Confused Flour Beetle)
Trichoptera, characteristics and life history of, 230–231
metamorphosis of, 37
tabulation of, 247
Trimerotropis (*see* Grasshopper)
Trochanter, 20–21
True bugs, 72
mouth parts of, 93–94
(*See also* Hemiptera)
True flies, 32, 33
(*See also* Diptera)
Tsetse-fly, 314
Tumble-bug, 5
Tussock-moth, 39, 112, **349**
control of, 336
where to find, 351
Tympanum, 186

V

Vagina, 107
Value of insects, 294–300
Van Dyke, E. C., 322
Vegetarians, 66, 71–77
scavenging, 87–88
Vehicles for insecticides, 328
Ventriculus, 26
Veratrum album, 323
Veratrum viridis, 323
Vertebrata, characteristics of, 8
Vespa, 256
Vespidae, 256
Vespinae, 256
Vespula, 258, 261, 264, 276
Vespula pensylvanica, 277–278
(*See also* Western Yellowjacket)
Vespula vulgaris, 278
(*See also* Common Yellowjacket)
Viceroy Butterfly, 170
Viviparous insects, 121–123
Voices of insects, 174–187
(*See also* Sounds)

W

Walking-stick, **171,** 172
Walnut-husk Fly, 339
Warble, Ox, 83

Wasp, 116
  braconid, 58, **341, 342**
  crabronid, 39, 86
  exoskeleton of, 14
  gall-, 74, **75,** 123, 194, 354
  ichneumon, 120–121, **239**
  Tarantula Hawk, **239**
  Thread-waisted Sand, 81, 87, 197, **239**
  vespine, 256–258
    (*See also* Hymenoptera; Yellowjackets)
Watch-winding Cicada, 185
Water-boatmen, 149, 356
Water-bug, 80, 356
  Giant, **17,** 18, **44, 78,** 80, **94, 102,** 103, **118,** 119, 129, **199,** 224, **355**
Water-scavenger beetles, 133, **151**
Water-scorpion, 80, 103
Water-strider, 9, 148
Water-tiger, 102, 356
  adults of, 132–133
Weevil, Alfalfa, 318
  Common Bean, 312
  Cotton-boll, 310, 318, 333
  New York, 333
West Coast Ten-lined June-beetle, 174, 176, **228**
Western Corsair, **223**
Western Dobson larva, **152,** 153, **212**
Western Parsley Butterfly, life history of, 55–65
    (*See also* Swallowtail butterfly)
Western Skipper, **233,** 247
Western Yellowjacket, nest of, **262, 265, 268, 272**
  queen of, **277**–278
Wheat Midge, 332
Wheat-stem Maggot, 312
Wheeler, William Morton, 253, 256
Whirligig-beetles, 355
White ants (*see* Termites)
White-lined Sphinx Moth, 71, 247, **296**
White-tail Dragon-fly, 242
Wing pads, 36
Wingless Hanging-fly, **102, 229,** 230
Wingless Scorpion-fly, 246
Wings, 12, 14, 21
Wire-worms, 310
Woolly Bear caterpillar, 71, 85, **160, 344**
Worm, Apple (*see* Codling Moth)
  canker-, 336
  Corn Ear-, 311–312
  Imported Cabbage, 303
  measuring-, **171, 172**
  Northern Corn Root-, 322, 332
  Oriental Silk-, **67,** 71, 72
  Tomato-, 170
  wire-, 310
Wormwood, 318

Y

Yellowjacket, 4, 112–113, 256–278
  castes of, **257**–259
  Common, **257, 267, 270, 277,** 278
  Diabolical, **259, 260**
  food of, 266–269
  nests of, 259–261, **273, 275**
  where to find, 354

Z

Zootermopsis angusticollis (*see* Common Dampwood Termite)